NEURAL PHYSIOPATHOLOGY

PROGRESS IN NEUROBIOLOGY

I. NEUROCHEMISTRY

II. ULTRASTRUCTURE AND CELLULAR CHEMISTRY OF NEURAL TISSUE

III. PSYCHOPHARMACOLOGY

IV. THE BIOLOGY OF MYELIN

V. NEURAL PHYSIOPATHOLOGY

NEURAL PHYSIOPATHOLOGY

Some Relationships of Normal to Altered Nervous System Activity

Edited by

ROBERT G. GRENELL, Ph.D.

Professor of Neurobiology in Psychiatry, University of Maryland School of Medicine, Baltimore, Maryland

With Twenty-Eight Participants

A HOEBER MEDICAL BOOK

Harper & Row, Publishers

PROGRESS IN NEUROBIOLOGY: V. NEURAL PHYSIOPATHOLOGY

Printed in the United States of America

 For information
address Hoeber Medical Division,
Harper & Row, Publishers, Incorporated
49 East 33rd Street, New York 16, N. Y.

Library of Congress catalog card number: 62-18339

GM

CONTENTS

LIST OF PARTICIPANTS

GEORGE H. BISHOP, Ph.D. Professor Emeritus of Neurophysiology, Washington University School of Medicine, St. Louis

MARY A. B. BRAZIER, D.Sc. Research Anatomist and Physiologist, Brain Research Institute, University of California, Los Angeles

BRITTON CHANCE, Ph.D., D.Sc. Chairman, Department of Biophysics and Physical Biochemistry, University of Pennsylvania School of Medicine, Philadelphia

HALLOWELL DAVIS, M.D. Director of Research, Central Institute for the Deaf; Research Professor of Otolaryngology and Professor of Physiology, Washington University School of Medicine, St. Louis

JOHN C. ECCLES, D. Phil., Sc.D. Professor of Physiology, Australian National University, Canberra, Australia

FRANK R. ERVIN, M.D. Associate in Psychiatry, Harvard Medical School and Massachusetts General Hospital, Boston

ALEXANDER GEIGER, M.D. Professor of Neurophysiology, Department of Psychiatry, University of Illinois College of Medicine, Chicago

R. S. GEIGER. Research Associate, Research Laboratories, Department of Psychiatry, University of Illinois College of Medicine, Chicago

ROBERT G. GRENELL, Ph.D. Professor of Neurobiology in Psychiatry, University of Maryland School of Medicine, Baltimore

HERBERT H. JASPER, M.D. Professor of Experimental Neurology, Department of Neurology and Neurosurgery, Montreal Neurological Institute, Montreal

CLIFFE D. JOEL, Ph.D. Instructor in Biological Chemistry, Department of Chemistry, Harvard Medical School, Boston

Manfred L. Karnovsky, Ph.D. Associate Professor of Biological Chemistry, Departments of Chemistry and Pathology, Harvard Medical School, Boston

Keith F. Killam, Ph.D. Associate Professor of Pharmacology, Stanford University, The School of Medicine, Palo Alto, California

G. P. McCouch, M.D. Professor Emeritus, Department of Physiology, The University of Pennsylvania, The Medical School, Philadelphia

H. W. Magoun, Ph.D. Professor of Anatomy and Member, Brain Research Institute, University of California, Los Angeles

Guido Majno, M.D. Associate Professor of Pathology, Harvard Medical School, Boston

Jack H. Mendelson, M.D. Associate in Psychiatry, Harvard Medical School and Massachusetts General Hospital, Boston

Jerome K. Merlis, M.D. Professor of Neurology and Clinical Neurophysiology, University of Maryland, The School of Medicine, Baltimore

Hugo W. Moser, M.D. Instructor in Neurology, Harvard Medical School, Boston

L. J. Mullins, Ph.D. Professor of Biophysics, University of Maryland, The School of Medicine, Baltimore

Austin H. Riesen, Ph.D. Professor of Psychology, Department of Psychology, The University of California, Riverside, California

Theodore Shedlovsky, Ph.D. Professor, Rockefeller Institute, New York City

Bernard L. Strehler, Ph.D. Chief, Section on Cellular and Comparative Physiology, Gerontology Branch, National Heart Institute, National Institutes of Health, Bethesda

Ichiji Tasaki, M.D. Neurophysiologist, Laboratory of Neurobiology, National Institute of Mental Health, National Institutes of Health, Bethesda

STEPHEN THESLEFF, M.D. Associate Professor of Pharmacology, Department of Pharmacology, University of Lund, Lund, Sweden

PATRICK D. WALL, D.M. Professor of Biology, Department of Biology, Massachusetts Institute of Technology, Cambridge, Massachusetts

W. GREY WALTER, Sc.D. Head, Department of Physiology, Burden Neurological Institute, Bristol, England

A. G. M. WEDDELL, M.A., M.D., D.Sc. Reader in Human Anatomy, Oxford University; Fellow, Oriel College, Oxford, England

INTRODUCTION

OVER the last few decades remarkable progress has been made in the understanding of the structure and operation of glia, neurons, and neuron nets. New methods and concepts, both theoretical and experimental, have not only made it necessary to ask new questions, but have also further clarified complex problems of both a gross and microscopic nature. These developments have given rise to a new outlook on both the functional activity of the neuron as an entity and on the role in the total organismic picture played by particular neuronal, interneuronal, and multineuronal structural arrangements.

On all levels from the molecular up, the activity of these structures is being related (i.e., attempts are being made to clarify possible relationships) to behavior and disease. As a result of these investigations, it was thought interesting to see what suggestions could be made about what happens in the organism when something goes wrong at a particular level in the nervous hierarchy. The sequence of the contributions follows a scheme starting with peripheral disturbances and moving into and up the central nervous system. In a few cases, certain specific questions were asked.

Examples of these are the contributions of Dr. Grey Walter and Dr. Keith Killam. Dr. Walter was asked to discuss the nervous system as an oscillatory physical system, making an attempt to show what can happen when such a system is not functioning normally. Dr. Killam was posed the question of why and how drugs may correct neural abnormality. In no case was it expected that the answers to such questions were at hand. The basic idea was to bring together available data and analyze it from this point of view, in order to see how far it was possible to go at the present time, and what ideas for further investigations appeared. With such a synthesis and somewhat unusual approach could one learn anything of changes in the nervous system that accompany learning, or perhaps, derive some clear understanding of such problems as the chemotherapeutic potential in nervous and mental disease?

In other words, by examining abnormal ("unphysiological") phenomena at various levels, perhaps we could increase our knowledge or research potential with regard to the behavioral process of nerve and brain; with regard to the clarification of the substance and activity of "mind"; and finally with regard to the role played by such processes in the integration and maintenance of the total organism.

It is not possible to express my gratitude to all those who have contributed to this symposium. I am deeply indebted to all of the participants for preparing their papers for publication. Particular thanks can be expressed only inadequately to the National Institute of Neurological Diseases and Blindness and its Council whose financial support and encouragement have made this series of volumes possible. To our many friends at The Upjohn Company of Kalamazoo, Michigan, go our thanks for their additional contribution. The Symposium was held under the auspices of the University of Maryland to which we also express our gratitude.

Our brief acknowledgements cannot be terminated without some expression of our thanks and admiration to Mr. Paul B. Hoeber and his staff. Their job of publication was made much more difficult as a result of the editor's sojourn in India. Without the patience, understanding, and efforts of Miss Claire Drullard this book would probably have never appeared at all.

ROBERT G. GRENELL

Trivandrum, India

NEURAL PHYSIOPATHOLOGY

CHAPTER 1

Some Aspects of the "Abnormal" Neuromuscular Junction

STEPHEN THESLEFF

WE have been studying the effects of motor innervation on the chemical sensitivity of skeletal muscle. Interest in this subject was evoked by the observation that an excess of acetylcholine (ACh) reduced the chemosensitivity of a muscle, and subsequently this has led to an investigation of the opposite phenomenon, i.e., that of denervation supersensitivity.

First, I should like to relate our experimental results and then to briefly discuss their main implications.

Our studies were made on isolated mammalian skeletal muscle with electrical micromethods for drug application and recording. The technique used is illustrated by Figure 1-1. It is possible by an electric current to release iontophoretically constant quantities of ACh from the tip of a fine micropipette (5, 14). By careful manipulation of the pipette a close-range and localized application of ACh to the receptor structure of a single muscle fiber is achieved. At a sensitive "spot" iontophoretically released ACh

The author's work has been sponsored by the Swedish Medical Research Council, the Muscular Dystrophy Associations of America, Inc., and the Air Research and Development Command, United States Air Force, through its European office.

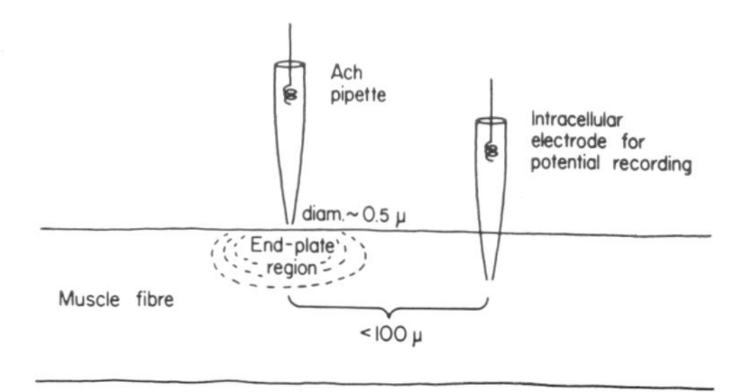

FIG. 1-1. A schematic illustration of the ACh-pipette and the intracellular electrode in their position at the motor end-plate of a single muscle fiber.

produces a transient membrane depolarization with a rapid time course. This potential change is recorded by a capillary microelectrode inserted into the muscle fiber close to the point of drug application. By moving the drug-pipette and the intracellular recording electrode to various parts of a muscle fiber it is possible to determine the distribution and relative sensitivity of ACh receptors in various parts of the fiber.

NERVE DEGENERATION

In an innervated muscle ACh produces depolarization only when applied to the end-plate region of a muscle fiber (Fig. 1-2

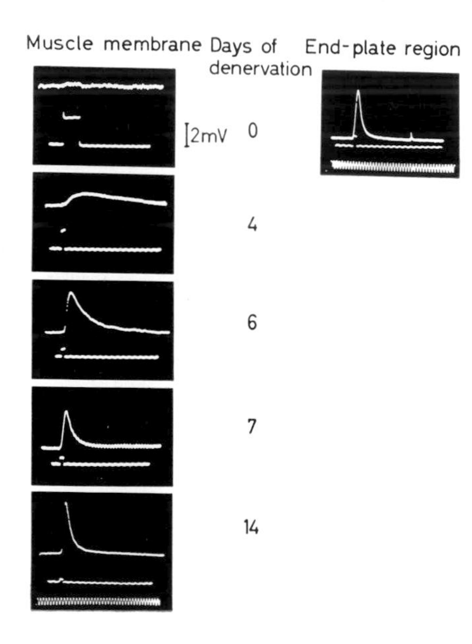

FIG. 1-2. An illustration of the sensitivity of innervated and denervated muscle fibers (cat's tenuissimus) to iontophoretically applied ACh. The membrane potential of the fiber is recorded in the upper tracing, and the current passing through the pipette in the lower tracing of each record. In an innervated muscle ACh produces membrane depolarization only when applied to the end-plate region (*upper right record*) but has no effect when released outside this area of the membrane (*upper left record*). After denervation the whole muscle becomes sensitive to ACh, which, wherever applied to the membrane, causes a potential change (*subsequent records*). Time marker, 100 c/s (2).

and lower records in Fig. 1-3). The area sensitive to ACh is small and covers normally not more than 1 mm. of the fiber length.

Following motor denervation, however, the entire muscle membrane becomes sensitive to locally applied ACh (2, 9). A few days after denervation iontophoretically released ACh produces depolarizations outside the former end-plate region, and one week later the whole muscle membrane is uniformly as

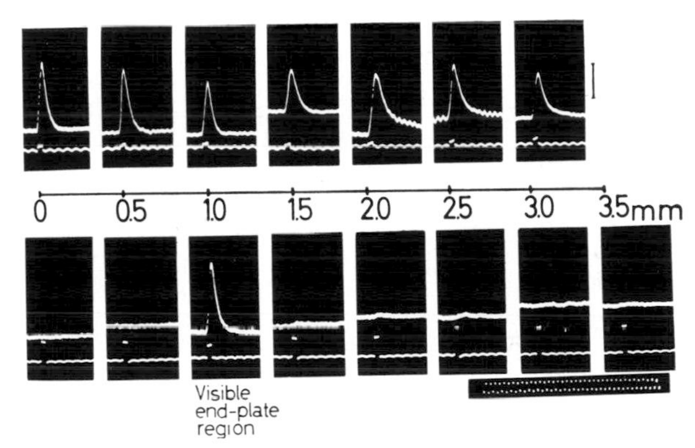

FIG. 1-3. The sensitivity of a muscle fiber of the cat's tenuissimus to locally applied ACh was tested by moving the tip of an ACh-pipette close to the cell membrane at points separated by distances of about 0.5 mm. In an innervated fiber (*lower records*) only the visible end-plate region is sensitive to ACh. In a 14-day denervated fiber a constant pulse of ACh produced a potential change at each point of the membrane, as is shown in the upper records. Time marker, 100 c/s; voltage calibration, 2 mV (2).

sensitive to ACh as the former end-plate region (Figs. 1-2 and 1-3).

The spread of chemosensitivity occurs from the end-plate toward the tendons. The sensitivity of the end-plate region to ACh is not increased by denervation. It retains about its original responsiveness to the drug and it is not affected by the process which renders the rest of the cell membrane equally sensitive to ACh.

The new ACh receptors which are formed in the muscle membrane after denervation have properties similar to those at an innervated end-plate (2). Thus, in a denervated muscle ACh displaces the membrane potential toward an equilibrium value of about —10 mV. The reaction between ACh and the receptors proceeds even when no sodium is present and in the absence of a resting potential, as shown at the innervated end-plate by del Castillo and Katz (6). Furthermore, the mode of action of drugs such as carbachol and tubocurarine is not altered by denervation. However, drugs with anticholinesterase activity do not potentiate the effects of locally applied ACh in a denervated muscle. Presumably the denervated muscle membrane is, in a practical sense, devoid of cholinesterase (2).

EFFECTS OF BOTULINUM TOXIN

The conversion, following denervation, of the muscle membrane into an ACh-sensitive surface is presumably due to the absence of some influence exerted when the motor innervation is intact. To elucidate whether or not the chemical transmitter agent provided such an influence, use has been made of botulinum toxin (18).

Characteristic of botulinum poisoning is a lack of transmitter release from cholinergic nerves while otherwise nerve and muscle are unaffected by the toxin (13, 15, 20). As shown by Professor B. Katz the ultrastructure of motor nerve terminals is not altered by botulinum toxin, and electrophysiological results indicate that the toxin selectively blocks the mechanism responsible for the release of the chemical transmitter from the motor nerve (18).

When transmitter release is blocked by botulinum toxin the muscle fibers become sensitive to applied ACh along their entire length. About two weeks after the administration of the toxin, ACh released from the tip of a micropipette produces depolarizations with a rapid time course wherever applied to the muscle membrane (Fig. 1-4, upper records). The whole surface of the membrane becomes as sensitive to ACh as the end-plate which maintains its original responsiveness to the drug. The uniform sensitivity of the muscle membrane to ACh is similar to that which is observed in chronically denervated muscles.

When transmitter release is reduced but not completely abolished, as shown by the occurrence of spontaneous miniature end-plate potentials at a slow rate, the receptor area is enlarged but it does not cover the whole muscle fiber (Fig. 1-4).

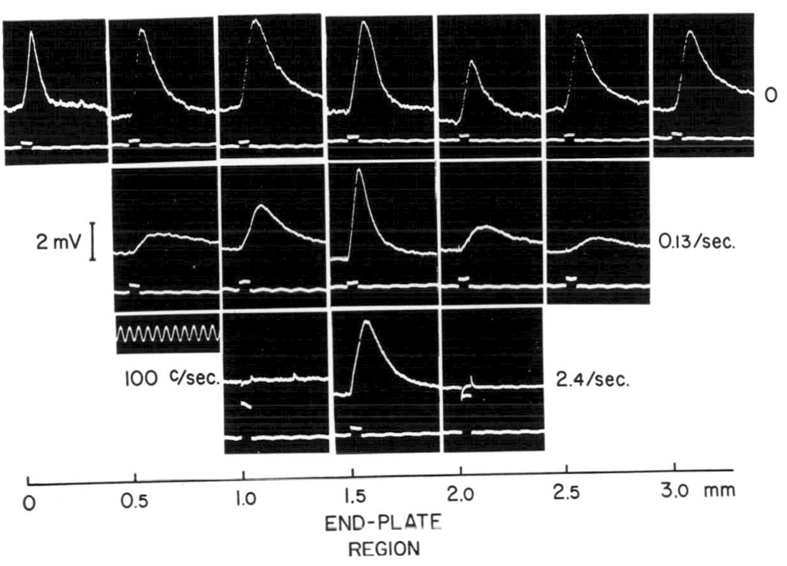

FIG. 1-4. In a tenuissimus muscle of the cat, intoxicated three weeks earlier with a small amount of botulinum toxin, muscle fibers were observed in which the ACh-sensitive surface varied in size. The fiber illustrated by the upper records was uniformly sensitive to applied ACh over a distance of at least 1.5 mm. at each side of the end-plate. The size of the ACh-sensitive surface in two other fibers was smaller (*middle and lower records*). The respective frequency of miniature end-plate potentials is shown by right-hand figures (18).

Since, as mentioned, botulinum toxin is without effect on the morphological structure of motor nerve endings it may be concluded that lack of transmitter release and not nerve degeneration is responsible for initiating the process which causes the high and uniform chemical sensitivity of chronically denervated muscles.

EFFECTS OF DECENTRALIZATION

The possibility that the extension of chemosensitivity, following denervation, was due to inactivity has been investigated by isolation of the motor mechanism of the cat's spinal cord as described by Tower, Bodian, and Howe (19). The surgical procedure consisted of transection of the spinal cord between L_4 and L_5 and again below the sacral region. All intervening dorsal roots were cut intradurally on both sides. In such a segment the ventral horn cells are intact but deprived of all ingoing impulses. During the first five to ten days after the operation, spontaneous electrical impulses were absent in the hind legs, but subsequently motor unit potentials and fasciculations were observed. Spontaneous transmitter release recorded as miniature end-plate potentials was not markedly influenced by the operation (11).

The size of the ACh-sensitive surface in muscle fibers increased somewhat after decentralization, but even three weeks after the operation it covered less than 2 mm. of the fiber length. Therefore, inactivity alone cannot be responsible for the extension of the receptor surface after denervation. Consequently, it has to be considered that lack of transmitter release per se causes the afore-mentioned change in chemosensitivity. Furthermore, one may conclude that spontaneous transmitter release in the absence of nerve impulses is enough to maintain the chemosensitivity of a muscle at about its normal innervated level.

FETAL MUSCLE

The results presented have shown that following motor nerve degeneration or lack of transmitter release the whole muscle membrane is converted into an ACh-sensitive surface. This suggests that a uniform chemical sensitivity probably is the original state of the muscle membrane and that this is modified upon innervation by transmitter release from the motor nerve.

This view has recently been substantiated by investigations made by Diamond and Miledi (7). They studied the sensitivity of fetal and newborn rat muscle to ACh. By microapplication of the drug and intracellular recording from single muscle fibers they showed that the fibers in the fetal diaphragm muscle were sensitive to ACh over their whole surface. Shortly after birth when a functional innervation was established, the chemical sensitivity receded starting from the tendons toward the end-plate.

We have confirmed these findings in the fetal rabbit and cat diaphragm muscle.

EFFECTS OF APPLIED ACh AND OF REPETITIVE NERVE STIMULI

Up to now I have dealt with the effects of a reduced transmitter release on the chemical sensitivity of skeletal muscle. To present a more complete picture of the influence of innervation, however, the effects of an excess of ACh should also be considered.

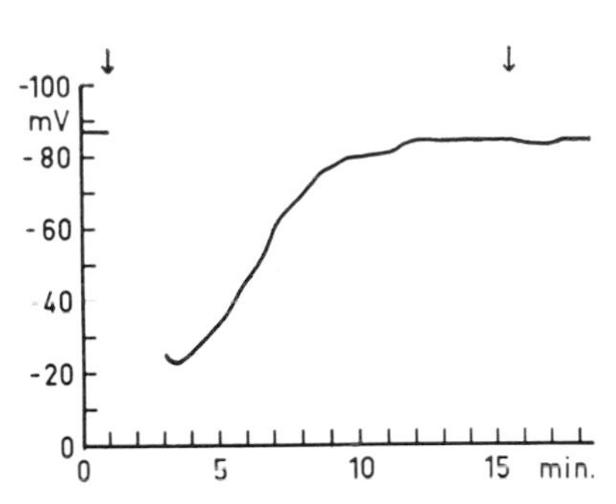

FIG. 1-5. Continuous recording of the resting membrane potential at the end-plate region of a single fiber of the frog's sartorius muscle. At the *arrows*, ACh-iodide was added to the muscle bath giving a concentration of 10^{-5} w/v (16).

When ACh is given by intra-arterial injection into a normal innervated mammalian muscle, a depression of its excitability to nerve stimulation develops. The depressant effect of the drug is confined to the end-plate since the response of the muscle to direct electrical stimulation is unaltered (3).

The experiment illustrated in Figure 1-5 shows that following application of ACh in a concentration exceeding 10^{-6} w/v the initial depolarization at the end-plate declines and the membrane potential is restored to about its original value. A neuromuscular block develops during the period of depolarization and persists despite repolarization of the membrane. The muscle remains unresponsive to nerve stimulation as long as ACh is in the muscle bath, and its chemical sensitivity is only restored after a prolonged period of washing in Ringer's solution (16).

The time course of receptor "desensitization" by applied ACh has been studied with microapplication of the drug to sensitive "spots" in the end-plate region (1, 12). With this method, both onset of and recovery from desensitization were fast as compared with the time courses observed with bulk application of ACh (Fig. 1-6). The degree and speed of desensitization increased with the dose while the recovery time was relatively constant.

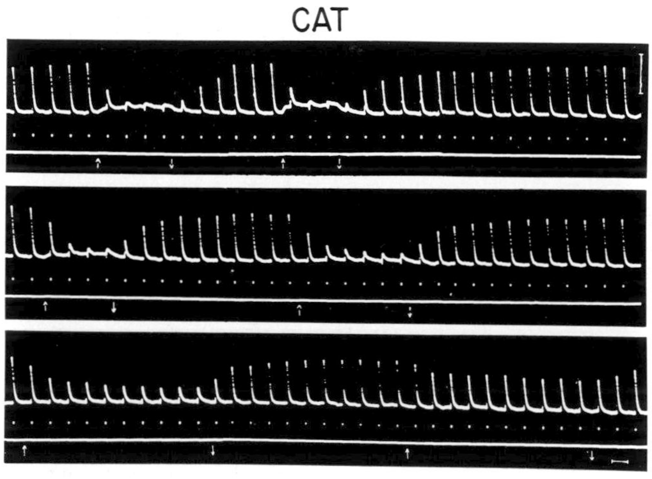

FIG. 1-6. "Desensitization" of end-plate receptors in the cat's tenuissimus muscle produced by different conditioning doses of ACh. Double-barrel ACh-pipettes were used, test pulses and conditioning currents being passed through separate channels. The development of desensitization is seen by reduction in amplitude of the brief test response during each conditioning period. *Arrows* indicate duration of conditioning dose. Voltage scale, 5 mV. Time marker, 1 sec. (1).

Repetitive motor nerve stimulation also renders the end-plate refractory to locally applied ACh (17). In the isolated phrenic-diaphragm preparation of the rat, nerve stimulation at a frequency higher than 30–40/sec. causes a reduction in the response to the applied ACh, and with stimulation frequencies of 60/sec. or more the response sometimes is completely abolished (Fig. 1-7).

The effect of varying the duration of the period of tetanic stimulation is that, at stimulation frequencies above 40/sec., a maximum of desensitization occurs within 0.2 sec. of starting the stimulation. At frequencies below 20/sec. even prolonged stimulation produces no observable desensitization. The time for complete recovery of the sensitivity of the end-plate to ACh was about 0.2 sec. when the preceding period of nerve stimulation had produced a partial reduction of the test response.

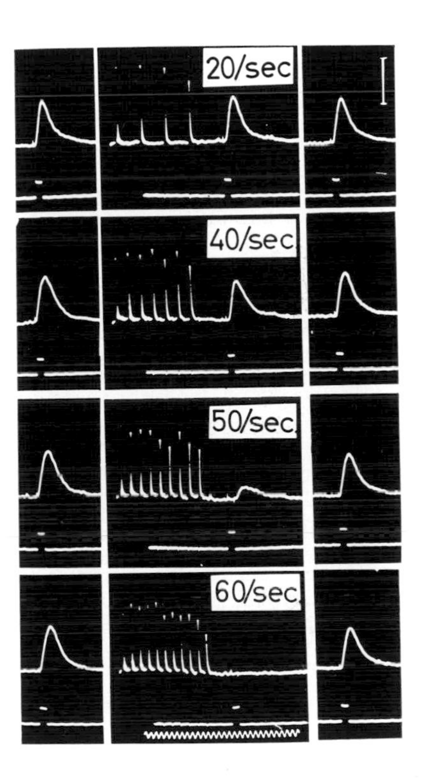

FIG. 1-7. End-plate desensitization produced in the rat diaphragm preparation by repetitive nerve stimulation at frequencies of 20, 40, 50, and 60/sec. The entire period of stimulation (150 msec.) is shown in each record. Responses to test pulses of ACh are shown: 5 sec. before nerve stimulation (*left-hand records*); 50 msec. after the end of stimulation (*middle records*); 5 sec. later (*right-hand records*). The current pulse responsible for the release of ACh is monitored in the lower tracing of each record. Time marker, 100 c/s; voltage calibration, 10 mV; monitor calibration (voltage scale) = 3.3×10^{-7} A (17).

As shown by this investigation, a short period of high-frequency nerve stimulation produced a marked reduction in the chemical sensitivity of the end-plate. Simultaneously with desensitization, a decline in amplitude of successive end-plate potentials has been observed (8, 17). Since a reduction in amplitude of end-plate potentials is likely to cause a failure of neuromuscular transmission, the desensitization process presumably is one of the causes of Wedensky inhibition.

CONCLUSIONS

The experimental findings which I have presented suggest that at an early phase of innervation the genuine state of a muscle fiber is one with a uniform sensitivity to ACh and that upon functional innervation the chemosensitive area decreases in size, the decrease being initiated and modified by the transmitter release. The motor nerve has, according to this view, two functions: first, to initiate mechanical activity in muscle, and, second, to control the size of its chemoreceptor surface.

Whether the "second" function of the nerve also applies to organs other than skeletal muscle remains to be shown. Considering the close similarity of the denervation process in various types of tissues (4), it, however, would be rather surprising if the mechanism varied markedly. A particularly challenging possibility is that presynaptic transmitter activity might determine the extension of the receptor region in neurons. In the central nervous system such a possibility could provide a means by which interneuronal pathways were established.

There are no experimental clues to the nature of the mechanism by which transmitter release can affect the size of the receptor surface in a muscle. However, it might be worth while to speculate about various possibilities.

The observation that following innervation the chemosensitivity of a muscle fiber is reduced from the tendons toward the end-plate suggests that the change in the distribution of ACh-receptors is not primarily caused by a substance entering the fiber at the end-plate region. It is more likely that formation and/or activation of chemoreceptors require the presence of a substance formed inside the muscle fiber. If such a substance in an innervated fiber was present only in the nervous part and following denervation everywhere in the fiber, the spatial sequence of the receptor change would be more obvious. Furthermore, if the ACh-receptor combination to be "effective" required a substance formed inside the fiber, an excess of ACh could be expected to deplete the membrane of this substance. The experimentally observed degree and time course of desensitization with applied ACh can fit such a mechanism (12). Following denervation the metabolic reactions of skeletal muscle undergo striking changes (10). Therefore, it is possible that the resulting alteration in the chemical composition of the muscle in some way is connected with the increase in the chemical sensitivity.

Because of the electric cable conductor properties of a muscle fiber an increase of its chemosensitive surface makes it supersensitive to drugs. Figure 1-8 is a diagram of a model with electrical properties similar to those of a muscle fiber. A potential difference (e.g., the membrane potential) between A and B can be reduced by short-circuiting either a fraction, or all, of the

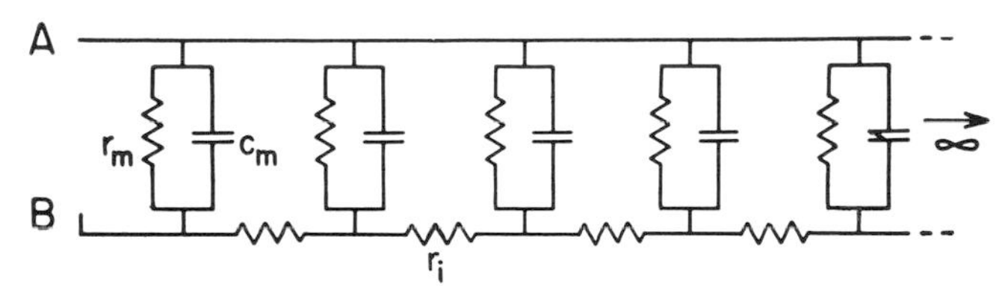

FIG. 1-8. A diagram of an electric model with cable conductor properties similar to those of a muscle fiber: r_m = membrane resistance; r_i = longitudinal resistance of myoplasm; c_m = membrane capacity (2).

parallel resistors r_m. In an innervated fiber only the end-plate is affected by ACh, i.e., only a fraction of the total effective resistance between the inside and the external medium is reduced. A relatively larger reduction of the resistance in the end-plate, according to Ohm's law, is, therefore, needed in order to produce a given membrane potential change. From membrane constants obtained for mammalian muscles it can be estimated that the sensitivity to ACh should through this mechanism increase after denervation by a factor of 10–500 depending upon whether 100 or 20 μ are taken as the diameter of the active end-plate membrane (2). In our opinion the extension of ACh-sensitivity, in combination with the lack of cholinesterase and an increased electrical excitability, provides an adequate explanation for the phenomenon known as denervation supersensitivity.

Almost nothing is known about the distribution of chemosensitivity in normal and diseased human skeletal muscle. Besides in chronically denervated muscle there are no indications that the afore-mentioned processes are of clinical importance. It is, however, my hope that these results obtained in animal experiments will encourage others to make similar studies in man.

REFERENCES

1. Axelsson, J., and Thesleff, S. The "desensitizing" effect of acetylcholine on the mammalian motor end-plate. *Acta physiol. Scandinav. 43:* 15, 1958.
2. Axelsson, J., and Thesleff, S. A study of supersensitivity in denervated mammalian skeletal muscle. *J. Physiol. 147:* 178, 1959.
3. Brown, G. L., Dale, H. H., and Feldberg, W. Reactions of the normal mammalian muscle to acetylcholine and to eserine. *J. Physiol. 87:* 394, 1936.
4. Cannon, W. B., and Rosenblueth, A. *The Supersensitivity of Denervated Structures.* The Macmillan Company, New York, 1949.
5. del Castillo, J., and Katz, B. On the localization of acetylcholine receptors. *J. Physiol. 128:* 157, 1955.
6. del Castillo, J., and Katz, B. Local activity at a depolarized nerve-muscle junction. *J. Physiol. 128:* 396, 1955.
7. Diamond, J., and Miledi, R. The sensitivity of foetal and newborn rat muscle to acetylcholine. *J. Physiol. 149:* 50 P, 1959.
8. Eccles, J. C., Katz, B., and Kuffler, S. W. Nature of the "endplate potential" in curarized muscle. *J. Neurophysiol. 4:* 362, 1941.
9. Elmqvist, D., and Thesleff, S. A study of acetylcholine induced contractures in denervated mammalian muscle. *Acta pharmacol. et toxicol. 17:* 84, 1960.
10. Gutmann, E. Metabolic reactions of denervated and reinnervated muscle. *Am. J. Phys. Med. 38:* 104, 1959.
11. Johns, T. R., and Thesleff, S. Effects of decentralization on the chemical sensitivity of skeletal muscle. *Acta physiol. Scandinav. 51:* 136, 1961.
12. Katz, B., and Thesleff, S. A study of the "desensitization" produced by acetylcholine at the motor end-plate. *J. Physiol. 138:* 63, 1957.

13. LAMANNA, C. The most poisonous poison. *Science. 130:* 763, 1959.
14. NASTUK, W. L. Membrane potential changes at a single muscle end-plate produced by transitory application of acetylcholine with an electrically controlled microjet. *Federation Proc. 12:* 102, 1953.
15. STEVENSON, J. W. Bacterial neurotoxins. *Am. J. M. Sc. 235:* 317, 1958.
16. THESLEFF, S. The mode of neuromuscular block caused by acetylcholine, nicotine, decamethonium and succinylcholine. *Acta physiol. Scandinav. 34:* 218, 1955.
17. THESLEFF, S. Motor end-plate "desensitization" by repetitive nerve stimuli. *J. Physiol. 148:* 659, 1959.
18. THESLEFF, S. Supersensitivity of skeletal muscle produced by botulinum toxin. *J. Physiol. 151:* 598, 1960.
19. TOWER, S., BODIAN, D., and HOWE, H. Isolation of intrinsic and motor mechanism of the monkey's spinal cord. *J. Neurophysiol. 4:* 388, 1941.
20. WRIGHT, G. P. The neurotoxins of Clostridium botulinum and Clostridium tetani. *Pharmacol. Rev. 7:* 413, 1955.

DISCUSSION

DR. ECCLES: There are about three questions I would like to ask. First, you have shown us what happens when you stop activity at the junction with what, I must say, are most impressive results. Very little happens when you have just inactivity of the nerve with the miniature still going. What happens if you prevent the miniatures being stimulated? Do you then get the spreading sensitivity?

Another question about neurons. I don't see how this can be of significance in the sensitizing of neurons because each synapse has its own area of application of transmitter. I would think the diffusion of the transmitter into space is so rapid that it wouldn't make any appreciable difference. However, that may be so, and I may have the wrong idea.

The last question is this. If you have multiple innervating fibers and if you cut one and knock it out, what happens to the other junction, and is the sensitivity at the remaining junction increased?

Dr. Thesleff: As for the first question, we have tried to study the effect of curarization, i.e., whether it produces changes similar to denervation or not. There are several difficulties. One has to keep the animal completely curarized for long periods. We have had cats completely curarized for two weeks and did not observe a denervation effect. However, every other measure which puts an animal in bad shape, immobilizing, paralyzing, or other means, has delayed the denervation process. So the results have not been conclusive.

The second question was about the neurons. This was just a hypothesis, and I don't think I should discuss it without further evidence.

The third question about partial denervation has been answered by work done by R. Miledi in London. He denervated one end-plate in muscles with two end-plates, and could show that the sensitivity of the denervated end-plate increased while the one which was still innervated remained about normal.

Dr. Wolman: In your desensitizing with the return of the membrane potential to baseline is there an increased membrane conductance which might account for the shortening of the sensitivity?

Dr. Thesleff: We have studied the membrane resistance of a muscle fiber at the end-plate in an innervated fiber by measuring the resistance from a point inside the fiber to the outside medium and have not been able to demonstrate any change in conductance during the desensitization process.

Dr. Trent: I am very much interested in the time required for the development of supersensitivity. After both denervation and bionecrosis you require one week. Obviously there is some time required for the degeneration of the nerve fibers and the time of bionecrosis. Have you any time required for supersensitivity after denervation is achieved?

Dr. Thesleff: We have studied this, and the miniatures were abolished about 36 hours after cutting the nerve. We have observed the first detectable increase in size of the receptor surface about 40 hours after cutting the nerve. After that you can follow the increase at about two-hour intervals and detect an increase.

Dr. Killam: Do you have any information about the distribution of cholinesterase after denervation?

Dr. Thesleff: There is some confusion about this point. Some claim that there is a decrease in total cholinesterase activity and some that there is a notable increase. I think most agree that the cholinesterase at the end-plate is reduced.

Dr. Eccles: Is there any curve for the spread of chemosensitivity along the fiber? Is it a smooth curve or are there any breaks? Does it increase a certain number of hours after or does it go smoothly?

Dr. Thesleff: This is very difficult to answer with the techniques we have used. It is my feeling that it goes smoothly.

Dr. Davis: I might make a general comment. I think it is interesting that there seems to be some property of the tissue, in this case the muscle fiber, which tends to keep active to a certain degree when it is not activated due to these procedures. The sensitivity increases, and more likely given a certain amount of stimulation it will contract, and vice versa, with greater activity leading to an impeding of the excitation. There is perhaps some sort of general regulatory principle at work here, the tissue tending to some equilibrium of medium degree. If we extend this concept to our concept of the central nervous system, then it is a process exactly the opposite of learning. It is something more in the nature of forgetting or avoiding getting into too much of a rut. It is a negative rather than a positive feedback.

Dr. Eccles: It seems to me that a kind of mechanism ties into this which might be of more general interest. When you do get this sensitivity speeding along the muscle fiber after denervation, it is very important because the whole fiber is in a receptive state. We do know that you can make effective end-plates anywhere along a muscle after it has been denervated. So there is, if you like, a teleological relationship in what you have found.

CHAPTER 2

Abnormal Connections in the Central Nervous System

JOHN C. ECCLES

CRITERIA FOR DEFINING ABNORMAL CONNECTIONS

THE patterns of connections in the central nervous system have been intensively investigated ever since the concept of the neuron was defined in the latter part of the nineteenth century (2, 3, 20, 21, 35). The structural independence of each nerve cell or neuron necessitated the postulate that functional connections occurred at specialized zones in regions of close contact, for which Sherrington (31) introduced the term "synapse." Thus, in establishing a particular pattern of nervous connection, it is not sufficient merely to show that the axons of certain neurons enter into close anatomical relationship with other neurons; the existence of functional synaptic relationship must also be established, as also whether it is excitatory or inhibitory.

The immense complexity of the connections between neurons in the central nervous system has made it a task of great difficulty to discover the principal pathways, and much has yet to be done at this initial stage of the investigation of nervous connections. Until criteria are established for defining the range of variability that can properly be described as normal, it is not profitable to discuss the problem of abnormal connections or aberrancies, as they may conveniently be called. For this reason attention will be restricted to abnormal central connections of the large afferent fibers of mammalian muscles (groups Ia and Ib from annulospiral endings and Golgi tendon organs respectively), since these connections have been investigated with more precise detail than any other connections in the central nervous system (9, 12, 15, 22). In particular the monosynaptic connections from group Ia afferent fibers onto motoneurons have been quantitatively evaluated by intracellular recording from over 1000 motoneurons belonging to 23 different hindlimb muscles and four forelimb muscles. Other central connections of the Ia and Ib afferent fibers of muscles have been much less rigorously investigated; hence, in these cases problems deriving from abnormal connections can be much less clearly defined and will be but briefly referred to.

It will be conceded that the method of recording EPSP's (excitatory postsynaptic potentials) intracellularly from individual motoneurons of a muscle gives more information on the patterns of monosynaptic connection than does the alternative method of testing populations of motoneurons by facilitation of reflexes. The former method has the further advantage of giving a valid quantitative measure of the various monosynaptic connections on any motoneuron, or, otherwise expressed, of the receptor fields from which a motoneuron draws its monosynaptic innervation (cf. refs. 6, 25). For example Figure 2-1*a* and *b* are tracings of EPSP's produced in typical soleus and medial gastrocnemius motoneurons by maximal group I afferent volleys in five different muscle nerves; and in Figure 2-1*c* and *d* pathway widths depict the mean sizes of the EPSP's produced in the whole of the population of soleus and gastrocnemius motoneurons that has been so investigated. It will be evident from Figure 2-1 that the receptive field from which a motoneuron draws its monosynaptic innervation is concentrated on its own muscle, i.e., it is preponderantly homonymous, but it is also subsidiarily derived from other muscles, i.e., heteronymously, particularly from those of related functions; for example, from lateral gastrocnemius and soleus in the case of medial gastrocnemius motoneurons (Fig. 2-1*b*, *d*). At present only two criteria are of value in attempting to decide if a particular instance of the

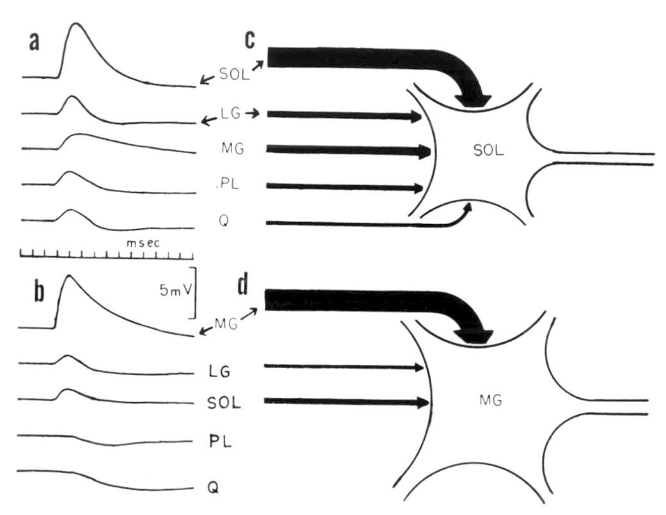

FIG. 2-1. *a*, Tracings of intracellular potentials produced by monosynaptic excitatory action on a soleus motoneuron. Each tracing is the mean of about 40 superimposed records and is produced by a maximum group Ia volley from the indicated muscle nerve, **SOL, LG, MG, PL,** and **Q** being for the nerves to soleus, lateral gastrocnemius, medial gastrocnemius, plantaris, and quadriceps muscles respectively. These monosynaptic EPSP's are often distorted in their latter part by polysynaptic IPSP's (see **LG, PL,** and **Q** traces), but their summit height is not appreciably affected. *b*, As in *a* but for a medial gastrocnemius motoneuron, the plantaris and quadriceps volleys generating only polysynaptic IPSP's. Same time and potential scales for all traces. *c* and *d* show diagrammatically the mean intensities of activation of a soleus and medial gastrocnemius motoneuron respectively by the Ia pathways of the gamma loops through the various muscles, the intensity being indicated by the widths of the channels. Note that soleus motoneuron is shown with a small size and thinner axon (modified from ref. 9).

monosynaptic receptive field is normal or aberrant: first, the frequency with which it is observed for that species of motoneuron; second, whether or not functional significance can be attributed to it.

The concept of the γ-loop control of motoneuronal activation (17, 18, 19) gives functional meaning to the restriction of the monosynaptic receptive field of a motoneuron to the muscle supplied by that motoneuron and to the synergic muscles, as is seen with the gastrocnemius motoneuron in Figure 2-1*b* and *d*. As

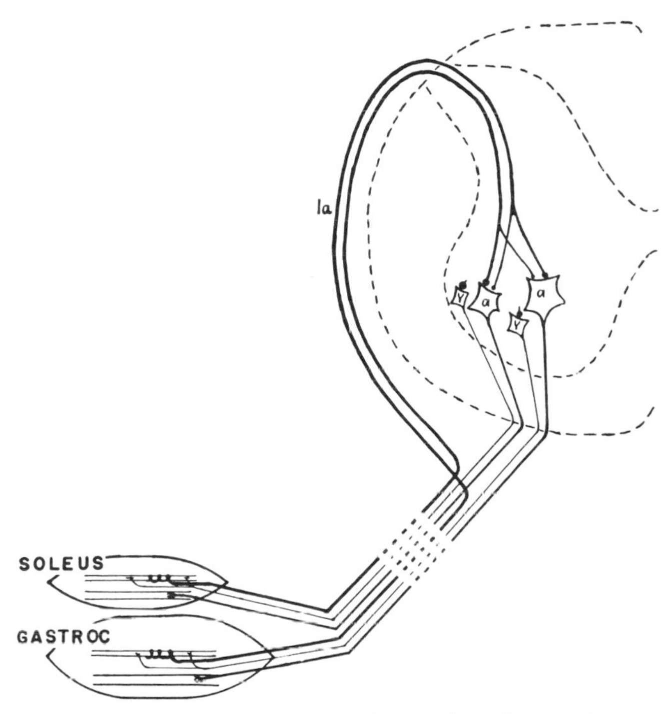

Fig. 2-2. Diagram of gamma-loop pathways for soleus and gastrocnemius motoneurons to show overlapping central connections of the gamma loops for these two synergic muscles. The small motoneurons labeled γ are activated by the synaptic knobs on their surface to discharge impulses to the muscle spindles, with the consequent activation of the annulospiral endings that discharge up the large Ia afferent fibers that monosynaptically activate the (α) motoneurons.

indicated in Figure 2-2 for soleus and gastrocnemius muscles, γ-loop operation occurs via the discharge of impulses from γ motoneurons along the γ-efferent fibers to the muscle spindles of a muscle, with the consequent activation of the annulospiral endings and discharge of impulses along the Ia afferent fibers which monosynaptically excite the α motoneurons to discharge impulses and so evoke a contraction of that muscle and its synergists. If the Ia afferent fibers from a muscle monosynaptically excited motoneurons not synergic with that muscle, the γ-loop mechanism would be likely to cause contraction of muscles having divergent functions, with the consequent risk of incoordinated movement. Thus, in this simplest view of the activation of motoneurons, all expansion of monosynaptic receptive fields beyond the synergic muscles should be regarded as aberrant.

It will be readily agreed that, when muscles act across two joints, the so-called double-joint muscles, it is appropriate for γ-loop operation that the Ia receptive field of their motoneurons should include the single-joint muscles acting synergically at one or the other joint. In addition, it is appropriate that the motoneurons of these latter two groups of single-joint muscles should include the double-joint muscle in their receptive fields. The reciprocal monosynaptic excitatory action in one example can be expressed as: tibialis anticus (ankle flexor) $\rightleftharpoons$ extensor digitorum longus (double-joint; ankle flexor plus digital extensor) $\rightleftharpoons$ extensor digitorum brevis (digital extensor); and two other examples are known (6). Such expansions of the receptive fields of motoneurons must be regarded as normal, on the grounds both of their frequency of occurrence and of their functional meaning.

Even when the investigation of monosynaptic receptive fields is restricted to muscles operating across the simple hinge-joints of the knee, ankle, or digits, the respective motoneuronal receptive fields sometimes expand to muscles whose action is entirely exerted at an adjacent joint, as for example in Figure 2-1*a*, *c*, where the knee extensor, vasto-crureus, is in the receptive field for soleus motoneurons, which act solely in ankle extension. Though no functional meaning can yet be given to that expansion of the receptive field beyond synergic muscles, it cannot be regarded as an aberrancy because it is present with almost every soleus motoneuron (9), and because a comparable connection occurs in the forelimb, where the shoulder extensor, supraspinatus, is in the receptive field for motoneurons of the single-joint elbow extensors, caput laterale, caput mediale and anconaeus (15). These expansions of the receptive field are not reciprocal, but there is reciprocity between the monosynaptic connections of the knee and hip extensors: vasto-crurcus ⇄ hip extensors (adductor femoris, biceps anterior, semimembranosus).

ABERRANCIES IN A NORMAL ANIMAL

If functional meaning is eventually to be given to these various expansions of the Ia receptive fields of motoneurons, it seems necessary to consider the integrated behavior of the limb as a basis of understanding, rather than each joint as an independent entity. However, even when allowance is made for such a possible development, there are examples of monosynaptic excitation which must be classed as aberrant on the grounds both of their rarity and of the unlikelihood that they can be given any functional meaning. Examples of particular relevance to our experimental investigations on aberrant connections are the reciprocal monosynaptic connections from the post-tibial extensor muscles (gastrocnemius, plantaris, and flexor digitorum longus) to the peroneal muscles (peroneus longus, brevis, and tertius). Not only are these monosynaptic actions uncommon, occurring in about 7 per cent of the various test situations (range 2 to 15 per cent of the peroneus motoneurons in different experiments), but they are also very small, contributing on the average about 1 per cent of the total monosynaptic excitatory action on the individual motoneurons. A further reason for regarding such monosynaptic excitatory connections as aberrant is that an inhibitory action was much more common for precisely the same Ia afferent pathways, being present with almost half the motoneurons, e.g., from the post-tibial extensor muscles onto 22 out of 49 peroneus motoneurons (12).

Other examples of indubitable aberrancies are shown in Figures 2-3 and 2-4 (9). In Figure 2-3 a biceps-semitendinosus volley had a small monosynaptic excitatory action on a vastus lateralis motoneuron instead of the usual Ia inhibitory action,

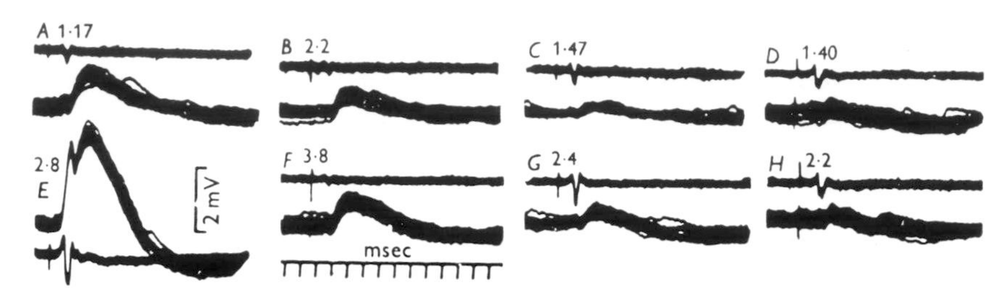

FIG. 2-3. Lower traces in all but *E* are intracellular records from a vastus lateralis motoneuron, internal positivity (depolarization) being signaled upward. The other traces are recorded by an electrode making contact with the L_6 dorsal root as it enters the spinal cord, negatively being signaled downward. *A, E* are evoked by volleys in vastus lateralis nerve; *B, F,* crureus nerve; *C, G,* rectus femoris nerve; *D, H,* biceps-semitendinosus nerve. Strengths of stimulation are indicated relative to respective thresholds. All intracellular traces are at same speed and amplification (9).

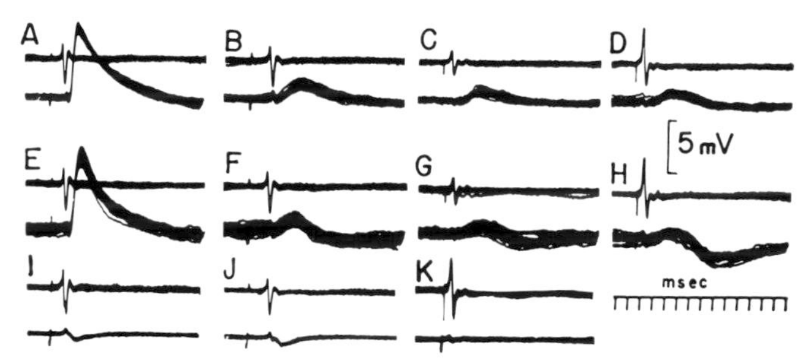

FIG. 2-4. As in Figure 2-3, but for a motoneuron of the semitendinosus-biceps posterior nucleus; *I, J,* and *K* were recorded extracellularly in close proximity to the motoneuron. (Ventral roots were cut; therefore, antidromic identification was not possible.) *A, E,* and *I* are evoked by volleys in the semitendinosus-biceps posterior nerve; *B, F,* and *J,* by gastrocnemius-soleus nerve; *C, D, G, H,* and *K,* by quadriceps nerve. Depolarizing current applied during *F, G,* and *H.* Strengths of stimulation are indicated relative to the respective thresholds. All intracellular traces are at same speed and amplification, as also are the extracellular traces, *I, J,* and *K* (9).

which was observed on adjacent vastus motoneurons. Figure 2-4 is remarkable because the presumed biceps-semitendinosus motoneuron there illustrated was one of nine in close proximity that displayed aberrant monosynaptic connections from gastrocnemius (*B, F*) muscle and also from quadriceps (*C, D, G, H*); whereas at other segmental levels in this spinal cord there were no aberrant connections onto the biceps-semitendinosus motoneurons. Apparently there was a region where the development of specific connections was defectively controlled.

Aberrant connections are of particular interest when considering the mode of development of specific connections in the nervous system. A remarkable instance of specific connections is provided by the Ia afferent fibers from gracilis muscle, which, besides monosynaptically exciting gracilis and sartorius motoneurons at L_5 level, descend for about two segments down the spinal cord to make an exclusive monosynaptic connection with the motoneurons of another knee flexor, the semitendinosus; and, reciprocally, semitendinosus afferent fibers ascend two segments to exert a strong monosynaptic excitation exclusively on gracilis motoneurons. A comparable condition has already been noted with the vasto-crureus afferent fibers that descend about two segments in order to make an almost exclusive connection with soleus motoneurons. It does not seem possible that these highly selective intersegmental connections are established by the growth of fibers in from the primitive spinal ganglia along the easiest channels between tissue planes. On such an explanation it would be expected that aberrant connections to the many other species of motoneurons would be far more frequent than is normally observed.

ORIGINS OF ABERRANCIES

One possible explanation of the development of selective connections is that some specific chemical or physicochemical property of the group Ia fibers provides a "selective contact guidance" during growth; and, furthermore, limits the possibility of their functional connection, so that it occurs only to those motoneurons that have a complementary specificity (32, 38). An influence of a muscle on the motoneurons innervating it was postulated by Wiersma (40) and Weiss (36, 37, 39). This postulate of a "modulating" influence of muscle on motoneurons, "myotypic specification," has been developed by Sperry (32, 33, 34) and Weiss (39) into the concept that the motoneuron could in this way be conditioned to attract and retain one type of synaptic contact rather than another, there being some kind of chemical affinity or "specification" between a nerve cell and the synaptic knobs in contact with it. Specification as a controlling factor is further suggested by the finding that no motoneuron receives both excitation and inhibition from the group Ia fibers of any particular muscle (15). The postulated myotypic specification must be distinguished from the chemical transmitter mechanism at synaptic junctions; the former is responsible for the actual existence of the synapses, the latter for their functional operation. Yet it seems very probable that there is a relationship; else the specification could cause the development of synaptic contacts that were functionless because the chemical transmitter was ineffective.

At present the only alternative to the explanation by specification is that initially all varieties of functional connection are made by the ingrowing Ia fibers, and this virtual randomness of connection is gradually shaped to the specific adult patterns by a process of "resculpturing," by means of which all inappropriate connections regress, while there is a complementary enhancement of those synaptic connections "corresponding" to proper function (32).

EFFECT OF OPERATIVE CROSS-UNIONS

These postulated processes for the development of specific connections have been tested by operatively cross-uniting nerves to antagonistic muscles in very young animals (kittens 1–25 days old) and some months later by investigating the Ia receptive fields of the motoneurons with changed function (12). A control population of motoneurons together with suitable control Ia afferent pathways was ensured by leaving one or more muscles of each synergic group with unmolested nerve supply, as is indicated diagrammatically in Figure 2-5*B*. The nerves to medial gastrocnemius and to the peroneus muscles (longus, brevis, and tertius) were cross-united, and at the end of the final experimental investigation it was found by electrophysiological test

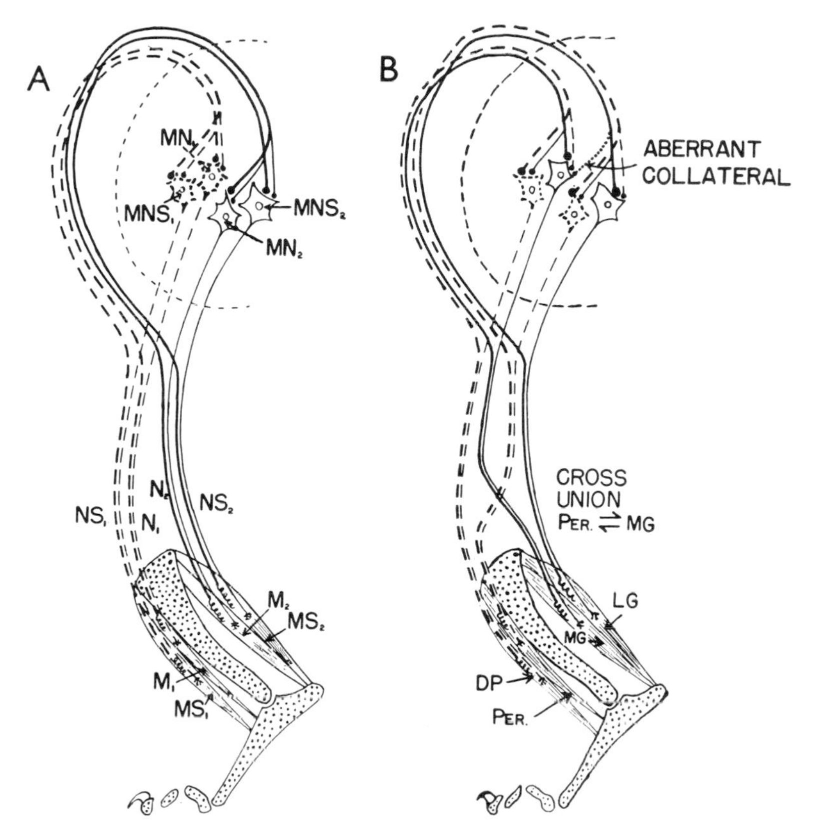

FIG. 2-5. *A*, Diagram showing the monosynaptic pathways for two pretibial muscles, $\mathbf{M}_1$ and $\mathbf{MS}_1$, and two post-tibial muscles, $\mathbf{M}_2$ and $\mathbf{MS}_2$. Only one group Ia afferent fiber ($\mathbf{NS}_1$, $\mathbf{N}_1$, $\mathbf{N}_2$, and $\mathbf{NS}_2$) and motoneuron ($\mathbf{MS}_1$, $\mathbf{MN}_1$, $\mathbf{MN}_2$, and $\mathbf{MN}_2$) with motor fiber is shown for each muscle, the afferent fibers being distinguished by their thicker lines. The afferent and efferent pathways for muscles functioning as flexors are shown by broken lines. It will be seen that the afferent fibers have monosynaptic action on the motoneuron of their own muscle and, to a less extent, on that of the synergic muscle, as shown by the thinner collateral branch. $\mathbf{MS}_1$, $\mathbf{MS}_2$, $\mathbf{MNS}_1$, and $\mathbf{MNS}_2$ are the muscles and motoneurons of the synergists that are used as controls. *B*, Diagram showing changed peripheral connections when regeneration has followed the cross-union. The change in function is shown by the change in broken line designation. In the spinal cord the dotted line shows the abberant connections that developed from the Ia afferent fibers of post-tibial extensors to the motoneurons of the peroneal muscles when nerves to medial gastrocnemius and to the peroneal muscles were cross-united (12).

that the cross-union was complete, there being not even one stray fiber. However, an unavoidable complication was the chromatolytic degeneration and death of many (about 70 per cent) motoneurons and spinal ganglion cells that follow nerve section in very young animals.

Figure 2-6 illustrates the intracellular responses evoked by a variety of nerves in a peroneal motoneuron that had become an ankle extensor through reinnervating medial gastrocnemius muscle. In the ensemble of the responses evoked by the various nerve volleys as indicated, the membrane potential change is the difference between the intracellular and extracellular records, as given by the two superimposed traces, the continuous line and the dotted line respectively. It is immediately evident that depolarizing potentials with the characteristic brief latency of monosynaptic EPSP's were set up by lateral gastrocnemius, plantaris, and flexor digitorum longus volleys in *F*, *G*, and *H*, respectively. On the other hand, in *C* and *D* the biceps-semitendinosus and semimembranosus afferent volleys had no monosynaptic action. The EPSP produced by the lateral gastrocnemius plus plantaris afferent volleys (*I*) was nearly as large as that generated homonymously in *A*, or by the afferents from the normal synergic muscles in *B*. The series with graded strengths of stimulation (*J–M*) shows this monosynaptic EPSP was produced by the lowest threshold group I afferent fibers and hence is attributable to the group Ia fibers (8, 10).

Altogether, in the 11 experiments with this cross-union operation, satisfactory intracellular investigations were made on 102 peroneal motoneurons that had reinnervated medial gastrocnemius muscle. In addition, 59 normal peroneal motoneurons were investigated in order to provide a control series. The upper section of Table 2-1 enables a comparison to be made between the frequency with which monosynaptic connections occur in the cross-united and the control series of peroneal motoneurons. The receptive field of the peroneal motoneurons reinnervating medial gastrocnemius had greatly expanded into the post-tibial extensor muscles, particularly to the lateral gastrocnemius (6 to 40 per cent), which is the most effective synergist to the medial gas-

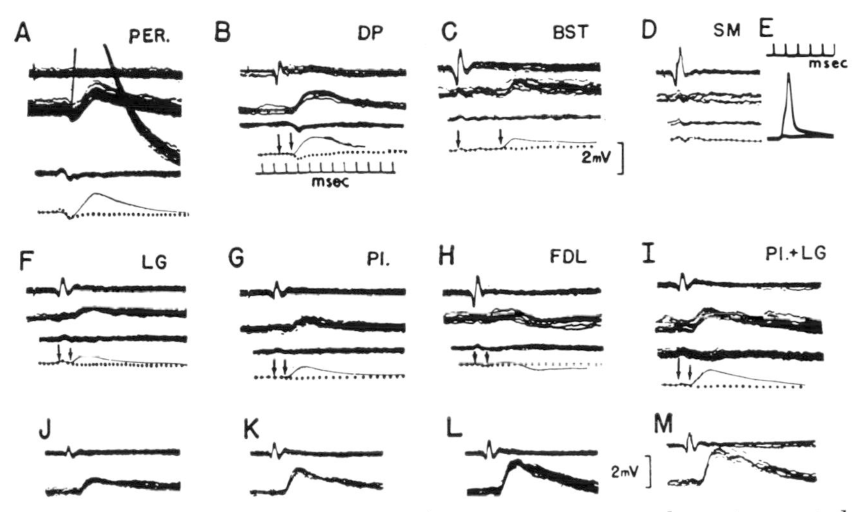

FIG. 2-6. Intracellular responses of a Per. motoneuron that reinnervated MG muscle. The three records of each ensemble *A–D* and *F–I* are each formed by the superposition of about 20 faint traces and show from above downward; the potential produced by an afferent volley at the dorsal root entry at mid-L_7 segmental level, negativity being upward; the intracellular potential of a Per. motoneuron having a membrane potential of −75 mV and spike potential of 109 mV, positivity being upward; the potential produced by the same volley, but with a just extracellular position of the microelectrode. Below the three records there is a superimposed tracing of the intracellular (*continuous line*) and extracellular (*dotted line*) records showing the time course of the potential change across the neuronal membrane. With *A* the stimulus to the Per. nerve was just at threshold for the axon of the motoneuron, producing an antidromic spike potential in about half the intracellular traces (*middle series*), which is shown at much lower amplification in *E*. *B–D* and *F–I* were produced by a maximum group I afferent volley in nerves indicated by the symbols: **DP** = deep peroneal; **BST** = biceps-semitendinosus; **SM** = semimembranosus; **LG** = lateral gastrocnemius; **PL** = plantaris; **FDL** = flexor digitorum longus. With **PL** plus **LG** the two volleys were synchronized. Same time scale for all records and same potential scale for all intracellular and extracellular records except *E*. The *two arrows* in the superimposed traces give the central synaptic delay. *J–M* show responses to **PL** plus **LG** volleys at the height of post-tetanic potentiation, being evoked by stimuli of increasing strength from *J* to *M*, *J* being so weak that it was submaximal for group Ia and below the Ib threshold. Same time scale for all intracellular record (12).

trocnemius. In the lower part of Table 2-1 the mean monosynaptic EPSP's were calculated by dividing the aggregate of the EPSP's observed for that nerve volley by the total number of motoneurons. For example, the aggregate EPSP for the action

Table 2-1

Tabled results for the 11 experiments with cross-union of Per. and MG nerves together with 12 control experiments. The monosynaptic EPSP's in motonuerons (arranged in rows) are shown for volleys in five different muscle nerves (arranged in columns). The upper part of the table gives the number of Per. cells responding by recognizable EPSP's over the total so investigated, the upper row giving the series for cross-union, i.e., for Per. motoneurons reinnervating MG, and the lower row the control series. The lower part of the table gives the mean EPSP in mV for the total Per. cells so investigated, the upper row again giving the series for cross-union (Per. motoneurons reinnervating MG), and the lower row the control series.

	Nerve volleys				
Motoneurons	DP	Per.	LG	PL	FDL
Cross-Union Per. → MG	92/102	85/100	41/102	17/101	23/95
Control Per. → Per.	40/56	59/59	3/52	1/54	6/54
Cross-Union Per. → MG	1.50	1.17	0.20	0.05	0.08
Control Per. → Per.	0.94	3.66	0.015	0.01	0.04

The abbreviations for nerves and motoneurons are as follows: DP = deep peroneal; Per. = peroneus longus, brevis, and tertius; MG = medial gastrocnemius; LG = lateral gastrocnemius plus soleus; PL = plantaris; FDL = flexor digitorum longus plus flexor hallucis longus.

of lateral gastrocnemius volleys on peroneal motoneurons was 20.3 mV, which gives a mean of 0.20 mV for the 102 motoneurons so investigated. Again the lateral gastrocnemius leads the other post-tibial extensor muscles in respect of the potency of its receptive field, which had increased more than tenfold above the control value (0.20/0.015).

In Figure 2-6 plantaris was more effective than lateral gastrocnemius, but Figure 2-7 illustrates the more usual situation with much greater effectiveness of the aberrant monosynaptic connections from lateral gastrocnemius. As illustrated in Figure 2-6 there was no development of aberrant connections from biceps-semitendinosus or semimembranosus afferent fibers onto the peroneal motoneurons with changed function.

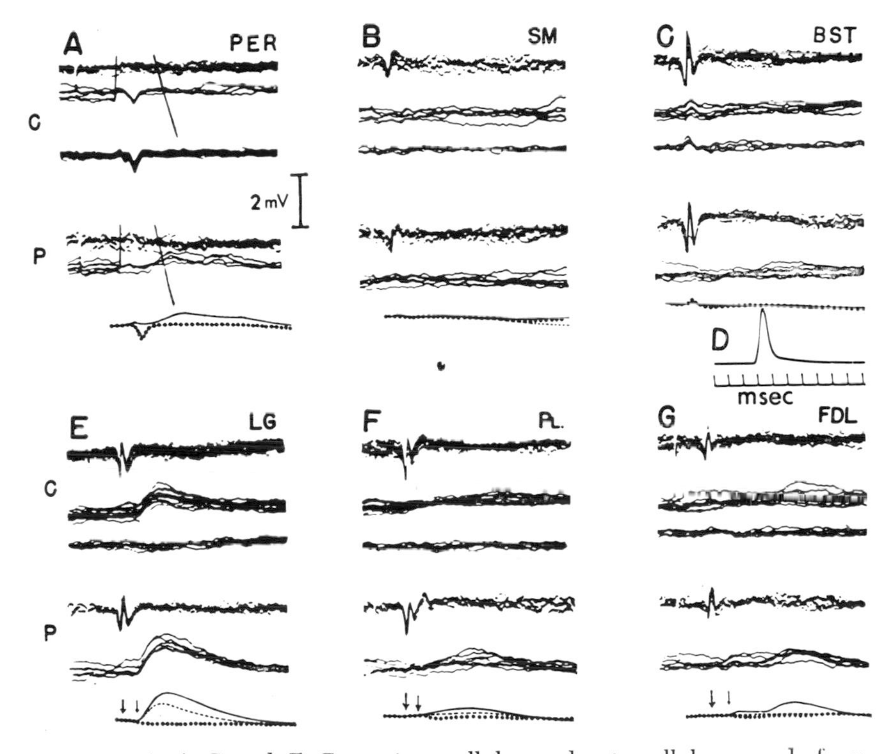

FIG. 2-7. *A–C* and *E–G* are intracellular and extracellular records from a Per. motoneuron that reinnervated MC muscle (membrane potential of −76mV and spike potential of 76 mV, arranged to show intracellular records before, row **C** and after post-tetanic potentiation, row **P**). Between **C** and **P** are the corresponding extracellular records, while below **P** are the superimposed tracings of the two intracellular (*broken line*, **C**; *continuous*, **P**) and the extracellular (*dotted line*) records, the *arrows* giving the approximate central synaptic delays. The afferent volleys are identified as in Figure 2-6. *D* shows the intracellular antidromic spike evoked by a Per. volley, and recorded at much lower amplification. Same time scale for all records, and all but *D* at same amplification. The afferent volley records are mid-L_7 level, negativity being upward (12).

Similar investigations have been made with the complementary component of the cross-union operation of Figures 2-6 and 2-7, namely, on the medial gastrocnemius motoneurons reinnervating peroneal muscles. Little or no increase in aberrancy was observed (12). Failure of cross-union to alter the Ia receptive fields of motoneurons also occurred with both species of motoneurons in six preliminary cross-unions between the nerves to the peroneal muscles and to the lateral gastrocnemius-soleus muscle (7).

Since the receptive field for peroneal motoneurons reinnervating medial gastrocnemius muscle expanded particularly to the acquired synergic muscle, lateral gastrocnemius (Table 2-1), it is an attractive postulate that this expansion results from the transformed motoneuron function and is specifically related thereto. However, an alternative explanation would attribute the expanded receptive field to a nonspecific sprouting of primary afferent fibers that was evoked by the degenerating central terminals of those spinal ganglion cells dying from the chromatolysis, as mentioned above. Such nonspecific sprouting has been found to occur after hemisection of the spinal cord (28), and also has been observed in the peripheral nervous system (16, 29). Experiments now in progress may enable a decision to be made between these two alternative explanations, but already there are good grounds for regarding nonspecific sprouting as responsible for no more than a small fraction of the developed aberrancy (12).

It thus appears likely that the major part of the developed aberrancy in Table 2-1 arises on account of some specific growth that is attributable to such processes as "myotypic specification" or "resculpturing." The resculpturing hypothesis is not supported because it predicts that there would be a loss of monosynaptic connections from the control synergic muscles that function as antagonists after the cross-union, i.e., that there would be a decrease in the EPSP's produced by the deep peroneal nerve on the transformed peroneal motoneurons, whereas in Table 2-1 there is actually an increase from a mean value of 0.94 to 1.50 mV. On the other hand, the postulated process of myotypic specification would account for the large increase in the monosynaptic activation by lateral gastrocnemius of peroneal motoneurons reinnervating medial gastrocnemius muscle. It has to be postulated, first, that the medial gastrocnemius muscle fibers effect some retrograde change up the motor axons reinnervating them, and, second, that there is a consequent transformation of the surface specificity of their motoneurons, the original peroneal motoneurons, which thereby attract synaptic connections from the closely related lateral gastrocnemius Ia afferent fibers in the vicinity (cf. the dotted line of Fig. 2-5*B*). The lack of close proximity of the control motoneuronal nuclei may explain the failure of aberrancy to develop with other examples of transformed motoneuronal function, as referred to above.

However, even if myotypic specification is responsible for the observed aberrancies in Table 2-1, the magnitude of this effect is far less than would be expected for a process that is postulated to account for the embryological development of specific connections. Possibly specification is much more effective at the very early stage of development. As postulated by Weiss (37) and Sperry (32, 33, 34), one can envisage the growing nerve fiber as chemically sensing the surfaces along which it grows, and being specifically attracted by the chemical properties of some surfaces and not by others. There are now many lines of evidence which suggest that the development of synaptic connections can be explained only by some such postulate of surface specificity. For example, group Ia and Ib primary afferent fibers of muscle appear never to make functional synaptic connections on the same nerve cell, whether this be a motoneuron, an interneuron of the intermediate nucleus, a cell of Clarke's column, or a cell of origin of the ventral spinocerebellar tract (11, 27, 30). Apparently these two types of fiber differ in respect of the surfaces which attract them.

The central pathways for the inhibitory action of group Ia afferent fibers are also of interest when considering the specificity of pathways. It can first be stated that no single exception has been found to the rule that the pathway for inhibitory action on motoneurons or the cells of origin of the dorsal and ventral spinocerebellar tracts always includes an interneuron (1, 4, 5, 13, 14, 15). The dogmatic statements to the contrary (23, 24) are based upon miscalculations of the latency of central inhibitory action. When this is experimentally determined by measuring the time between the entry of the inhibitory volley into the spinal cord and the onset of the first inhibitory action on the reflex spike discharge, the central inhibitory latency is about 0.2 msec. *longer* than the latency of the intracellularly recorded inhibitory postsynaptic potential, a discrepancy that is attributable to the conduction time of impulses from their site of initiation to the recording electrode on the ventral root (1). Presumably Ia impulses cannot liberate inhibitory transmitter substance; therefore, they have to be relayed by special inhibitory interneurons before they can exert an inhibitory action. Hence it is readily appreciated why group Ia impulses never exert a monosynaptic inhibitory action, and this rule invariably obtains also for the aberrant connections developing after cross-union of nerves.

ABERRANT CONNECTION TO DORSAL SPINOCEREBELLAR TRACT

The connections which afferent fibers from muscle and skin establish with the cells of origin of the dorsal spinocerebellar tract (DSCT) have now been investigated so thoroughly that there are good grounds for recognizing certain types of connection as aberrant. Lundberg and Oscarsson (26) have shown that the great majority of fibers in the DSCT belong to five clearly defined functional groups. However, out of the several hundred fibers that were investigated, there were several stemming from cells in Clarke's column that exhibited connections characteristic of each of two different groups. For example, fibers receiving the typical monosynaptic connections from group I muscle afferents also received monosynaptically from cutaneous afferent fibers; and there was one example of a fiber that exhibited the very specific monosynaptic connection from afferent fibers of the pressure receptors in the foot pad and that also received monosynaptically from group I muscle afferents. Finally, there were two examples of DSCT fibers that were typically activated by groups I and II muscle afferents, but from the contralateral side.

It seems probable that more intensive investigations of the individual fibers of other tracts will disclose the existence of aberrancies comparable with those of the DSCT. When the manner of development of connections in the central nervous system is taken into account, it is remarkable that aberrancies are of such rare occurrence. It would seem that the problem confronting us is not: How do aberrancies come to exist; but rather: How does it come about that aberrancies are so uncommon. Presumably it has to be postulated that, in development, the establishment of functional synaptic connections is controlled very effectively by the chemical sensing of surfaces that has already been referred to. However, the existence of aberrancies shows that this process is not 100 per cent efficient. Possibly during development the postulated factors of myotypic specification and resculpturing are operative in reducing the incidence of aberrancies, so that, eventually, they are almost completely eliminated from the adult nervous system. It will be appreciated that, on account of the necessity for convergent excitatory action at each synaptic relay, the nervous system will readily eliminate functional disturbances arising from relatively rare aberrant pathways.

REFERENCES

1. Araki, T., Eccles, J. C., and Ito, M. Correlation of the inhibitory postsynaptic potential of motoneurones with the latency and time course of inhibition of monosynaptic reflexes. *J. Physiol. 154:* 354–377, 1960.
2. Cajal, S. R. Sur les fibres nerveuses de la couche granuleuse du cervelet et sur l'évolution des élèments cérébelleux. *Internat. Mschr. Anat. Physiol. 7:* 12–31, 1890.
3. Cajal, S. R. Sur l'origine et les ramifications des fibres nerveuses de la moelle embryonnaire. *Anat. Anz. 5:* 85–95, 1890.
4. Curtis, D. R., Eccles, J. C., and Lundberg, A. Intracellular recording from cells in Clarke's column. *Acta physiol. Scandinav. 43:* 303–314, 1958.
5. Curtis, D. R., Krnjevic, K., and Miledi, R. Crossed inhibition of sacral motoneurones. *J. Neurophysiol. 21:* 319–326, 1958.
6. Eccles, J. C. Monosynaptic excitatory patterns and the connec-

tions of group Ia afferent fibres from muscle. *21st International Congress of Physiological Sciences.* Pp. 87–93, 1959.

7. Eccles, J. C. Plasticity at the simplest levels of the nervous system. Pp. 217–244. In *The Centennial Lectures.* Edited by J. T. Culbertson. G. P. Putnam's Sons, New York, 1959.
8. Eccles, J. C., Eccles, R. M., and Lundberg, A. Synaptic actions on motoneurones in relation to the two components of the group I muscle afferent volley. *J. Physiol. 136:* 527–546, 1957.
9. Eccles, J. C., Eccles, R. M., and Lundberg, A. The convergence of monosynaptic excitatory afferents on to many different species of alpha motoneurones. *J. Physiol. 137:* 22–50, 1957.
10. Eccles, J. C., Eccles, R. M., and Lundberg, A. Synaptic actions on motoneurones caused by impulses in Golgi tendon organ afferents. *J. Physiol. 138:* 227–252, 1957.
11. Eccles, J. C., Eccles, R. M., and Lundberg, A. Types of neurone in and around the intermediate nucleus of the lumbo-sacral cord. *J. Physiol. 154:* 89–114, 1960.
12. Eccles, J. C., Eccles, R. M., and Magni, F. Monosynaptic excitatory action on motoneurones regenerated to antagonistic muscles. *J. Physiol. 154:* 68–88, 1960.
13. Eccles, J. C., Fatt, P., and Landgren, S. The central pathway for the direct inhibitory action of impulses in the largest afferent nerve fibres to muscle. *J. Neurophysiol. 19:* 75–98, 1956.
14. Eccles, J. C., Hubbard, J. I., and Oscarsson, O. Intracellular recording from cells of the ventral spinocerebellar tract. *J. Physiol. 158:* 517–543, 1961.
15. Eccles, R. M., and Lundberg, A. Integrative pattern of Ia synaptic actions on motoneurones of hip and knee muscles. *J. Physiol. 144:* 271–298, 1958.
16. Edds, M. V. Collateral nerve regeneration. *Quart. Rev. Biol. 28:* 260–276, 1953.
17. Eldred, E., Granit, R., and Merton, P. A. Supraspinal control of the muscle spindles and its significance. *J. Physiol. 122:* 498–523, 1953.
18. Granit, R. *Receptors and Sensory Perception.* Yale University Press, New Haven, 1955.
19. Granit, R., and Kaada, B. R. Influence of stimulation of central nervous structures on muscle spindles in cat. *Acta physiol. Scandinav. 27:* 130–160, 1952.
20. His, W. *Zur Geschichte des menschlichen Rückenmarks und der Nervenwurzeln.* Leipzig, 1886.

21. HIS, W. Die Neuroblasten und deren Entstehung im embryonalen Marke. *Abh. sächs. Ges. (Akad.) Wiss. 15:* 311–372, 1889.
22. LAPORTE, Y., and LLOYD, D. P. C. Nature and significance of the reflex connections established by large afferent fibers of muscular origin. *Am. J. Physiol. 169:* 609–621, 1952.
23. LLOYD, D. P. C. Spinal mechanisms involved in somatic activities. *Handbook of Physiology: Neurophysiology 2:* 929–949, 1960. Edited by John Field. American Physiological Society, Washington, D. C.
24. LLOYD, D. P. C., and WILSON, V. J. Functional organization in the terminal segments of the spinal cord with a consideration of central excitatory and inhibitory latencies in monosynaptic reflex systems. *J. Gen. Physiol. 42:* 1219–1231, 1959.
25. LUNDBERG, A. Integrative significance of patterns of connections made by muscle afferents in the spinal cord. *21st International Congress of Physiological Sciences.* Pp. 100–105, 1959.
26. LUNDBERG, A., and OSCARSSON, O. Functional organization of the dorsal spino-cerebellar tract in the cat. VII. Identification of units by antidromic activation from the cerebellar cortex with recognition of five functional subdivisions. *Acta physiol. Scandinav. 50:* 356–374, 1960.
27. LUNDBERG, A., and WINSBURY, G. J. Functional organization of the dorsal spino-cerebellar tract. VI. Further experiments on excitation from tendon organ and muscle spindle afferents. *Acta physiol. Scandinav. 49:* 165–170, 1960.
28. MCCOUCH, G. P., AUSTIN, G. M., LIU, C. N., and LIU, C. Y. Sprouting as a cause of spasticity. *J. Neurophysiol. 21:* 205–216, 1958.
29. MURRAY, J. G., and THOMPSON, J. W. The occurrence and function of collateral sprouting in the sympathetic nervous system of the cat. *J. Physiol. 135:* 133–162, 1957.
30. OSCARSSON, O. Functional organization of the ventral spino-cerebellar tract in the cat. *Acta physiol. Scandinav. 42:* Suppl. 146, 1957.
31. SHERRINGTON, C. S. The central nervous system. In Foster's *A Text Book of Physiology.* 7th ed. Macmillan, London, 1897.
32. SPERRY, R. W. Mechanisms of neural maturation. In *Handbook of Experimental Psychology.* Edited by S. S. Stevens. John Wiley & Sons, Inc., New York, 1951.
33. SPERRY, R. W. Regulative factors in the orderly growth of neural circuits. *Growth: Symposium. 10:* 63–87, 1951.

34. SPERRY, R. W. Physiological plasticity and brain circuit theory. In *Biological and Biochemical Bases of Behaviour.* Pp. 401–424. Edited by H. F. Harlow and C. N. Woolsey. University of Wisconsin Press, Madison, 1958.
35. WALDEYER, H. W. G. Uber einige neuere Forschungen im Gebiete der Anatomie des Zentralnervensystems. *Deutsche med. Wchnschr. 17:* 1213–1281, 1891.
36. WEISS, P. Selectivity controlling the central-peripheral relations in the nervous system. *Biol. Rev. 11:* 494–531, 1936.
37. WEISS, P. The problem of specificity in growth and development. *Yale J. Biol. & Med. 19:* 235–278, 1947.
38. WEISS, P. The deplantation of fragments of nervous system in amphibians. I. Central reorganization and the formation of nerves. *J. Exper. Zool. 113:* 397–461, 1950.
39. WEISS, P. Central versus peripheral factors in the development of coordination. In *Patterns of Organization in the Central Nervous System. Res. Publ. Ass. Nerv. Ment. Dis. 30:* 3–23, 1952.
40. WIERSMA, C. A. G. An experiment on the "Resonance Theory" of muscular activity. *Arch. néerl. Physiol. 16:* 337–345, 1931.

DISCUSSION

DR. ECCLES: When performing a cross-union operation the afferents are cut, but the synaptic connections of the uncut afferents form the basis of the experimental results. These were not at all affected by the operative procedures and they were the ones that gave the significant increases in monosynaptic action. I am looking at the results from the motor neuron point of view; that is at the field from which it receives monosynaptic innervation, and in the light of the afferents that were not molested at all originally.

The effects I showed were very small as a consequence of the crossing, not nearly enough to explain the selectivity of connections that were originally developed. But, if we can find a trace of changed connections after birth, I think we would be likely to find a much greater effect before birth at an early developmental stage; hence it should be possible in this way to explain plausibly how specific development occurs.

DR. WALL: Dr. Eccles, I would like to ask you three questions. First, do you believe that you would have been able to demonstrate the aberrant connections in a normal animal with natural stimuli? We have observed aberrant monosynaptic connections using electrical stimuli, but have been unable to find such connections using natural stimuli. Your results here contradict Sperry's behavioral results. Second, do you believe that some of your results could come from sprouting of aberrant connections in the manner shown for normal dorsal root fibers by McCouch and Alston following the deafferentation of a region? Third, there are not only changes in the dorsal root ganglia in these experiments, but also changes in the motoneurones after section of their axons. Could some of your results be explained by the changes of excitability of neurones whose axons were cut?

DR. ECCLES: The first question concerned aberrant connections and how they might arise from afferent impulses excited by electrical as distinct from adequate stimulation. I assume that when I stimulate nerves electrically the impulses are identical with those produced by adequate stimulation, but with different temporal relations. Adequate stimulation fails to produce that synchronization which is so important when you are seeking for very small connections that would be probably undetectable with stimulation of receptors. Of course, these results are in contradiction to Sperry's experiments. These are the cross-union experiments that he did in the 1940's on rats and monkeys and which he reviewed in 1945. He was observing limb movements, not even muscle contractions. We have been working with much more finesse with this intracellular recording from motoneurones because we probably can detect if there is one single aberrant monosynaptic connection on a motoneurone.

This brings me to the second point, which concerns the aberrant connections that there are likely to be preoperatively. I did specify something like 3 out of 56 peroneus motoneurones had aberrant monosynaptic connections from lateral gastrocnemius nerve in the control animals. This was the total number, for even a single aberrant connection probably would have been detectable. After the cross-union the number of aberrancies was increased to 41 out of 102. I do not think that these can be accounted for by increase in the sizes of the actions of aberrant connections that previously were too small to be detected.

I assume that the third question concerns the possibility that the changes produced in the motoneuronal membrane as a consequence of the cutting of the motor axon in the cross-union operation could lead also to an increase of previously undetectable EPSP's to a size that makes them overt. Experiments with intracellular recording from motoneurones with cut motor axons have shown that on the contrary there is a considerable depression of their monosynaptic responses.

DR. McCOUCH: In regard to the aberrant connections found under normal conditions I would like to call attention to the fact that the biceps is partly a flexor and partly an extensor, and to the fact that the rectus contracts in the flexor reflex as well as in the extensor. From crureus, one can easily inhibit the entire quadriceps. You cannot do so from rectus.

DR. ECCLES: What Dr. McCouch says on the biceps is important. This large muscle has an anterior part that functions as a hip extensor and a posterior part that is a knee flexor. However, there is no clear anatomical separation between these two components, and some of the motoneurones innervating the posterior portion have monosynaptic connections more related to hip extensors than to knee flexors. For example, in the innervation of the posterior biceps you will find some motoneurones with synaptic connections that indicate an extensor function rather than a flexor. There is a worse problem that I feared Dr. McCouch was going to raise. There is a slip of biceps that goes down and joins in the tendon Achilles and so should function as an ankle extensor. Perhaps the motoneuron of Figure 2-4 innervated this slip of muscle.

CHAPTER 3

Higher Functions of the Nervous System

H. W. MAGOUN

THE most striking recent progress in the biology of higher neural activity is unquestionably that in the electrophysiology of behavior. Study of learned behavior and analysis of the mechanism of learning have been especially advanced by a marriage between the electrical recording techniques of Western neurophysiology and the classical Pavlovian approaches to study of conditional reflexes, cultivated so extensively in the USSR. These advances have formed the subject of a number of recent international meetings, among which have been: the Moscow Colloquim on *EEG and Higher Nervous Activity* (13), the Montevideo Symposium on *Brain Mechanisms and Learning* (27), and the Macy Conference Series on *CNS and Behavior* (1).

The present paper will survey some of the recent advances which exemplify Western approaches to this field, and then review contributions to analysis of the orienting reflex, an important area of current Soviet research.

ELECTROCORTICAL CONDITIONING

While pioneering studies of the electrical activity of the brain during learning were undertaken in the USSR by M. N. Livanov and A. B. Kogan, from the 1930's on, and more recently have been extended by a considerable number of Soviet investigators (26), their findings are just now becoming available in English translation, and Western knowledge of them is still regrettably limited.

Western studies in this field similarly began in the thirties when Durup and Fessard (5), in a study of the alpha-blocking response to visual stimulation, noted that an associated click of their camera soon itself elicited blocking, even when the visual

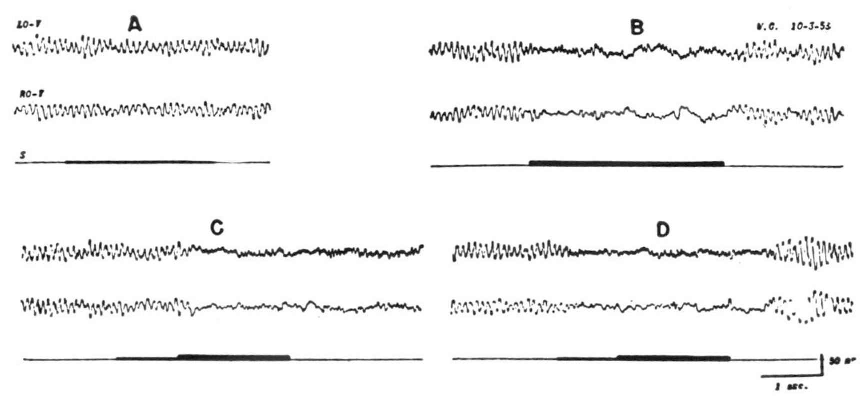

FIG. 3-1. Records of electrical activity from the brain of a normal human subject, illustrating the establishment of a conditional blocking of occipital alpha rhythm. The initial lack of response to a tone stimulus (thin black signal) is seen in *A*. The unconditioned alpha blockade to bright light stimulation (thick black signal) is seen in *B*. When the signals are first paired, in *C*, the tone stimulus preceding the light is ineffective. By the ninth trial, in *D*, however, the tone stimulus evokes a conditional alpha-blocking response before the light appears (17).

stimulus was not presented. Their adventitious finding was confirmed and extended by Jasper and Shagass (12) and by other investigators. More recently the method has been employed, particularly by Morrell and his associates (17-22), as a means of studying the formation of temporary connections in the brain during simulated conditioning procedures.

Such "learned" blocking of the alpha rhythm is illustrated in Figure 3-1. An initial lack of cortical response to a tone stimulus (thin signal line, in *A*) can be compared with the unconditional blocking of the occipital alpha rhythm induced by a bright light stimulus (thick signal line, in *B*). In the first paired trial (*C*), the lack of response to the tone can again be compared with the alpha blocking when the light appears. By the ninth trial (*D*), however, alpha blocking occurs in response to the tone, before the light stimulus is presented. At this initial stage, conditional alpha blocking is displayed widely over the cortex; subsequently, it becomes confined to the occipital region, i.e., to the projection area of the unconditional stimulus.

In such study of the formation of new functional links in the brain, direct examination of changes in central electrical activity is proposed to possess advantages over the inference of central neural processes from observations of peripheral behavior. The relations of electrocortical conditioning to motor performance are not invariably direct, however (3), and attention has also been called to the problem of differentiating in these experiments between conditional and unconditional signals (4). On its initial presentation, what is later to be called the conditional stimulus may also evoke widespread potentials and a generalized alpha-blocking reaction, so that the animal needs to become habituated before further conditioning can proceed (14).

In a later variation of electrocortical conditioning, Morrell and Jasper (18) employed intermittent rather than steady photic stimulation as the unconditional stimulus and, at a stage between the initial general and the final focal desynchronization of the EEG, observed in the visual cortex a conditional or tone-induced repetitive response, the frequency of which was that of the photic stimulus (Figs. 3-2, 3-3). These experiments with intermittent photic stimulation were extended by Yoshii, *et al.* (32–34), who found that the "conditioned repetitive discharges were earlier in onset, higher in amplitude, and more constant in subcortical structures, especially in the mesencephalic reticular formation" (Fig. 3-2). In subsequent study, Yoshii and Hockaday (35) found that this conditional frequency-specific response was prevented by bilateral lesions in nonspecific thalamic nuclei.

Morrell (21, 22) has likewise supported the involvement of nonspecific mechanisms of the brain stem in electrocortical conditioning. It is his view that the initially generalized activation pattern is mediated by the mesencephalic reticular system, while the subsequent focal EEG activation, limited to the receiving area for the unconditional stimulus, is subserved by intralaminar

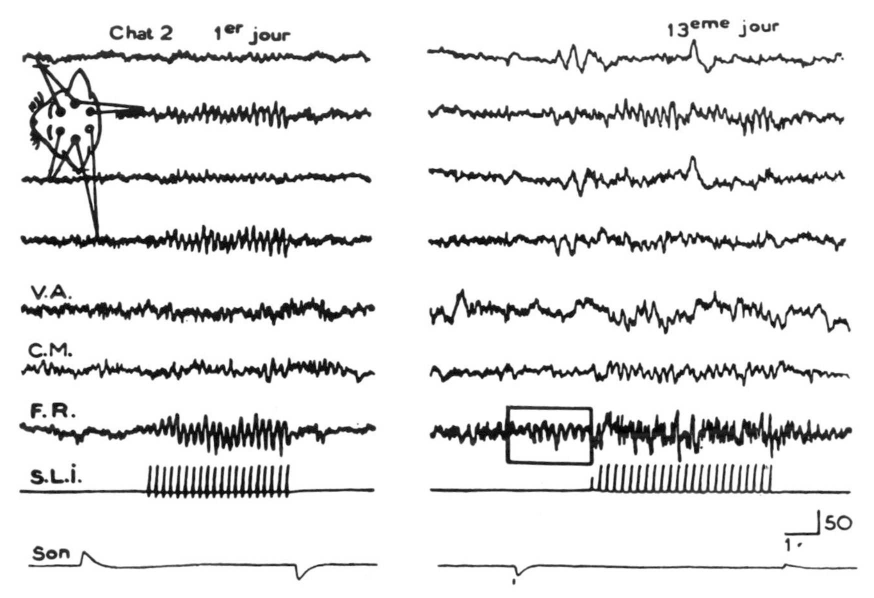

FIG. 3-2. Records of electrical activity in cortical and subcortical regions of the cat's brain showing responses to tone (**Son**) and intermittent photic (**S.L.I.**) stimulation. On the first day, the sound is without effect, and one observes only the unconditioned driving of the occipital and reticular activity at a frequency of the light flashes. On the thirteenth day, the sound evoked a conditional response, at the same frequency as the rhythmic light flashes, recorded only from the reticular formation.

The first four channels record activity from fronto-temporal and temporo-occipital regions, the lower three from the thalamic nucleus ventralis anterior (**V.A.**), the center median (**C.M.**), and the mesencephalic reticular formation (**F.R.**) (34).

and midline thalamic nuclei. The disturbing effects of discharging epileptiform foci in the amygdala provided further evidence for the involvement of subcortical structures in such conditional learning (19), interference being referable either to the seizure within the amygdala itself or within the cephalic brain stem into which such seizures readily propagate.

In a similar way, it has been recently proposed by Gastaut (7, 8) that closure in conditional learning is not completed within the cortex, for section between the cortical analyzers or removal of one of them does not prevent closure. Alternatively, he proposes that closure is established at sites of convergence of input

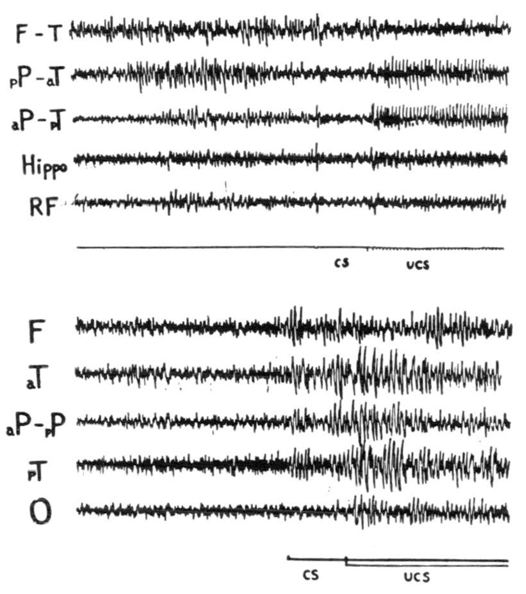

FIG. 3-3. Records of electrical activity in cortical and subcortical regions of the cat's brain show (*upper*) an initial absence of response to a tone stimulus (**cs**) and a frequency-specific discharge to an unconditioned seven-per-second photic stimulus (**ucs**). On the next day (*below*) the conditional tone stimulus evokes widespread frequency-specific responses in the cortex.

Channels record from frontal (**F**), parietal (**P**), temporal (**T**), and occipital (**O**) cortical regions and from the hippocampus (**Hippo**) and midbrain reticular formation (**RF**) (35).

within the reticular formation or the nonspecifically projecting thalamic nuclei. As seen in Figure 3-4, Gastaut (8) conceives of the setting up of a focus of excitation in the reticular formation, by way of collaterals from the afferent paths for the unconditional stimulus, with the establishment of connections between it and the cortex, and with the subsequent domination of localized thalamo-cortical projections over more diffuse ones from the lower brain stem, as the ultimate changes become focal rather than generalized. Paradoxically, these developments of Western neurophysiology, concerned initially with study of the electrical activity of the cerebral cortex, have come to emphasize the

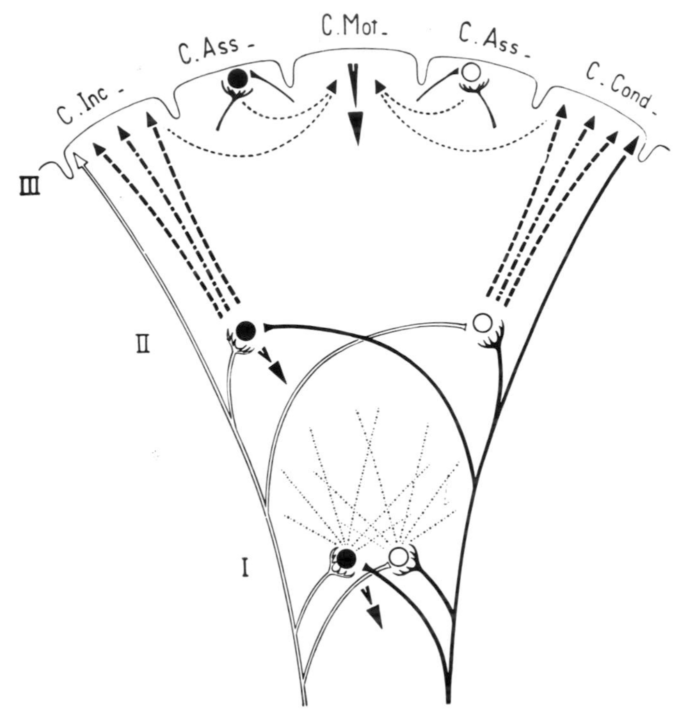

Fig. 3-4. Diagram of the proposed subcortical and cortical levels of the brain involved in the formation of a conditional reflex. **I.** The midbrain reticular formation. **II.** Thalamus. **III.** Cortex. The white pathway (*left*) is that of the unconditioned stimulus (S); the black path (*right*), that of the conditional stimulus (s). The circles represent reticular neurons on which the hetereogenous stimuli converge. The unconditioned (**C. Inc**), the conditional (**C. Cond**), associational (**C. Ass**), and motor (**C. Mot**) cortical areas are shown (8).

importance in the conditioning process of subcortical mechanisms, particularly of nonspecific systems in the reticular formation and thalamus of the brain stem.

Additional Western emphasis upon the importance of subcortical mechanisms in conditioning has come from study of the

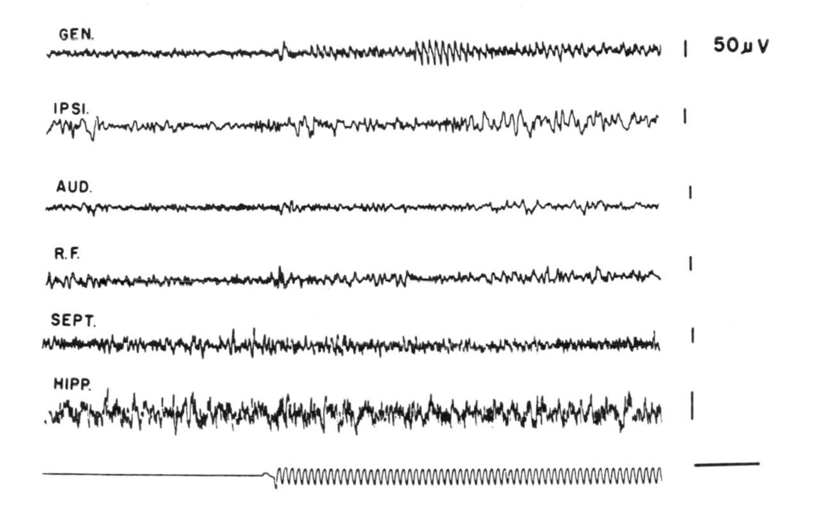

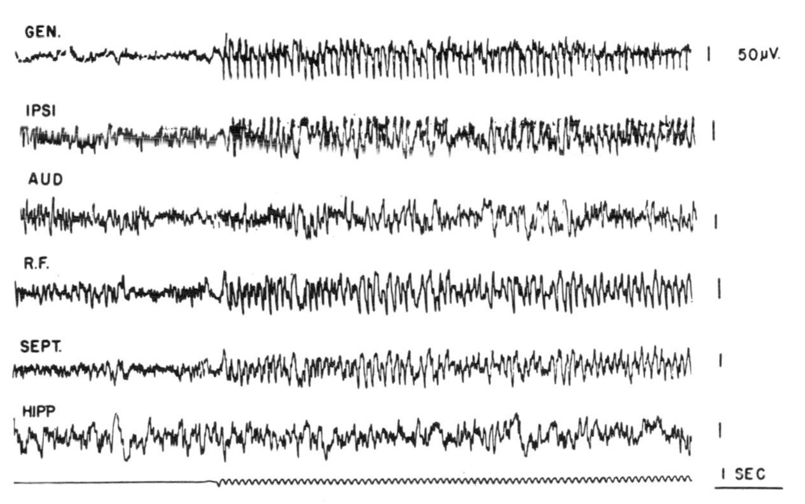

FIG. 3-5. Records of electrical activity from cortical and subcortical regions of the cat's brain, showing (*upper*) the minimal and restricted response to repetitive photic stimulation (signal) after habituation; and (*lower*) the marked increase in amplitude and the widespread generalization of responses when reinforcement is introduced.

Channels are, from above downward: **GEN.**—lateral geniculate body; **IPSI.**—visual cortex; **AUD.**—auditory cortex; **R.F.**—midbrain tegmentum; **SEPT.**—septum; **HIPP.**—hippocampus (14).

role of reinforcement in learning. Valuable progress has been made by monitoring tracer responses evoked in central neural stations by afferent stimulation, before and during reinforcement procedures. In the experiments of John and Killam (14), novel photic stimuli which initially evoked widespread high-amplitude central activity were repeatedly presented, unpaired with any consequence, until the amplitude of evoked potentials

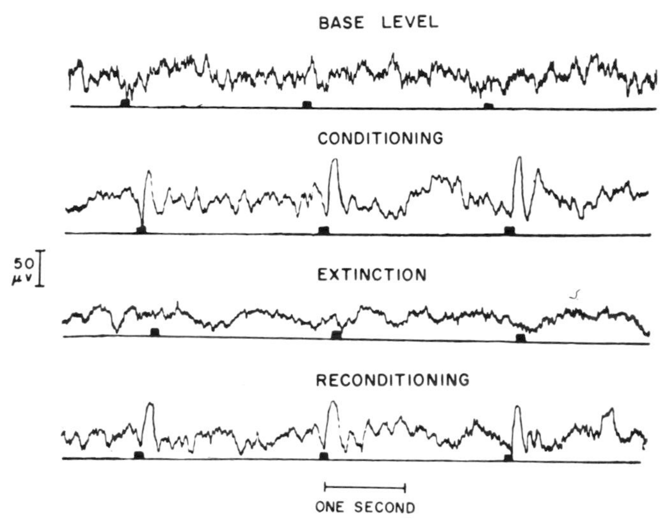

FIG. 3-6. Records of electrical activity from the monkey's hippocampus, showing variations in the responses evoked by tone stimuli (signal). From above downward are responses: in the control period, during reinforcement with sugar pellets in conditioning, after extinction, and during subsequent reconditioning (with food reward again presented) (10).

became reduced and their distribution confined to the visual pathway, a stage described as habituation (Fig. 3-5 *Upper*). Immediately thereafter, when negative reinforcement was introduced, by pairing shocks to the feet with the tracer stimuli, central responses again became widely generalized and displayed a marked increase in amplitude (Fig. 3-5 *Lower*). In similar experiments of Galambos (6) and Hearst, *et al.* (10), tone-evoked responses in the hippocampus were conspicuously augmented when positive reinforcement was introduced (Fig. 3-6).

These recent findings, along with those of Jouvet (15), Hernandez-Peon (11), and Worden (31), demonstrate the important role of reinforcement in increasing the amplitude and generalizing the distribution of afferent signals in the brain. It would no longer seem necessary, in accounting for the establishment of temporary connections, to search for potential sites of convergence between signals in the different analyzers. During reinforcement, afferent signals become so widely distributed in the brain that the problem would seem rather to lie in determining in which of many possible regions new functional relationships become established. It has even been proposed recently that central reinforcement systems be given a place of importance along with that of the analyzers in conditional reflex theory (16).

ANALYSIS OF THE ORIENTING REFLEX

In contrast to the West, recent developments in the USSR have come in large part from research based upon more classical Pavlovian discoveries and concepts. In 1950, in Moscow, the Academy of Sciences of the USSR and the Academy of Medical Sciences of the USSR jointly sponsored a Moscow Conference on *The Physiological Teaching of Academician I. P. Pavlov* (24), the resolutions of which were influential in extending on many fronts the study of higher nervous activity, inaugurated and developed so extensively by Pavlov and his associates from the turn of the century.

One of the most fruitful of these programs has studied the Pavlovian orienting or investigatory reflex, which forms an initial step in the establishment of conditional learning. The progress of this program has formed the subject of three annual conferences on the orienting reflex, held in Kiev in 1958, 1959, and 1960. Some of the findings were also presented by Voronin and Sokolov (30) at the Moscow Colloquim on *EEG and Higher Nervous Activity* in 1958, and the current status of the program was surveyed by Sokolov (29) at the Macy Conference on *CNS and Behavior* in 1960. From these several sources, and from a valuable recent review by Razran (25), the following synthesis and interpretation are attempted.

The orienting reflex, whose role lies in alerting or attracting attention, differs from adaptive reflexes in a number of ways. It is not specific to the modality of stimulation. Its responses are initially generalized, though later they may become restricted to a part of the body or to a region of the brain most closely related to the evocative stimulus. Additionally, unlike specific reflexes, the orienting reflex tends to habituate rapidly upon repetition of stimulation.

The important role played by the orienting reflex in conditioning seems to be related to its attention-attracting properties. Attention is attracted only by stimuli which possess significance, either because of their novelty or for their reinforcement-provoking features. In essence, conditioning seems to consist of associating an indifferent or conditional stimulus with a significant or unconditional one, for a sufficient number of times, until the former becomes a signal for the latter, i.e., until the previously indifferent stimulus acquires significance for the subject. The orienting reflex is thus of initial importance for conditioning in evoking the subject's attention.

Once the conditional reflex has become stabilized, the orienting reflex can additionally provide a means by which the conditional response can temporarily be reduced or prevented by so-called external inhibition. In this situation, the action of the external inhibitor seems to lie in distracting the subject's attention from the conditional signal, so as to prevent evocation of what, under the circumstances, might be an inappropriate response.

The orienting reflex includes somatic, visceral, and EEG alterations, which enhance the discriminatory power of the analyzers, so as to enable them to gain more information about the unusual properties of the evocative stimulus, and so prepare the subject for dealing with it. Movements of the eyes, head, or body may occur. There are usually changes in respiration and heart rate. There is a vasodilatation of the head vessels, a vasoconstriction of the finger vessels, and a galvanic skin response. There is a generalized EEG arousal reaction, or blocking of the alpha-rhythm by low-voltage fast discharge. As Razran (25) has pointed out, unlike other reaction patterns of the organism, that of the orienting reflex does not manage the stimuli initiating it but is merely reactive to their presence. As he indicates, the reaction patterns of the orienting reflex are thus more preparatory than consumatory and are preadaptive rather than adaptive in nature.

The aspect of novelty is the prepotent feature of stimuli evoking the orienting reflex. Its typical induction by nonstereotyped stimulation has given rise to the concept that the orienting reflex is not initiated directly by the stimulus, in the customary sense of the term, but rather by a change in its modality, intensity, temporal pattern, or other parameter. A comparison of present with previous stimulation seems to be of major importance, with an orienting reflex being evoked at every point of disagreement in such comparison. This reflex is induced whenever new stimuli are discordant with, rather than accordant or coincident with, earlier stimulation.

The concept of a cortical neuronal model has been devised by Sokolov to account for this induction of the orienting reflex by stimuli whose characteristic feature is their nonstereotyped quality. This neuronal model is conceived as a cell assembly which preserves information about the modality, intensity, duration, and order of presentation of earlier stimuli, with which analogous aspects of novel stimulation may be compared. According to the hypothesis, the orienting reflex is evoked whenever, upon such comparison, the parameters of the novel stimulus do not coincide with those of the neuronal model. The orienting reflex is considered to be the result, then, not of stimulation itself, but rather of impulses caused by the difference between such stimulation and the established model.

When properties of novel stimulation differ from those of the neuronal model, this discordance is proposed to generate corticifugal discharge to the brain stem reticular system, the increased activity of which evokes the orienting reflex. In this schema, therefore, cortical feedback to the brain stem reticular system is conceived as evoking the orienting reflex, and an important significance is attached to cortical control of reticular excitability, as distinct from influences proceeding more directly from peripheral receptors.

In the contrasting situation, when novel stimuli are coincident with the proposed neuronal model, there is no excitatory discharge from the cortex to the reticular system, and the orienting reflex is not induced. Moreover, upon repetition, such accordance of stimulus and model is suggested to generate corticifugal inhibitory discharge to the brain stem, which blocks input to the reticular formation by way of collaterals from afferent paths, and so provides the basis for habituation. In this view, habituation is a consequence of inhibition at central afferent relays between peripheral receptors and the reticular formation, the inhibitory influences being corticifugal in derivation and generated by an accordance between novel stimulation and an established neuronal model.

This general concept, that incoming stimuli are matched with a model created by previous stimulation, tends to fractionate the classical consideration of a stimulus as a unitary phenomenon. All but the briefest stimuli are suggested to be composed of at least two differentiable parts: one formed by the beginning of the stimulus, whose match with the model is likely to be discordant and hence excitatory; and a second, consisting of the subsequent prolongation of the stimulus, whose match with the model is more likely to be accordant and so induce inhibition. Upon repeated presentation of the same stimulus, its beginning may become a conditional signal for the stage of prolongation, and the resulting habituation can be attributed to the elaboration of a type of inhibitory conditional reflex.

Sokolov's hypothesis (29), which is diagramed in Figure 3-7, thus acknowledges the participation of subcortical mechanisms in the orienting reflex but proposes that they are managed and dominated by cortico-reticular influences. These cortico-reticular influences are in turn proposed to be a consequence of the comparison of novel stimuli with neuronal models established in the cortex by previous stimulation. Discordance between novel input and the model evokes excitatory cortico-reticular discharge and triggers the orienting reflex. Accordance of input and model not only fails to provoke an orienting reflex but additionally induces inhibitory cortico-reticular influences responsible for habituation.

It will be apparent from this research program on the orienting reflex that investigators in the USSR are well informed of developments in other parts of the world and are taking active steps

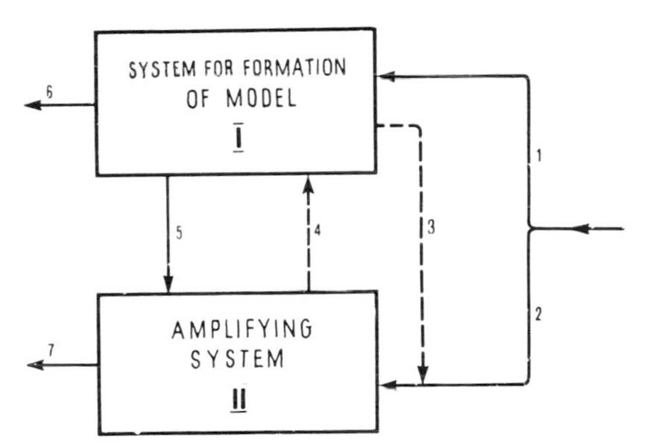

FIG. 3-7. Schema of the brain mechanisms involved in the orienting reflex. *I*, Cortical neuronal model; *II*, Amplifying system in brain stem reticular formation.

Functional connections are: (**1**) specific pathway from receptor to cortical neuronal model; (**2**) collateral afferent path to reticular formation; (**3**) negative feedback from cortical model to afferent reticular collateral; (**4**) ascending reticular activating pathway to cortex; (**5**) cortico-reticular connections signaling con- or discordance between afferent stimuli and the cortical neuronal model; (**6**) corticifugal pathways for specific responses; (**7**) reticulofugal pathways for nonspecific somatic and visceral responses (29).

to interrelate their own observations with them. By so doing, as in this instance, valuable new points of view may be introduced both into Western and Soviet thinking. In this way, indication is once more provided that a breakdown of insularity in science is generally contributory to progress. By increasing translation and study, Western scientists are beginning to follow the reciprocal example of Soviet investigators and to acquaint themselves with current research developments in the USSR. It is a particular pleaure to have had an opportunity to make reference to the findings and concepts of Sokolov and his associates on this occasion.

REFERENCES

1. Brazier, M. A. B., editor. *CNS and Behavior* (Transactions of the First, Second and Third Macy Conferences). Josiah Macy, Jr. Foundation, New York, 1958, 1959, 1960.
2. Brazier, M. A. B. An exploration of the EEG in terms of its statistical characteristics, in *Symposium in Neural Mechanisms, Information Theory and Behavior.* VA Hospital, Battle Creek, Michigan, 1960.
3. Chow, K. L., Dement, W. C., and John, E. R. Conditioned EEG potentials and behavioral avoidance response in cat. *J. Neurophysiol. 20:* 482, 1957.
4. Doty, R. W. Brain stimulation and conditioned reflexes, in *CNS and Behavior,* edited by M. A. B. Brazier. Josiah Macy, Jr. Foundation, New York, 1959.
5. Durup, G., and Fessard, A. L'électroencéphalogramme de l'homme; observations psycho-physiologiques relatives à l'action des stimuli visuels et auditifs. *L'Année Psychol. 36:* 1, 1935.
6. Galambos, R. Electrical correlates of conditioned learning, in *CNS and Behavior,* edited by M. A. B. Brazier. Josiah Macy, Jr. Foundation, New York, 1959.
7. Gastaut, H. État actuel des connaissances sur l'électroencéphalographie du conditionnement. *EEG Clin. Neurophysiol.* Suppl. 6: 133, 1957.
8. Gastaut, H. Some aspects of the neurophysiological basis of conditioned reflexes and behavior, in *Neurological Basis of Behavior* (Ciba Foundation Symposium), edited by G. E. W. Wolstenholme and C. M. O'Connor. Little Brown & Co., Boston, 1958.
9. Gershuni, G. V. Central regulation of discharges in the peripheral nervous system. *Fiziol. zhlur. 45:* 772, 1959.
10. Hearst, E., Beer, B., Sheatz, G., and Galambos, R. Some electrophysiological correlates of conditioning in the monkey. *EEG Clin. Neurophysiol. 12:* 137, 1960.
11. Hernandez-Peon, R., Scherer, H., and Jouvet, M. Modification of electrical activity in cochlear nucleus during "attention" in unanesthetized cats. *Science. 123:* 331, 1956.
12. Jasper, H. H., and Shagass, C. Conditioning the occipital alpha rhythm in man. *J. Exper. Psychol. 28:* 373, 1941.

13. JASPER, H. H., and SMIRNOV, G. D., editors. *EEG and Higher Nervous Activity* (Moscow Colloquium, 1958). *EEG Clin. Neurophysiol.* Suppl. 13, 1960.
14. JOHN, E. R., and KILLAM, K. F. Electrophysiological correlates of avoidance conditioning in the cat. *J. Pharmacol. & Exper. Therap. 125:* 252, 1959.
15. JOUVET, M., and HERNANDEZ-PEON, R. Mechanismes neurophysiologiques concernant l'habituation, l'attention et le conditionnement. *EEG Clin. Neurophysiol.* Suppl. 6: 39, 1957.
16. MAGOUN, H. W. Subcortical mechanisms for reinforcement, in *EEG and Higher Nervous Activity*, edited by G. Smirnov and H. H. Jasper (Moscow Colloquium, 1958). *EEG Clin. Neurophysiol.* Suppl. 13, 1960.
17. MORRELL, F., and ROSS, M. Central inhibition in cortical conditioned reflexes. *AMA Arch. Neurol. & Psychiat. 70:* 611, 1953.
18. MORRELL, F., and JASPER, H. H. Electrographic studies of the formation of temporary connections of the brain. *EEG Clin. Neurophysiol. 8:* 201, 1956.
19. MORRELL, F., ROBERTS, L., and JASPER, H. H. Effect of focal epileptogenic lesions and their ablation upon conditioned electrical responses of the brain in the monkey. *EEG Clin. Neurophysiol. 8:* 217, 1956.
20. MORRELL, F., NAQUET, R., and CASTAUT, H. Evolution of some electrical signs of conditioning: I. Normal cat and rabbit. *J. Neurophysiol. 20:* 574, 1957.
21. MORRELL, F. Some electrical events involved in the formation of temporary connections, in *Reticular Formation of the Brain*, edited by H. H. Jasper. Little Brown & Co., Boston, 1958.
22. MORRELL, F. Electroencephalographic studies of conditioned learning, in *CNS and Behavior*, edited by M. A. B. Brazier. Josiah Macy, Jr. Foundation, New York, 1959.
23. PALESTINI, M., DAVIDOVICH, A., and HERNANDEZ-PEON, R. Functional significance of centrifugal influences upon the retina. *Acta Neurol. Latino-Americana. 5:* 113, 1959.
24. PAVLOV, I. P. *Scientific Session on the Physiological Teachings of Academician I. P. Pavlov.* Foreign Language Publication House, Moscow, 1951.
25. RAZRAN, G. *A Survey of Experiments in Interoceptive Conditioning, Semantic Conditioning and the Orienting Reflex. Psychol. Rev. 68:* 81, 1961.

26. Rusinov, V. S., and Rabinovich, M. Y. Electroencephalographic researches in the laboratories and clinics of the Soviet Union. *EEG Clin. Neurophysiol.* Suppl. 8, 1958.
27. Delafresnaye, J. F., editor. *Brain Mechanisms and Learning* (CIOMS Symposium, Montevideo, 1959). Blackwell, Oxford, 1961.
28. Sharpless, S., and Jasper, H. H. Habituation of the arousal reaction. *Brain. 79:* 655, 1956.
29. Sokolov, E. N. Neuronal models and the orienting influence, in *CNS and Behavior,* edited by M. A. B. Brazier. Josiah Macy, Jr. Foundation, New York, 1960.
30. Voronin, L. G., and Sokolov, E. N. Cortical mechanisms of the orienting reflex and its relation to the conditioned reflex, in *EEG and Higher Nervous Activity* (Moscow Colloquium, 1958), edited by H. H. Jasper and G. B. Smirnov. Suppl. 13, 1960.
31. Worden, F. G. Neurophysiological contributions to the understanding of schizophrenia, in *Schizophrenia, an Integrated Approach,* edited by A. Auerbach. Ronald Press Co., New York, 1959.
32. Yoshii, N. Principes méthodologiques de l'investigation electroencéphalogique du comportement conditionné. *EEG Clin. Neurophysiol.* Suppl. 6: 75, 1957.
33. Yoshii, N., Matsumoto, J., and Hori, Y. Electroencephalographic study on conditioned reflex in animals, Abst. of Reports, *IV Internat. Cong. EEG Clin. Neurophysiol.,* p. 79, 1957.
34. Yoshii, N., Pruvot, P., and Gastaut, H. Electroencephalographic activity of the mesencephalic reticular formation during conditioning in the cat. *EEG Clin. Neurophysiol. 9:* 595, 1957.
35. Yoshii, N., and Hockaday, W. J. Conditioning of frequency-characteristic repetitive EEG response with intermittent photic stimulation. *EEG Clin. Neurophysiol. 10:* 487, 1958.

DISCUSSION

Dr. Jasper: There are so many ways that one might approach the topic assigned to Dr. Magoun, namely, the mechanisms of interference with the higher functions of the nervous system, that choice of the many aspects of this complex problem to present at this symposium must be difficult. It is obvious that this is too large a subject to be adequately discussed in the confines of the present portion of this symposium. Dr. Magoun has solved this dilemma by not attempting to review the great masses of literature available on this subject but has confined himself to introducing a fascinating working hypothesis of one aspect of brain function proposed by Dr. Sokolov of Moscow.

The concept of some form of "model" or "stereotype" in the brain with which incoming stimulus patterns are compared for the determination of definite subsequent action is not new in the field of psychoneurophysiological thinking. It is not the same, however, as the problem of the engram studied so thoroughly and considered so extensively and intelligently by the late Professor Karl Lashley, with the final conclusion, after a lifelong search, that he had still been unable to find a suitable neurophysiological basis for this conception.

The hypothesis of Dr. Sokolov, if it is to be a useful one, must be susceptible to objective testing in the laboratory. One might well ask where one would look for the neurophysiological substratum of such hypothetical neuronal models. Dr. Penfield has suggested that such models may be found in the cortex of the temporal lobe from his observations on the effects of electrical stimulation of this area of cortex in man producing recollections of complex memories and changes in perception and the interpretation of stimuli-producing illusions. However, this is not the only interpretation that might be made of these results of electrical stimulation in man, for it may well be that the disturbance in neuronal function caused by the crude electrical stimulus destroys the functional identity of neuronal models situated immediately beneath the stimulating electrodes, making it unlikely that these particular neurons represented a part of the true assembly of neurons responsible for the neuronal patterns causing the recollection of the particular perception or memory. One could argue that the stimulated neurons of the temporal lobe acted merely as triggers for the release of circuits elsewhere which, once activated, generated the pattern responsible for a specific recollection or memory image.

It is of interest to recall that, even though experiences may be reactivated by electrical stimulation of areas of temporal cortex in one hemisphere, the removal of all of this temporal cortex and adjacent regions with the subjacent hippocampal and amygdaloid formations does not result in a loss of these memories. Following removal, the patient recalls in detail all of the events of the operative procedure and the experiences he had during electrical stimulation in vivid detail. This is complete proof that the essential neuronal circuits for these particular experiential recollections did not lie in the stimulated temporal cortex. It is quite possible, however, that such "engrams" are always laid down bilaterally so that the temporal cortex of the opposite hemisphere could serve this recall process in the absence of the one stimulated. This is, of course, only speculation. It has been clearly demonstrated that without the amygdaloid hippocampal systems on both sides memory recording of certain types is not possible in man. This does not prove, of course, that these structures are essential for the preservation of memory patterns since old memories prior to the operative removals are retained and many skills remain unaltered following this procedure. This leads to the complex problem of the nature of the function of the limbic systems in the laying down of memory patterns, which we cannot discuss adequately here.

From our microelectrode studies of cortical elements during learning processes in monkeys we have the impression that neuronal circuits in widespread areas of the cortex are simultaneously active in a bewildering variety of patterns during the formation of a simple conditioned response to a particular conditioning stimulus pattern. Of course, the complexity of distribution of neuronal processes responsible for the hypothetical "neuronal model" is not necessarily against the validity of the general hypothesis as was suggested by Dr. Sokolov.

As to the hypothesis itself it seems to me that it is not necessarily a very useful one for it would appear to prescribe a relatively rigid conception of simple excitatory effects which are supposed to result from concordance of incoming stimulus patterns with this cortical model. Likewise, the use of the terms "excitation" and "inhibition," so common in the Russian theoretical literature, which we find of little use in our understanding of cortical function when interpreted rigidly in terms of true inhibition of cortical neuronal activity in a given area of cortex or brain stem.

In attempts to study the unit neuronal representation of such states of "inhibition" or "excitation" as would be proposed by such theories, one finds that frequently more cortical units become involved in repetitive activity in areas presumably inhibited, while in others less cortical units seem to be active in states which might be called excitatory or in a state of excitation. In all cases we have had the opportunity of examining functional conditions of the cortex responsible for given behavioral acts that have involved a complex of excitatory and inhibitory patterns in different neuronal elements in a given area of cortex. What is more important, perhaps, is that the functional alteration in neuronal discharge cannot be suitably described in terms of either excitation or inhibition when viewed at the unit level, but rather the reorganization of patterns of firing in relation to the conditioned stimulus or to the mode of behavioral response, sometimes representing an over-all increase in number per second and at other times a decrease, but with all, a change in temporal pattern and in number of units activated at different levels, and in different circuits of the cortex. This is a qualitative change which can be described only in a spatial-temporal sequence. The description of such changes in terms of simple excitation or inhibition, it seems to me, is misleading and not a fruitful hypothesis upon which to base studies of the neurophysiological basis of higher brain functions.

For example, we have observed in the parietal lobe during an avoidance conditioning experiment, where a monkey learns to withdraw his hand in response to a conditioned intermittent light stimulus and to not withdraw the hand in response to such a stimulus delivered at a different frequency, that certain elements in the parietal cortex can be conditioned to respond in grouped synchrony with the conditioning stimulus and to be inhibited in response to the differential stimulus which is identical except for its frequency, and the fact that it has not been reenforced in the conditioning trials. In terms of the Pavlovian theory one would have to admit that some form of unit inhibition has been established to one frequency of stimulation and excitation to the other, but as a matter of fact the units which were conditioned to follow the frequency of the conditioning light stimulus were often firing less frequently during this following than they were before, indicating that in one sense there was more inhibition, or reduction in number of discharges per second, rather than an over-all excitation. This serves to illustrate how inadequate are the conceptions of excitation and inhibition used in the Russian theory when one attempts to apply them to the function of single neurons taking part in the conditioning process.

Another difficulty that I find with Dr. Sokolov's theory, as it has been presented by Professor Magoun, is that it does not consider the positive aspects of neuronal "models." This might be illustrated by a question to Dr. Magoun asking him whether there would be an excitatory or an inhibitory effect upon his own behavior should he be walking down Broadway at Times Square on an Easter Sunday meeting hundreds and hundreds of individuals on the way. Would it be those individuals passing by whose "models" did not correspond to an existing "model" in his brain which would cause him to be excited or alerted or would it be the chance meeting of a certain individual who would correspond to an existing "model" in his brain which would cause him to be most interested or excited. It would seem to me that meeting a familiar "body" would cause more of an excitatory response than the hundreds of unfamiliar bodies. Of course, should Dr. Magoun be walking down Broadway after theater hours in the evening and a series of "models" of a different kind pass by it is possible to conceive that the novelty of each "model" might cause an excitation process to occur, as prescribed in Sokolov's theory. In brief, the theory of Sokolov applies only to the repetition of unre-enforced stimulus patterns causing habituation, while it does not account for the more usual re-enforcement of specific stimulus patterns which give them significance in behavior. In the latter case it would be the concordance, not the discordance, of the incoming pattern with the "model" which would be critical for the release of a particular behavior pattern, or recognizable and familiar conscious experience.

In studies of the habituation process in cats with Dr. Sharpless we have found that behavioral habituation to a given frequency of sound is specific to this frequency, and not to other frequencies, and it can be established in animals without the cortical auditory receiving areas. In addition, by recording of auditory-evoked potentials from the cortex of these animals during habituation to definite frequencies of click, to a point of no behavioral response to a specific click frequency, we found no decrease in cortical electrical responses but rather a slight increase, at a time when the animal failed to show any behavioral or arousal response to the stimulus, as determined by changes in the cortical EEG. We were thus forced to conclude that this type of habituation did not occur by means of changes in the primary receiving system to the cortex and could occur even without the cortical relay. It seemed to be possible for such habituation to occur at subcortical levels alone, although we did not try removal of the limbic areas. However, these experiments involved only relatively simple stimuli with frequency discrimination to clicks or tones. It was stimulus specific as to the frequency of the sound, and did not involve habituation to other forms of stimulation or to other frequencies at the same time. It was long-lasting and could be established to last for several days without re-enforcement, diminishing in its intensity. However, these are rather simple types of habituation and when experiments were attempted to habituate an animal to the pattern of tones in a tonal sequence, with each element of the pattern constant but only in a different order, it was found that the cortex was necessary and seemed to participate definitely in such more complex pattern discriminations for the habituation process. This may well be more comparable to the type of "model-matching" process proposed by Dr. Sokolov.

Lest I be misunderstood in my critical approach to this hypothesis I wish to make it perfectly clear that I am well aware of the many attempts now being made by our Soviet colleagues to test such hypotheses by direct electrical recording methods with implanted electrodes in various parts of the brain, including microelectrode studies of both cortical and subcortical structures. During the recent symposium in Moscow, and since then from manuscripts received from our colleagues over there, I am impressed with the great progress being made in the attempt to confirm or test some of these working hypotheses by direct electrical recording methods. I am sure that in this way such hypotheses have been fruitful.

Finally, I would like to raise the question as to the nature of the participation of the brain stem in such higher brain functions as are the subject of the present discussion. In the model proposed by Dr. Sokolov the diagram indicates that the brain stem functions only as a booster, or nonspecific activator, subservient to commands from the cortex to "go" or "stop." In attempting to work out the nature of this process I have been unable to conceive of brain stem function in this manner without considering a fairly high degree of differential and integrative function possible by the brain stem itself, even though it goes without saying that function of the brain takes place constantly by interactions between cortex and brain stem and that the function of either cannot be conceived without the other.

When one imagines the complexity of the activity in neuronal networks distributed over the great expanded mantle of the cerebral cortex, and duplicated on both sides, the problem of understanding how all of this mass of simultaneous activity can be filtered out into a relatively simple and meaningful command for a definite though highly integrated and purposeful action seems almost overwhelming. It would seem to require a remarkable interaction of patterns distributed over wide areas of the cortex and somehow selected with a mechanism whereby the selected pattern becomes prepotent and possibly inhibiting all other patterns in determining a given course of motor action. The concept that in the brain stem there is required a remarkable convergence of impulses into relatively simple neuronal networks in this selective process seems to me to be an intriguing one. I would like to hear Dr. Magoun's most recent concept of what he now considers to be the possible integrative function of the brain stem in relation to the multitude of simultaneously active cortical processes.

It seems abundantly apparent that we are sadly in need of more comprehensive and experimentally useful working hypotheses of brain function in order to make progress in our understanding as well as to design significant experimental approaches to these problems. It seems clear that such higher level functions are not to be located in any particular part of the brain and that there is a remarkable interdependence of parts and even of patterns of incoming sensory stimuli.

The disintegration of higher level functions which is shown to occur when individuals are deprived for periods of time of normal input of sensory stimulation is a striking example of how higher level functions depend upon a stable input from the sensory environment of the brain. Distortions in sensory control also produce significant alterations in central and integrative functions, whether these distortions are produced by abnormal sensory input from the environment or by centrally acting drugs which alter the synaptic systems mediating sensory information to the brain.

Certainly, some regions of the brain are more highly specialized for higher integrative processes than are others and are those in which we find the greatest confluence and capabilities of interactions between the various sensory inputs and the patterns responsible for initiation of purposeful behavior. However, an understanding of the function of this mechanism cannot be obtained by consideration of these specialized areas themselves but must involve concepts which allow for multiple simultaneous variables in many interdependent neuronal systems and assemblies. The conceptual framework for such a theory of brain function has not yet been adequately formulated. We hope that future work and thought will give us more satisfactory guides to the experimental approach to these most complex problems.

Dr. Magoun: It would seem to me that Dr. Jasper's observation with Sharpless (28), that the amplitude of potentials evoked in the cortical receiving areas are not reduced during habituation, is really in agreement with Sokolov's hypothesis. The latter proposes that habituation is a result of corticifugal inhibition, blocking input to the reticular formation via collateral afferent relays. In turn, this corticifugal inhibition is conceived to be generated by an accordance of novel stimuli with an established cortical neuronal model. According to the theory, the maintenance of habituation in Sharpless and Jasper's experiments was dependent upon afferent signals continuing to reach the cortex without alteration. If, in their experiments, signals arrived at the cortex with other than their previous amplitude, their discordance with the model would have provoked an orienting reflex, instead of habituation. It may be mentioned, however, that recent observations of reduction of afferent transmission during habituation, both in auditory (9) and visual (23) pathways, are seemingly opposed both to Sokolov's theory and to the findings of Sharpless and Jasper.

Dr. Jasper has commented further that, in his experiments with Sharpless (28), behavioral habituation could be established to a given frequency of sound stimulus in animals lacking the cortical auditory receiving areas. Sokolov (29) proposes a cortical level for the comparison of novel input with an established model on two grounds, both derived from studies with human subjects. First, verbal signals are as effective as primary ones, and presumably are managed cortically. Second, during drowsiness, when delta and theta waves in the EEG imply an impairment of cortical function, habituation is no longer maintained.

It may be noted, however, that Sokolov's observations do not specifically implicate the cortical receiving areas or any other focal region of the hemisphere. Recent indications, some of them from Montreal, of the importance of the hippocampus, both for the retention of conditional reflexes in animals and for more general memory in man, suggest that the paleocortex of the hemisphere should seriously be considered in this connection, along with the large volume of neocortex outside the receiving areas.

Finally, with respect to the model of the orienting reflex, Dr. Jasper's curious analogy of a walk on Broadway illustrates the semantic difficulties inherent in conceptualization. As Dr. Brazier has proposed, in discussion of this terminology elsewhere

(1), Sokolov's word *novelty* may correspond best to the term of *low probability* employed in information theory (2). A familiar face on Broadway is improbable or unexpected, whereas the unknown crowds are highly probable and expected, and hence are not novel in Sokolov's sense of the word.

It is my understanding that information theory works on probability. The higher the probability of something occurring, i.e., the more you expect it, the less information you receive when it occurs. You were expecting it anyway, so what new have you learned? It is when something unexpected, of low probability, happens that you get the jolt, i.e., receive the maximum information. In Sokolov's model (29), events whose probability of matching the neuronal model is low are those which evoke the impulses registering discordance and initiate the orienting reflex.

As Dr. Jasper points out, features of this hypothesis have been proposed before. An unusually early expression of its more hedonistic aspects may be found in Bichat's *Physiological Research on Life and Death,* first published in 1800. Bichat wrote:

> The action of the mind on each feeling of pain or pleasure, arising from a sensation, consists in a comparison between that sensation and those which have preceded it. The greater the difference between the actual and past impressions, the more ardent will be the feeling. That sensation would affect us most which we had never experienced before.
>
> It follows, therefore, that our sensations make a greater or less impression upon us according to the frequency of their repetition, because the comparison becomes less sensible between their past and actual state. Every time that we see an object, hear a sound, or taste a dish, we find less difference between what we experience and what we have experienced.
>
> The nature of pleasure and of pain is thus to destroy themselves, to cease to exist, because they have existed. The art of prolonging the duration of our enjoyments consists in varying their causes.

Excessive emphasis may have been placed in this presentation upon the model which Sokolov and his associates have proposed.

If so, it can be pointed out in closing, that their hypothesis has been formulated, not as a feat of wheel-spinning, but to provide an explanatory synthesis of an impressive collection of data, gathered both from animal and human subjects, over a considerable period of past research, as well as to guide future investigatory efforts which give every expectation of continuing and increasing. Anyone who may have gained a misconception on this score should reassure himself by examining their original publications.

CHAPTER 4

Abnormal Excitatory Activity: Epilepsy

JEROME K. MERLIS

THE abnormalities which are demonstrable in the scalp electroencephalogram of epileptic man are varied. They range from a restricted disturbance involving only a small area of the underlying cortex to diffuse and bilateral disturbances which may involve cortex, subcortex, and brain stem. A consideration of a restricted cortical epileptogenic focus provides the most direct approach to a study of the mechanisms involved in hyperexcitable states of the neurons of the mammalian brain. The abnormal excitability of such a focus is evidenced not only by its spontaneous activity but also by its lowered threshold to electrical stimulation (45, 87, 88) and to various drugs, such as Metrazol (49).

SINGLE UNIT DISCHARGES

Recorded directly from the cortical surface with a microelectrode, the random cortical "spike" arising in such a focus has a duration of 5–60 msec. (46) and is to be distinguished from the much briefer soma or axon spikes. Figure 4-1 illustrates micro-

Some of the data presented herein were obtained in studies supported by a grant (B-1414) from the National Institute of Neurological Diseases and Blindness.

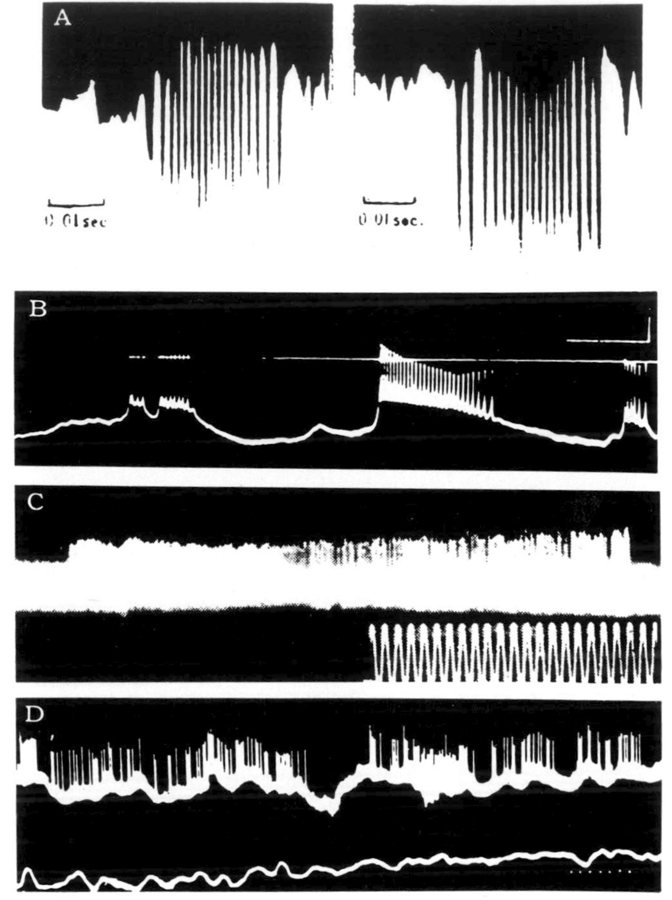

Fig. 4-1. Spontaneous discharges of "epileptic" units. *A*, Unit from pyramidal decussation after local application of strychnine to the motor cortex. Maximal frequency of discharge 890/sec. (After Adrian and Moruzzi, 1). *B*, Intracellular recording, cortical unit after local strychninization. Time—250 msec., amplitude—50 mV. (After Li, 60.) *C*, Cortical unit after local application of penicillin. Time—25 c/sec. (After Enomoto and Ajmone-Marsan, 29.) *D*, Cortical unit in a chronic alumina cream preparation. Lower trace is a surface macroelectrode recording. Time—10 msec. (After Schmidt, Thomas and Ward, 80.)

electrode recordings of single unit activity in experimental foci produced by various means and demonstrates that the characteristic feature is the occurrence of paroxysmal bursts of spikes repeating at frequencies up to 1000/sec. Most such recordings have been extracellular, and the exact origin of the spikes cannot be determined. Occasional intracellular recordings, as in Figure 4-1*B*, have demonstrated that the spike discharges may occur in association with a slower depolarization potential similar to the phenomena of impulse initiation studied intensively in spinal motoneurons. The occurrence of similar high-frequency bursts in single fibers of the medullary pyramid (Fig. 4-1*A*) in relation to a cortical strychnine spike indicates that the unit discharges, if not axonal spikes themselves, are capable of initiating such all-or-none propagated potentials.

It becomes pertinent to consider whether high-frequency unit discharge necessarily implies an abnormal state of the neuron. It is well known that sensory receptors, physiologically stimulated, may set up repetitive discharges at frequencies up to 1200/sec. (67, 74, 85) in their afferent fibers. The spontaneous activity of cerebral units is usually of considerably lower frequency, from 10–100/sec., with most units firing at frequencies of 50/sec. or lower (19, 25, 50, 63, 65, 75, 81, Fig. 4-2*A*). Occasional units firing spontaneously at much higher frequencies are reported (9, 66, Fig. 4-2*B*). Such high-frequency firing is usually attributed to cell injury by the microelectrode, and is usually of very brief duration. However, in examples such as those shown in Figure 4-2*B*, the units were held for periods up to one hour and the discharge frequency could be modified by stimulation of the cortex. When stimulated physiologically via sense organ discharge (Fig. 4-2*D*) or when excited by electrically induced afferent barrage (Fig. 4-2*C*), high-repetition frequencies are noted, rates of 500–1000/sec. (55, 62, 73, 74, 85) being not uncommon. Such high-frequency discharges are usually only of momentary duration, the discharge rate decreasing rapidly to lower values.

It is evident that the ability to discharge at high frequencies is not, of itself, an abnormal characteristic. Factors that dis-

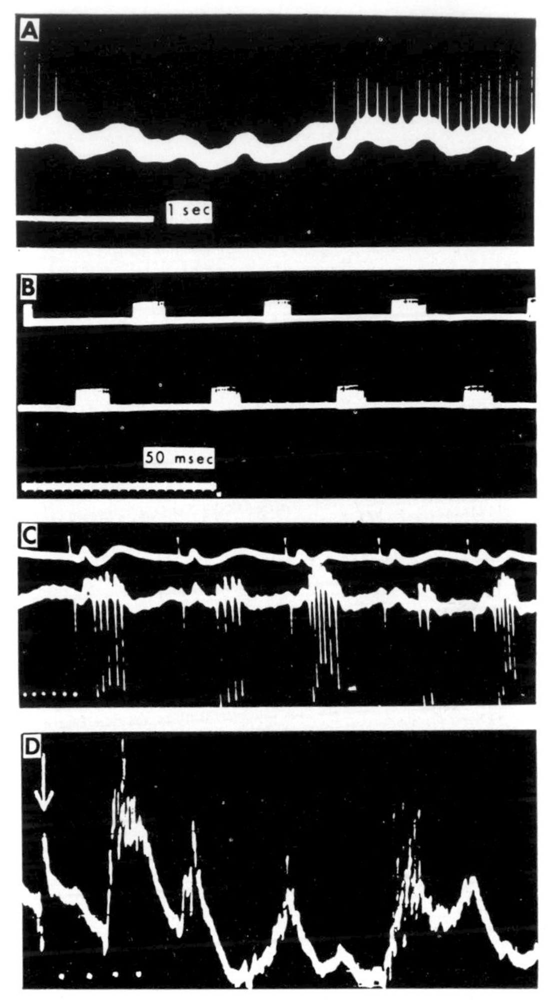

FIG. 4-2. Discharges of normal units. *A,* Spontaneous activity of Betz cell, low-frequency discharge. (After Martin and Branch, 66.) *B,* Spontaneous activity of Betz cell, high-frequency discharge. At beginning of each burst, frequency is about 1000/sec., declining to about 300/sec. at end of burst. (After Martin and Branch, 66.) *C,* Response of unit of somatosensory cortex to stimulation of thalamic sensory nucleus. Upper trace is from the surface of the cortex. Time—10 msec. (After Li, Cullen, and Jasper, 62.) *D,* Response of unit of visual cortex to light flash. Arrow marks stimulus artifact. Time—10 msec.

tinguish the epileptic neuron from the normal include its marked tendency to fire in such high-frequency bursts spontaneously and its ability to maintain the burst discharge for longer periods than ordinarily occur through afferent activation of a normal neuron. The term "spontaneous," in this area of neurophysiology, necessarily must be qualified in the sense of implying no apparent afferent influx. It need not be emphasized that all such units must be studied in a milieu of other neurons, and epileptic neurons, as well as normal ones, are influenced by afferent bombardment (1, 5, 90).

We may assume that a change in the pattern of afferent influx is not the essential determining influence in the paroxysmal high-frequency discharge of epileptic neurons and that their hyperexcitability is due to changes in their internal milieu giving rise to spontaneous discharge or increasing their responsiveness to the normally incident afferent flux. Li (61) has demonstrated intrinsic membrane instability in cortical units and emphasizes this as being an important factor influencing their discharge. The basic change in epileptic neurons could be one of membrane characteristics similar to the changes demonstrated in peripheral nerve and autonomic ganglia as a result of calcium deficiency (6, 15, 16). In this connection, mention may be made of the exaggeration of the normal spontaneous oscillations of excitability of nerve fibers which is produced by strychnine (31). Other possibilities are changes in the characteristics of the presynaptic terminal (e.g., greater release of transmitter substance), of the postsynaptic dendrite or soma membrane (e.g., greater responsiveness to transmitter substance), or in the dynamics of repolarization after impulse initiation. Any one, or a combination, of such changes might result in normal excitation producing abnormally intense or prolonged postsynaptic excitatory potentials. It is evident that any such modification would also influence the intensity and duration of bombardment through synaptic chains, open, closed, or reverberating, if such exist.

Relevant data obtained from studies of neurons of the mammalian brain are scanty, most of our concepts being based on analogy with information obtained from studies of spinal cord and from lower forms. Where specific data exist, frequently they are pertinent only to a special situation such as the strychnine focus, and generalization from the data becomes hazardous.

RELATIONSHIP OF THE UNIT DISCHARGE TO THE CORTICAL SPIKE

There is considerable variability in the data pertaining to the relationship of unit firing to the slower cortical waves, normal or paroxysmal. Adrian and Moruzzi (1) demonstrated a synchrony between spontaneous cortical waves and pyramidal fiber unit discharges and a similar relationship of strychnine waves ("spikes") to high-frequency discharges. They considered the strychnine wave as representing an hypersynchrony of elements whose normal activity gives rise to the spontaneous slow activity of the cortex. A more recent study by Whitlock *et al.* (90) reports similar findings, not only for pyramidal units, but for cortical units as well. Other workers find only occasional units firing in relation to the spontaneous slow cortical waves. Similarly, in the typical low-voltage fast EEG record of the cat, while awake, there is no obvious relationship of pyramidal unit discharge to the cortical fast waves (19).

A temporal relationship to the slow cortical responses evoked by afferent stimulation is frequently evident (9, 19, 57, 59, 62, 63, 65, 72, 73, 81, 85), although many units fire independently and some may cease their spontaneous discharges during such activation of the cortex (10, 19, 59, 62, 65, 72, 81, 85). It is now generally considered that the spontaneous rhythms of the cortex represent, in large part, slow potential changes of the nature of synaptic or dendritic potentials (47). Brazier (11, 12) has suggested that the cortical spike in an epileptogenic focus is an abnormal discharge of apical dendrites of pyramidal cells of the cortex. She argues that these spikes never have a duration less than 15 msec., the duration of the dendritic spike evoked by direct electrical stimulation. However, as already noted, Jasper indicates (46) that the cortical spike in an epileptic focus may be as brief as 5 msec.

In acute foci produced by the local application of various convulsant agents, Enomoto and Ajmone-Marsan (29) have reported a close parallelism between unit discharges and the paroxysmal cortical spike, with different units firing in different temporal relationship with the cortical event, but each unit tending to maintain a constant relationship. In the chronic alumina cream focus, Schmidt *et al.* (80) note a paucity of such relationship. This, together with differing form and behavior of unit potentials in a strychnine focus, presents the possibility of a fundamental dissimilarity between acute and chronic foci (84).

The demonstration of a relationship between unit firing and the cortical spike does not resolve the "chicken-egg" dilemma, and, as yet, there is no good evidence to indicate whether the pattern of unit firing determines the cortical event or vice versa (29).

AFTER-DISCHARGE

After-discharge is usually defined as activity continuing beyond the duration of an applied stimulus. In neuronal systems two types are well recognized; one is due to temporal dispersion of presynaptic bombardment and the other, repetitive discharge resulting from maintained depolarization at the postsynaptic membrane. In the case of random cortical spike discharges in epileptic foci, the term after-discharge is also applied to the repetitive discharge, usually of lower and decreasing amplitude, which follows the paroxysmal cortical spike. In experimental epileptic foci, the transition from interictal spike to sustained seizure discharge involves the development of such after-discharge activity in 90 per cent of the observations reported by Ralston (78, 79, Figs. 4-3, 4-10, 4-11).

It is difficult to apply the term after-discharge to a single cortical unit, since its normal spontaneous activity is frequently repetitive, and an increased frequency of discharge usually occurs in response to a physiological stimulus. However, the term has been used to characterize long-duration high-frequency discharges evoked by electrical stimulation. With low-intensity single shocks, Betz cells fire repetitively but briefly, at frequencies up to 500/sec. but longer-duration high-frequency discharges of cortical neurons (called after-discharge) may be evoked by repetitive stimulation (76).

As recorded from the surface, the cortical response to a single shock usually appears as a surface negative spike followed by a positive and then negative slower potential which may occlude

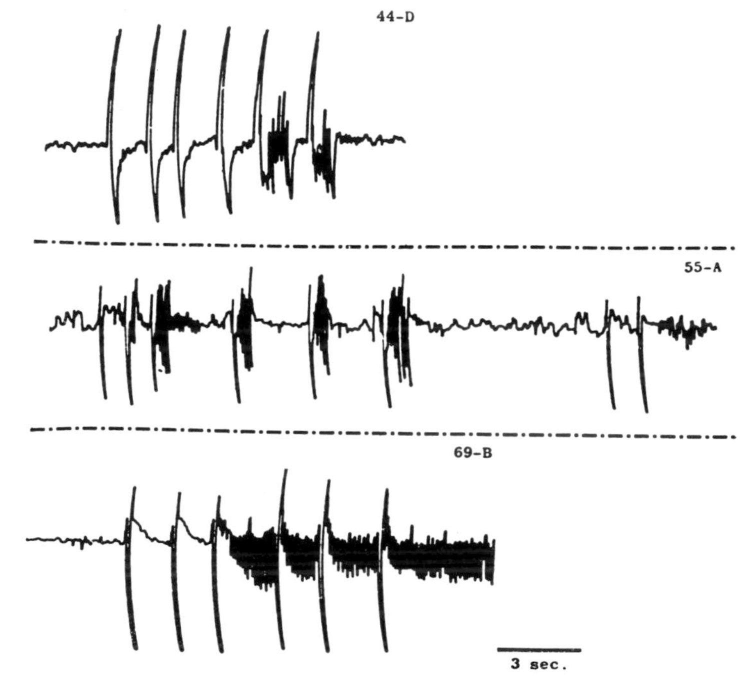

Fig. 4-3. Examples of spike after-discharge. **44-D**—cingulate; **55-A**—thalamic (CM); **69-B**—hippocampal (after Ralston, 78).

each other to some degree. The initial negativity is usually attributed to depolarization of the apical dendrites of pyramidal cells (20, 23). There is less general agreement concerning the interpretation of the later potentials, although it is frequently considered that the positivity signals invasion of deeper cortical elements, and Chang interprets the second negativity as representing the activity of intracortical neurons (20). Goldring *et al.* (40, 42) consider that the mechanisms of the later potentials have not yet been elucidated, but would agree that the initial and the late negativities are separate neuronal events which may be differentially influenced by a number of agents.

With repetitive stimulation, the cortical discharge may become self-sustaining, as an after-discharge. In the transition, Bonnet and Bremer (8, 14) describe a period of cortical inertia followed by decrease to disappearance of the initial negative spike with a sudden development of positivity. At optimal stimulation frequencies of 15–20/sec., the form of the potential becomes complex, and a stage of alternation appears. This is held to be crucial, for if stimulation is arrested before such alternation, no after-discharge develops, whereas it invariably appears if stimulation is continued up to this stage.

If it is accepted that the initial negative spike in response to each stimulus is a dendritic response, the reason for the decline of these spikes is not clear since it has been shown by Clare and Bishop (23) that there is an increase in the dendritic depolarization with increasing frequencies of direct stimulation up to 70/sec. These authors mention that with "prolonged stimulation something like fatigue intervenes" but do not define this further.

The alternation of potentials is ascribed by Bremer (14) to progressive lengthening of post-reactional subnormality, but why such lengthening is an essential for the development of self-sustained after-discharge is not explained. Seizures may be produced in the cortex by repetitive stimulation of a thalamic relay nucleus, and here alternation is not a feature, but there is an early increase of the negative phase of the evoked potential followed by a progressive decline of the response amplitude. If the stimulus is stopped at this time, paroxysm usually develops (54). Li *et al.* (62) have reported that such repetitive stimulation of the thalamus evokes after-discharge of cortical units which is associated with the decrease of the surface negative component of the evoked potential. Some units may fail to fire as the repetition rate is increased.

In the seizures evoked by repetitive physiological stimulation after subconvulsant dosage of Metrazol, even slow-frequency stimulation may be effective, without the interposition of alternation (Fig. 4-4). In this example, note that there is no significant decline of the negative component of the evoked potential, but that there is marked attenuation of the initial positivity.

Since normal neurons can be driven to after-discharge, it may be assumed that such discharges result from some exaggeration

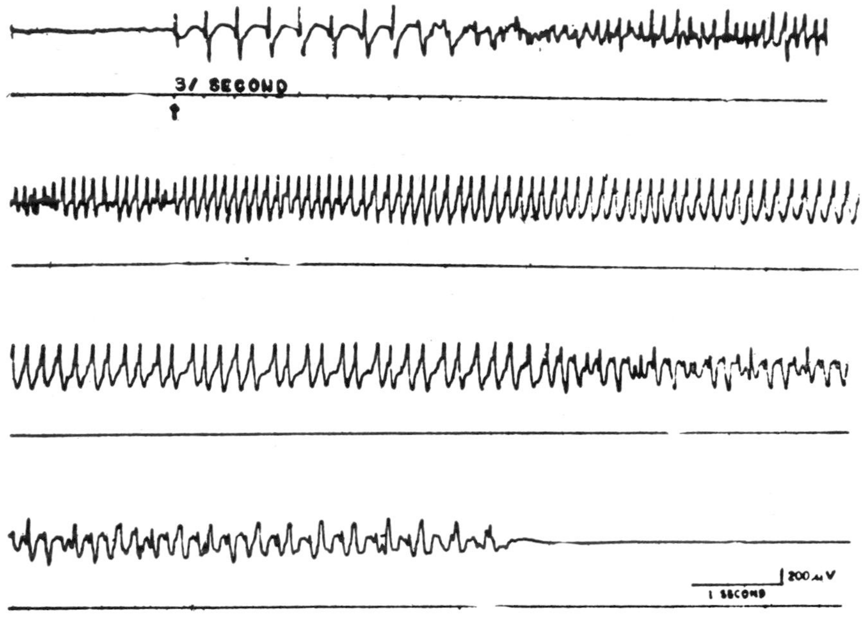

FIG. 4-4. Seizure produced by rhythmic auditory click stimulation after subconvulsant dosage of Metrazol IV in cat. Surface positivity signaled by upward deflection of pen.

of normal mechanisms of impulse initiation, i.e., that the difference between normal repetitive discharge and after-discharge is one of degree, rather than of kind. The possibility of long-duration synaptic bombardment is obvious and requires no further discussion. As regards possible changes in basic mechanisms of impulse initiation, after-discharge can be produced by abnormally enduring dendritic depolarization in synaptic regions such as muscle end-plate (53). In Li's studies of cortical units in a strychnine focus (57), there are frequent waves of polarization and depolarization suggesting changes in the membrane characteristics. The intensity of the repetitive discharge of a unit appears to be related to the degree of depolarization exhibited by that unit (Fig. 4-5).

With extracellular recording, Gerin (38) has recently reported significant amplitude changes of cortical units in the transition to after-discharge following repetitive electrical stimulation of

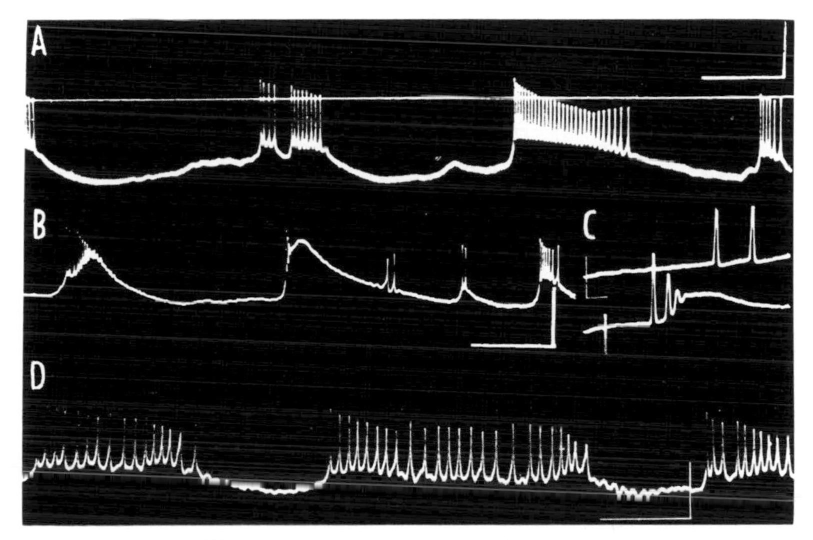

FIG. 4-5. Intracellular recordings of cortical units after local application of strychnine. *A*, about 10 minutes after strychninization; *B*, 15 minutes; *C*, and *D*, 40 minutes; in (*C*) an R-C coupled amplifier was used. Time—250 msec. in *A* and *B*; 5 msec. in *C*; 20 msec. in *D*. Amplitude 50 mV. (After Li, 60.)

the cortex. During stimulation which evokes repetitive discharge of a unit, there is a progressive decrease of unit spike amplitude, to total disappearance. At this stage, cessation of stimulation will be followed by after-discharge after a brief latency, with unit spikes beginning at low amplitude and gradually increasing. The decreasing amplitude during stimulation is considered to be due to increasing membrane depolarization until the depolarization level is so great as to prevent impulse generation. The increasing amplitude during after-discharge is attributed to the return of the state of polarization toward normal levels. However, the dynamics of the postulated repolarization process are far slower than in the normal cortical neuron and require the suggestion of various secondary hypotheses. An analysis of the amplitude variations with intracellular electrodes would be of great interest.

SLOW POTENTIALS

In the isolated cortical slab, Burns (17, 18) reports that "afterbursts" are related to the development of a sustained potential difference between surface and depth, with the surface positive. Properly oriented polarizing currents are sufficient to produce such bursts, and these are arrested by oppositely directed currents. Convulsive discharges have also been set up in nonisolated rabbit cortex by similar surface positive polarization (7, 41). The repetitive discharging activity is considered, by Burns, to be dependent on a polarization gradient between the two extremities of the pyramidal neurons due to differential repolarization. Euler and Green (32) argue that dendrites are not necessarily invaded by impulses, and that such an hypothesis would only be valid when active depolarization of dendrites occurs. In their studies of hippocampal units, they find such invasion correlated with an "inactivation process."

A somewhat similar concept of enduring dendritic depolarization being involved in the chronic alumina cream focus is proposed by Ward and Mahnke (89), who find standing potentials of 7–9 mV, surface negative, in such foci. This potential is attributed to mechanical deformation of dendrites in the cortical scar.

The role played by such slow or standing potentials is very difficult to define. The potential difference reported by Burns is surface positive, and Gloor *et al.* (39) have reported dendritic layer positivity during seizure of the hippocampal pyramidal cells. In a study of the steady potentials of the cortex produced by different convulsant drugs, it is reported that these may be of opposite polarity, although the patterns of the paroxysms are similar (86).

HYPERSYNCHRONY

A striking feature of the seizure discharge is the hypersynchrony of neuronal aggregates as evidenced by the high-amplitude rhythmic discharges recorded from the cortical surface (44). The techniques of single unit recording with one or two microelectrodes do not permit adequate demonstration of possible hypersynchrony, but it is inferred from the presence of a much greater number of spontaneously firing units than is found in normal cortex (80). A temporal relationship between the discharge patterns of two units is sometimes demonstrable in epileptic as well as in normal cortex (58).

Approximate synchrony between neurons may, of course, be achieved through established anatomic interconnection, with a dominant pacemaker group imposing its rhythm on neurons which are discharging at slower rhythms. Fessard (35) points out that postsynaptic influences which are subliminal for actual impulse initiation may also impose a faster rhythm on a group of autorhythmic neurons, but this requires that the rhythms of the pacemaker and of the secondary group be close to each other, and that a fairly rigid isorhythmicity be present. Rigid isorhythmicity is a situation which rarely exists in the mammalian central nervous system. Fessard suggests that, in the epileptic focus, conditions favor isorhythmicity through geographic proximity of neurons and multiple synaptic interconnection. However, unit recording clearly reveals that, although individual neurons may fire at high frequency, the interspike interval is very variable and is maintained at regular frequency for only exceedingly short periods, at best.

The electric fields generated during activity are frequently postulated as a mechanism for synchronization by ephaptic influence, by analogy with simpler systems such as a peripheral nerve. The influence of the field of a single cortical neuron must be small indeed. Tasaki *et al.* (83) found the maximal extracellular potential to be 2.5 mV and considered that fields of such small magnitude could play no more than a negligible role in the synchronization of normal spontaneous activity. Larger potentials have been recorded by some investigators (3, 66), although it is not always certain that these are not intracellular recordings. In any case, it is conceivable that, if properly oriented, the summed fields of a simultaneously acting group could exert a synchronizing influence. This mechanism is frequently postulated as active in the epileptic focus, but there is little direct evidence to support the concept. There is a tendency to consider that the epileptic discharge is essentially the activity of the pyramidal neurons whose cell bodies lie close together with a similar orientation of soma, axon, and dendrite. However, these cells represent only a fraction of the total number of cells present, and there are large numbers of smaller cells arranged in a much less regular fashion. The lower magnitude of unit potentials recorded from epileptic cortex as compared with normal units suggests that many of these smaller cells are also involved in the epileptic discharge (80), so that the electric fields are exceedingly more complex than would be represented by the usual diagram of three radially oriented large pyramidal cells. Subcortical neuronal aggregates may also be foci of epileptic discharge, and, in such nuclei, there is little evidence of any distinctive topographic arrangement of the units.

INHIBITORY MECHANISMS

Interactions between neurons will be more effective as the level of excitability is increased. Among the possible mechanisms involved in states of hyperexcitability is interference with normal inhibitory mechanisms. The presence of inhibitory homeostatic mechanisms protecting against seizure has been postulated by Jung and Tönnies (50, 51), but these are, as yet, ill defined and require description and explanation in neuronal terms. Various types of inhibitory phenomena have been demonstrated in units of the cerebral cortex. Discharges of individual cells may be arrested by afferent stimulation and reciprocal relationships of excitation, and arrest of different units has frequently been demonstrated (2, 4, 10, 19, 59, 65, 72). Figure 4-6 presents the simultaneous recording of two units with relation to a brief spontaneous surface cortical discharge in a chronic epileptic focus. One unit fires at high frequency whereas the spontaneous activity of the other is inhibited. It will be noted that the slow potential change of the surface outlasts the changes in unit activity and that the high-frequency discharge of the activated unit begins before there is any appreciable slow potential change.

A number of workers have demonstrated hyperpolarization of cortical units (10, 60, 61, 75, 82), and Kandel and Spencer (52) have presented evidence that hyperpolarization with inhibition

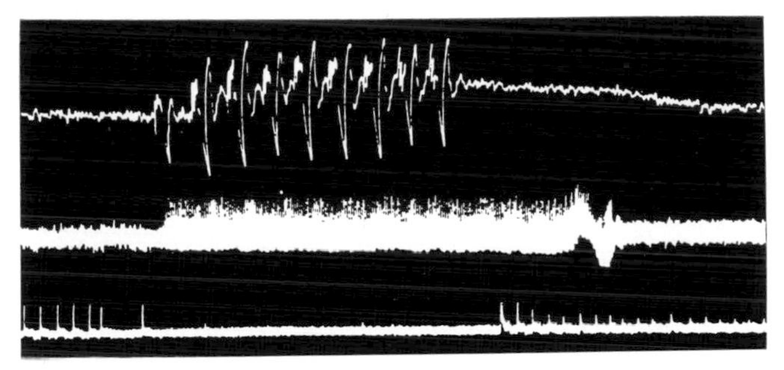

FIG. 4-6. Simultaneous recording of two units in epileptic focus. Double microelectrode with tips about 100 mμ apart. Upper trace is a D.C. surface recording of a spontaneous paroxysm. *Middle* trace shows a unit discharging at high frequency. *Lower* trace shows another unit whose spontaneous low-frequency discharge is arrested. (After Morrell, 70.)

of unit firing may be an important feature of seizure activity in hippocampal neurons. The action of strychnine on the spinal cord is considered to be due to blockade of inhibitory postsynaptic potentials (26), and its excitatory action on the cerebral cortex is attributed to the same mechanism (43, but also see 24).

PROPAGATION OF SEIZURE DISCHARGE

After-discharge, once established in a cortical locus, may project by direct anatomical pathways to other regions of the brain, or may propagate to adjacent cortex where one or more foci of self-sustained discharge may develop. As has been mentioned, propagation by projection also occurs after repetitive stimulation of subcortical nuclei (34). It is significant that normal physiologic stimulation, no matter how prolonged or intense, does not evoke seizure in the normal animal or man. It seems probable that the synchronous character of the afferent barrage in the experimental situation is the differentiating characteristic. A similar synchrony of efferent discharge from a focus during paroxysm may serve a similar function in evoking after-discharge from an area of projection.

Synchrony of input is not essential, for if the excitability characteristics of the neurons are changed, even a physiologically asynchronous afferent barrage may evoke paroxysmal discharge, as may be seen in the evoked discharges of an area of cortex after local application or systemic administration of strychnine or Metrazol. Doses of Metrazol which exert little influence on the time course of the response of the geniculate neurons to a flash may so raise the level of excitability as to produce irradiation to motor cortex and seizure discharge in the form of an efferent pyramidal tract burst (68, Fig. 4-7).

Ephaptic influences have been invoked as playing an important role in the propagation of the epileptic discharge to neighboring cortex. Analogy is made with the famous caffeine spike of Libet and Gerard (64) which will cross a cut in the brain if the cut surfaces are placed in close apposition. Strychnine tetanus in the spinal cord of the frog exhibits similar properties (13) as does the spreading depression of Leao in the cortices of various mammals (56). These striking demonstrations of ephaptic transmission of a disturbance cannot obscure the fact that such transmission of the epileptic discharge from epileptic focus to normal cortex has not been demonstrated. Morrell (69) has recently reported data suggesting that ephaptic spread into the hyperexcitable cortex of a mirror focus may occur. In these experiments, a basic change in the excitability of the neuronal population to be affected appears to be an essential. The experiments of Erickson (30) with multiple incisions of the cortex make it clear that the major mechanism in cortical propagation of the epileptic discharge is via synaptic pathways.

In the propagation of the electrically evoked paroxysm, there frequently is preferential spread to ipsilateral cortex and to the homotopic cortex of the opposite hemisphere (34). In some localities, synaptic organization and anatomical pathways ap-

FIG. 4-7. Responses to light flash in Metrazolized cat; two different preparations. Upper trace of each pair is from motor cortex, lower trace from medullary pyramid. Multiple records of 4–5 responses repeated at 1 flash every 2 sec. Time—2 msec. Amplitude—200 μV. (After Merlis and Misrahy, 68.)

parently favor propagation to certain specific regions. It may be noted, however, that the after-discharge of a given cortical region may sometimes spread to adjacent cortex preferentially and, at other times, to more distant regions without involvement of

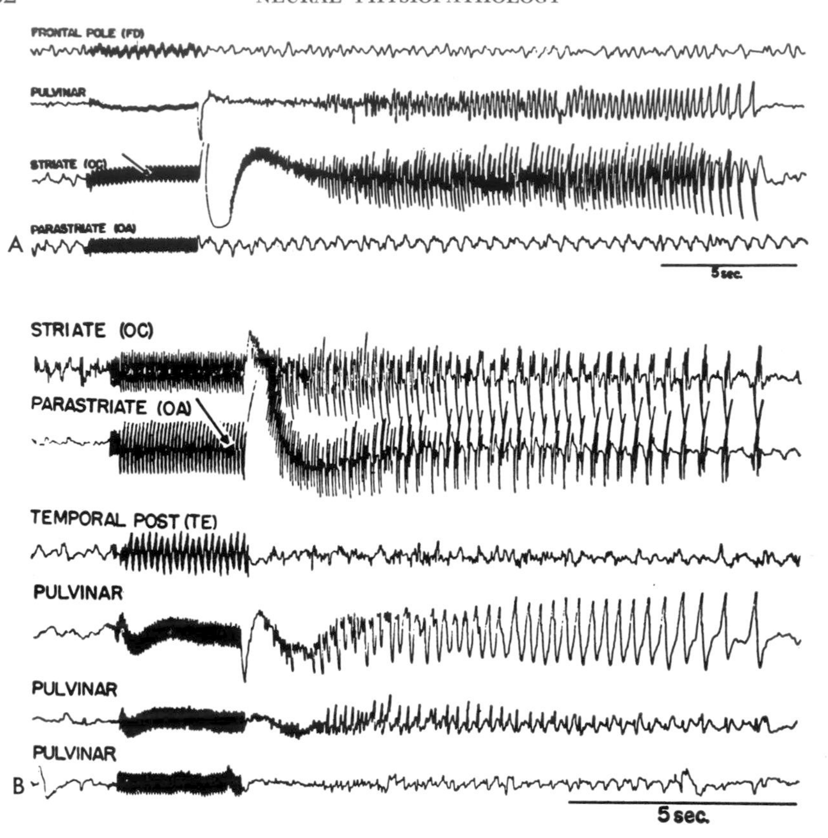

FIG. 4-8. Propagation of after-discharge induced by electrical stimulation of cortex. *A*, After-discharge from striate area conducted to pulvinar without conduction to adjacent parastriate area or to frontal pole. *B*, After-discharge from parastriate area conducted to striate area and to pulvinar, but not to posterior temporal cortex. (After Jasper, Ajmone-Marsan and Stoll, 48.)

neighboring areas as shown in Figure 4-8 (48). The factors which determine this variability have not yet been elucidated.

CESSATION OF DISCHARGE

A paroxysmal discharge, once begun, does not endure indefinitely. There is usually a progressive transition through a stage of rhythmic slow activity followed by bursts separated by periods of silence, the bursts becoming less and less frequent and finally ceasing, to be succeeded by a period of depression and then recovery through a phase of abnormally slow activity. The best-documented explanation for the slowing and cessation of discharge is the development of increasing post-reactional subnormality consequent upon the oxygen debt contracted during the period of hyperactivity (71). An interesting feature is that post-ictal exhaustion does not appear in an area of projection unless self-sustained paroxysmal discharge has occurred (46). Another possible factor is the depressing effect of excessive depolarization such as may be produced with excess acetylcholine at the neuromuscular junction (53), or by excessive stretch of invertebrate receptors (33). A similar mechanism has been demonstrated in the superior cervical ganglion, in which high-frequency stimulation may produce excitatory postsynaptic potentials but failure of the spike generation mechanism (27) and cerebral neurons may respond similarly. In intracellular recordings within a strychnine focus by Li (Fig. 4-5) it is noted that spikes decrease in amplitude and may fail at high levels of depolarization. Gerin's concept of such hyperdepolarization in the genesis of after-discharge has already been referred to (38), as has the possibility of activation of direct neuronal inhibitory mechanisms.

THE PHENOMENON OF THE MIRROR FOCUS

It has already been noted that, in the propagation of the discharge set up at a cortical focus, there may be projection to the homotopic area of the opposite hemisphere. After-discharge may continue in the area of projection after paroxysmal activity has ceased in the primary site. If a chronic focus is established, as with an alumina cream implant, by freezing, or cortical circumsection, a mirror focus may be established in the opposite hemisphere, evidenced by random spiking which may persist after complete removal of the primary focus (28, 46, 69, 87). It is apparent that changes of long duration occur in the neuronal aggregate of the mirror focus which become independent of sustained influence from the initiating disturbance.

The increased excitability of such a focus is demonstrated by the increase in magnitude of the direct cortical response to single shocks (28, 69). From preliminary studies, Morrell (69) suggests a change in the distribution of ribonucleic acid in the neuron as the underlying chemical basis for the development of the mirror focus. Other than this there has been mostly speculation as to possible chemical changes, with little investigation of the basic mechanisms of this highly significant transition of normal neurons into autonomously epileptic ones.

CONVULSANT DRUGS

Considerable attention has been focused on the actions of various convulsant drugs, and no detailed consideration can be attempted here. Unfortunately there has been a preoccupation

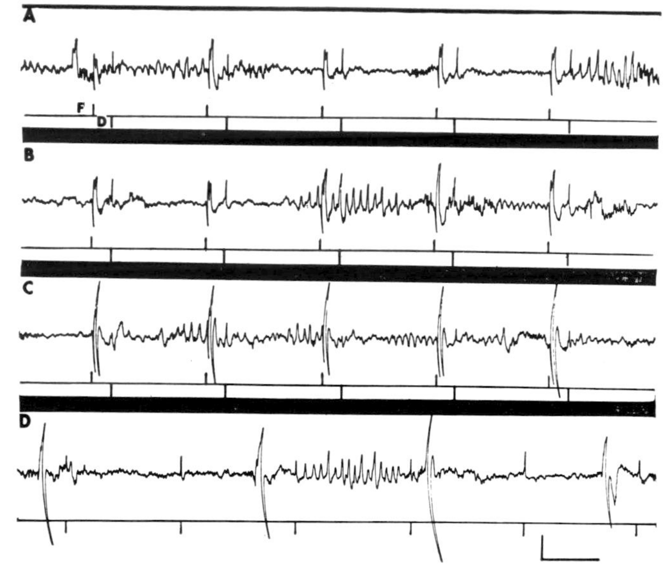

Fig. 4-9. Effect of local application of Metrazol to visual cortex on response to light flash and direct electrical stimulation. Flash signaled by **F**, direct cortical stimulus by **D**. Encéphale isolé cat. *A*, Control. *B*, 20 sec. after application of 5 per cent Metrazol. *C*, 15 sec. later. *D*, 10 sec. later, flash omitted. Note spontaneous discharges which are initially surface-negative; flash-evoked discharges are initially surface-positive. Time—0.5 sec., amplitude—200 μV.

with strychnine as the prototype of such drugs, and too frequently it has not been appreciated that the actions of strychnine are not necessarily typical of convulsants as a group.

Despite the large amount of observation concentrated on strychnine, there is a great deal of disagreement, not only as regards interpretation of the data available, but also in terms of experimental observation itself. As an example, we may cite the

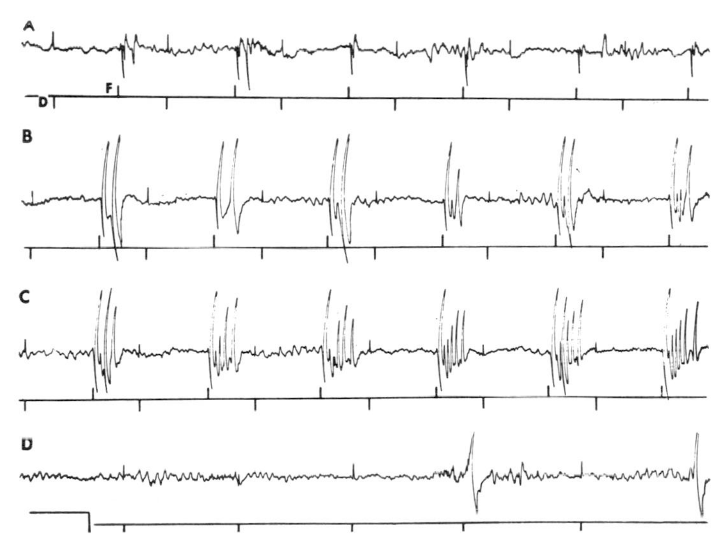

FIG. 4-10. Development of after-discharge; same preparation as in Fig. 4-9. *A*, Control. *B*, *C*, and *D*, strips taken at intervals of 15 sec. after application of Metrazol. Flash omitted in *D*.

disagreement as to whether or not strychnine augments the first or second negative potentials of the direct cortical response (21, 22, 24, 43). Both strychnine and Metrazol, locally applied to the cerebral cortex produce spontaneous cortical spiking, and Purpura and Grudfest (77) argue that this is due to blockade of inhibitory post-synaptic potentials (PSP's), in the case of strychnine, and augmentation of excitatory PSP's in the case of Metrazol. Gastaut *et al.* (36, 37) deny any influence of Metrazol on cortical activity, but our own data demonstrate a marked augmentation of physiologically evoked potentials, with no augmentation of the direct cortical response (DCR), shown in Figure

4-9. Indeed, the DCR is frequently diminished in amplitude, especially when it follows the augmented flash-evoked response at intervals up to 350 msec. In *D*, where the flash is omitted and only spontaneous spikes appear, the DCR is only slightly decreased as compared with the control amplitudes. Note that the

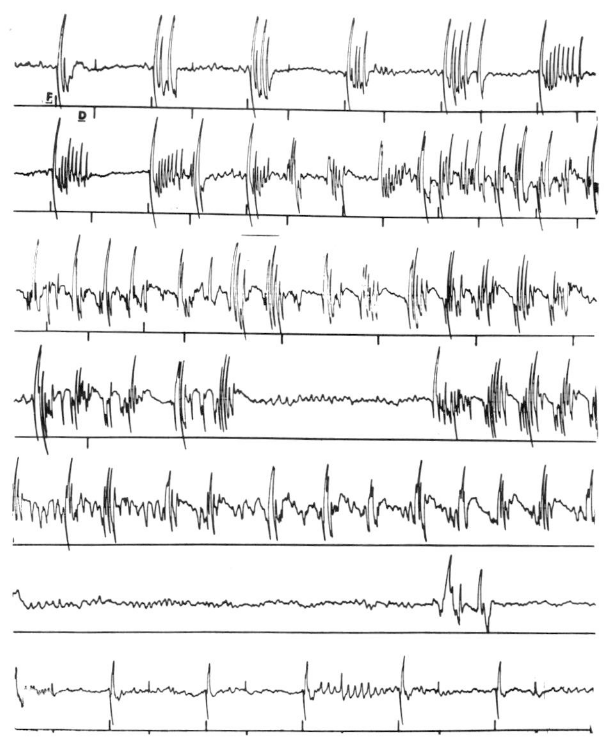

FIG. 4-11. Development of local self-sustained seizure after topical Metrazol. Continuous recording. Flash stopped in third strip, direct cortical stimulus stopped in fourth strip. Both stimuli applied in final strip after seizure.

spontaneous spikes sometimes begin with little or no initial positivity, suggesting that they arise very superficially. The locally augmented flash-evoked potentials may be followed by brief after-discharges as shown in Figure 4-10, and these may eventually lead to self-sustained seizure discharge as shown in Figure 4-11.

RÉSUMÉ

This discussion has been concerned largely with the area, called by Moruzzi, the "general physiology" of epilepsy (71). It has considered, necessarily briefly, some of the characteristics of epileptic or hyperexcitable neurons, and has mentioned some of the cellular mechanisms which may underlie the phenomena of the seizure discharge. It is apparent that paroxysmal bursts of high-frequency discharge with hypersynchrony and propagation may be produced by different agents in different ways.

There are, of course, many important gaps in our information and our understanding. The epileptic discharge produced by a convulsant drug may be ascribed to excitability changes produced by the drug through chemical action on the neuron or its processes, and a similar explanation can be applied to the chronic focus produced by physical or chemical damage. The chemical changes within the focus remain for the neurochemist, perhaps, to elucidate and thus to further our understanding.

A cogent question, and one which is misted in obscurity, concerns the mechanisms by which the normal neuron may become, through repetitive stimulation, at least temporarily epileptic. Put in another way, how are we to define the epileptogenic quality of synchronous bombardment? A better understanding of this phenomenon would do much to further our understanding of the basic mechanisms of the hyperexcitable or epileptic neuron.

REFERENCES

1. ADRIAN, E. D., and MORUZZI, G. Impulses in the pyramidal tract. *J. Physiol. 97:* 153–199, 1939.
2. AMASSIAN, V. E. Inhibition and occlusion in single cortical units. *Am. J. Physiol. 171:* 704–705, 1952.
3. AMASSIAN, V. E. Evoked single cortical unit activity in the somatic sensory areas. *EEG Clin. Neurophysiol. 5:* 415–438, 1953.
4. AMASSIAN, V. E. Studies on organization of a somesthetic association area, including a single unit analysis. *J. Neurophysiol. 17:* 39–58, 1954.

5. Arduini, A., and Whitlock, D. G. Spike discharges in pyramidal system during recruitment waves. *J. Neurophysiol. 16:* 430–436, 1953.
6. Arvanitaki, A. Recherches sur la réponse oscillatoire locale de l'axone géant de "Sepia." *Arch. internat. de physiol. 49:* 209–256, 1939.
7. Bishop, G. H., and O'Leary, J. L. The effects of polarizing currents on cell potentials and their significance in the interpretation of central nervous system activity. *EEG Clin. Neurophysiol. 2:* 401–416, 1950.
8. Bonnet, V., and Bremer, F. Analyse de modifications préconvulsives de la réaction cérébrale à une stimulus direct répété. *J. physiol. Paris 48:* 399–403, 1956.
9. Boyarsky, L. L., Sant'Ambrogio, G., and Frazier, D. Evoked slow and unit responses of the cerebral cortex following repetitive stimulation. *Am. J. Physiol. 198:* 511–514, 1960.
10. Branch, C. L., and Martin, A. R. Inhibition of Betz cell activity by thalamic and cortical stimulation. *J. Neurophysiol. 21:* 380–390, 1958.
11. Brazier, M. A. B. Neuronal structure, brain potentials and epileptic discharge. *Epilepsia.* Series III, *4:* 9–18, 1955.
12. Brazier, M. A. B. The development of concepts relating to the electrical activity of the brain. *J. Nerv. & Ment. Dis. 126:* 303–321, 1958.
13. Bremer, F. Le tétanos strychnique et le mécanisme de la synchronization neuronique. *Arch. internat. de physiol. 51:* 211–260, 1941.
14. Bremer, F. Les processus d'éxcitation et d'inhibition dans les phénomènes épileptiques. In Alajouanine, Th., *Bases Physiologiques et Aspects Cliniques de L'Epilepsie.* Masson, Paris, 1–35, 1958.
15. Brink, F., Bronk, D. W., and Larrabee, M. Chemical excitation of nerve. *Bull. N.Y. Acad. Sc. 47:* 457–485, 1946.
16. Bronk, D. W., Larrabee, M. G., Gaylor, J. B., and Brink, F. The influence of altered chemical environment on the activity of ganglion cells. *Am. J. Physiol. 123:* 24–25, 1938.
17. Burns, B. D. Intracortical integration. *EEG Clin. Neurophysiol.* Suppl. #4, 72–81, 1953.
18. Burns, B. D. The mechanism of after-bursts in cerebral cortex. *J. Physiol. 127:* 168–188, 1955.

19. Calma, I., and Arduini, A. Spontaneous and induced activity in pyramidal units. *J. Neurophysiol. 17:* 321–335, 1954.
20. Chang, H. T. Dendritic potentials of cortical neurons produced by direct electrical stimulation of the cerebral cortex. *J. Neurophysiol. 14:* 1–21, 1951.
21. Chang, H. T. An observation on the effect of strychnine on local cortical potentials. *J. Neurophysiol. 14:* 23–28, 1951.
22. Chang, H. T. Similarity in action between curare and strychnine on cortical neurons. *J. Neurophysiol. 16:* 221–233, 1953.
23. Clare, M. H., and Bishop, G. H. Properties of dendrites; apical dendrites of the cat cortex. *EEG Clin. Neurophysiol. 7:* 85–98, 1955.
24. Clare, M. H., and Bishop, G. H. Action of strychnine on recruiting responses of dendrites of cat cortex. *J. Neurophysiol. 20:* 255–274, 1957.
25. DeVito, R. V., Brusa, A., and Arduini, A. Cerebellar and vestibular influences on Deitersian units. *J. Neurophysiol. 19:* 241–253, 1956.
26. Eccles, J. C. *The Physiology of Nerve Cells.* The Johns Hopkins Press, Baltimore, 1957, pp. 270.
27. Eccles, R. M. Intracellular potentials recorded from a mammalian sympathetic ganglion. *J. Physiol. 130:* 572–584, 1956.
28. Eidelberg, E., Konigsmark, B., and French, J. D. Electrocortical manifestations of epilepsy in monkey. *EEG Clin. Neurophysiol. 11:* 121–128, 1959.
29. Enomoto, T. F., and Ajmone-Marsan, C. Epileptic activation of single cortical neurons and their relationship with electroencephalographic discharges. *EEG Clin. Neurophysiol. 11:* 199–218, 1959.
30. Erickson, T. C. Spread of the epileptic discharge. An experimental study of the after-discharge induced by electrical stimulation of the cerebral cortex. *AMA Arch. Neurol. & Psychiat. 43:* 429–452, 1940.
31. Erlanger, J., Blair, E. A., and Schoepfle, G. M. A study of the spontaneous oscillations in the excitability of nerve fibers with special reference to the action of strychnine. *Am. J. Physiol. 134:* 705–718, 1941.
32. Euler, C. V., and Green, J. D. Excitation, inhibition and rhythmical activity in hippocampal pyramidal cells in rabbit. *Acta physiol. Scandinav. 48:* 110–125, 1960.

33. Eyzaguirre, C., and Kuffler, S. W. Processes of excitation in dendrites and soma of single isolated sensory cells of lobster and crayfish. *J. Gen. Physiol. 39:* 87–119, 1955.
34. Faeth, W. H., Walker, A. E., and Andy, O. J. The propagation of cortical and subcortical epileptic discharge. *Epilepsia.* Series III, *3:* 37–48, 1954.
35. Fessard, A. Les mécanismes de synchronization interneuronique et leur intervention dans la crise épileptique. In Alajouanine, Th., *Bases Physiologiques et Aspects Cliniques de L'Epilepsie.* Masson, Paris, 37–60, 1958.
36. Gastaut, H., and Fischer-Williams, M. The physiopathology of epileptic seizures, in *Handbook of Physiology,* Vol. 1, edited by J. Field, H. W. Magoun, and V. E. Hall. American Physiological Society, Washington, pp. 329–363, 1959.
37. Gastaut, H., Naquet, R., and Fischer-Williams, M. The pathophysiology of grand mal seizures generalized from the start. *J. Nerv. & Ment. Dis. 127:* 21–33, 1958.
38. Gerin, P. Microelectrode investigations on the mechanisms of the electrically induced epileptiform seizure ("after-discharge"). *Arch. ital. de biol. 98:* 21–40, 1960.
39. Gloor, P., Sperti, L., Vera, C., and Ray, S. Investigations on the mechanisms of epileptic discharge in the hippocampus. Presented at Annual Meeting, *Am. EEG Soc.,* Cape Cod, June, 1960.
40. Goldring, S., Metcalf, J. S., Huang, S. H., Shields, J., and O'Leary, J. L. Pharmacological selectivity manifested by agents acting upon the cortical dendritic spike and its slow after-effects. *J. Nerv. & Ment. Dis. 128:* 1–11, 1960.
41. Goldring, S., and O'Leary, J. Experimentally derived correlates between ECG and steady cortical potential. *J. Neurophysiol. 14:* 275–288, 1951.
42. Goldring, S., O'Leary, J. S., Winter, D. S., and Pearlman, A. S. Identification of a prolonged post-synaptic potential of cerebral cortex. *Proc. Soc. Exper. Biol. & Med. 100:* 429–431, 1959.
43. Grundfest, H. General physiology and pharmacology of synapses and some implications for the mammalian central nervous system. *J. Nerv. and Ment. Dis. 128:* 473–496, 1959.
44. Jasper, H. The place of electroencephalography in clinical neurology: a retrospective and prospective study. *AMA Arch. Neurol. & Psychiat. 44:* 1345-1437, 1940.

45. JASPER, H. H. Electrical signs of epileptic discharge. *EEG Clin. Neurophysiol. 1:* 11–18, 1949.
46. JASPER, H. In Penfield, W., and Jasper, H. *Epilepsy and the Functional Anatomy of the Human Brain.* Little, Brown and Co., Boston, 1954.
47. JASPER, H. H. Discussion of Symposium on Dendrites. *EEG Clin. Neurophysiol.* Suppl. #10, 42–43, 1958.
48. JASPER, H., AJMONE-MARSAN, C., and STOLL, J. Corticofugal projections to the brain stem. *AMA Arch. Neurol. & Psychiat. 67:* 155–166, 1952.
49. JOHNSON, H. C., and WALKER, A. E. Response of experimental epileptic foci to intravenous and topical Metrazol. *EEG Clin. Neurophysiol. 4:* 131–139, 1952.
50. JUNG, R. Neuronal Discharge. *EEG Clin. Neurophysiol.* Suppl. #4, 57–71, 1953.
51. JUNG, R., and TÖNNIES, J. F. Hirnelektrische Untersuchungen uber Entstehung und Erhaltung von Krampfentladungen: Die Vorgange am Reizort und die Bremsfahigkeit des Gehirns. *Arch. f. Psychiat. 185:* 701–735, 1950.
52. KANDEL, E. R., and SPENCER, W. A. In Discussion, *Symposium on Basic Mechanisms in the Epileptic Discharge.* Annual Meeting, *Am. EEG Soc.,* Cape Cod, June, 1960.
53. KATZ, B., and THESLEFF, S. The interaction between edrophonium (Tensilon) and acetylcholine at the motor end plate. *Brit. J. Pharmacol. 12:* 260–264, 1957.
54. KING, R. B., SCHRICKER, J. L., and O'LEARY, J. L. An experimental study of the transition from normal to convulsoid cortical activity. *J. Neurophysiol. 16:* 286–298, 1953.
55. KUFFLER, S. W. Discharge patterns and functional organization of mammalian retina. *J. Neurophysiol. 16:* 37–68, 1953.
56. LEAO, A. A. P. Spreading depression of activity in the cerebral cortex. *J. Neurophysiol. 7:* 359–390, 1944.
57. LI, CHOH-LUH. Functional properties of cortical neurons with particular reference to strychninization. *EEG Clin. Neurophysiol. 7:* 475–477, 1955.
58. LI, CHOH-LUH. Synchronization of unit activity in the cerebral cortex. *Science. 129:* 783–784, 1959.
59. LI, CHOH-LUH. Some properties of pyramidal neurons in motor cortex with particular reference to sensory stimulation. *J. Neurophysiol. 22:* 385-394, 1959.

60. LI, CHOH-LUH. Cortical intracellular potentials and their responses to strychnine. *J. Neurophysiol. 22:* 436–450, 1959.
61. LI, CHOH-LUH. Single cell discharge in cortex. *Symposium on Basic Mechanisms in the Epileptic Discharge.* Annual Meeting, *Am. EEG Soc.,* Cape Code, June, 1960.
62. LI, CHOH-LUH, CULLEN, C., and JASPER, H. Laminar microelectrode studies of specific somatosensory cortical potentials. *J. Neurophysiol. 19:* 111–130, 1956.
63. LI, CHOH-LUH, CULLEN, C., and JASPER, H. H. Laminar microelectrode analysis of cortical unspecific recruiting responses and spontaneous rhythms. *J. Neurophysiol. 19:* 131–143, 1956.
64. LIBET, B., and GERARD, R. W. Control of the potential rhythm of the isolated frog brain. *J. Neurophysiol. 2:* 153–169, 1939.
65. MACHINE, X., and SEGUNDO, J. P. Unitary responses to afferent volleys in amygdaloid complex. *J. Neurophysiol. 19:* 232–240, 1956.
66. MARTIN, A. R., and BRANCH, C. L. Spontaneous activity of Betz cells in cats with mid-brain lesions. *J. Neurophysiol. 21:* 368–379, 1958.
67. MATTHEWS, B. H. C. Nerve endings in mammalian muscle. *J. Physiol. 78:* 1–53, 1933.
68. MERLIS, J. K., and MISRAHY, G. L. Corticospinal mechanisms in experimental seizures. *Epilepsia 1:* 527–537, 1960.
69. MORRELL, F. Lasting changes in synaptic organization produced by continuous neuronal bombardment. *Conference on Brain Mechanisms and Learning,* Montevideo, August, 1959. In press, Blackwell, London.
70. MORRELL, F. Discussion, *Symposium on Basic Mechanisms in the Epileptic Discharge.* Annual Meeting, *Am. EEG Society,* Cape Cod, June, 1960.
71. MORUZZI, G. *L'Epilepsie Experimentale,* Hermann, Paris, 1950.
72. MOUNTCASTLE, V. B. Modality and topographic properties of single neurons of cat's somatic sensory cortex. *J. Neurophysiol. 20:* 408–434, 1957.
73. MOUNTCASTLE, V., DAVIES, P., and BERMAN, A. Response properties of neurons of cat's somatic sensory cortex to peripheral stimuli. *J. Neurophysiol. 20:* 374–407, 1957.
74. PFAFFMANN, C. Afferent impulses from the teeth due to pressure and noxious stimulation. *J. Physiol. 97:* 207–219, 1939.

75. PHILLIPS, C. G. Intracellular records from Betz cells in the cat. *Quart. J. Exp. Physiol. 41:* 58–69, 1956.
76. PHILLIPS, C. G. Cortical motor threshold and the thresholds and distribution of excited Betz cells in the cat. *Quart. J. Exp. Physiol. 41:* 70–84, 1956.
77. PURPURA, D. P., and GRUNDFEST, H. Physiological and pharmacological consequences of different synaptic organizations in cerebral and cerebellar cortex. *J. Neurophysiol. 20:* 494–522, 1957.
78. RALSTON, B. L. The mechanism of transition of interictal spiking foci into ictal seizure discharges. *EEG Clin. Neurophysiol. 10:* 217–232, 1958.
79. RALSTON, B., and PAPATHEODORU, C. A. The mechanism of transition of interictal spiking foci into ictal seizure discharges. Part II: Observations in man. *EEG Clin. Neurophysiol. 12:* 297–304, 1960.
80. SCHMIDT, R. P., THOMAS, L. B., and WARD, A. A., JR. The hyperexcitable neuron. Microelectrode studies of chronic epileptic foci in monkey. *J. Neurophysiol. 22:* 285–296, 1959.
81. SEGUNDO, J. P., and MACHNE, X. Unitary responses to afferent volleys in lenticular nucleus and claustrum. *J. Neurophysiol. 19:* 325–339, 1956.
82. SPENCER, W. A., and KANDEL, E. R. Intracellular recordings of hippocampal neuron response to stimulation of deafferented fornix. Presented at Annual Meeting, *Am. EEG. Soc.*, Cape Cod, June, 1960.
83. TASAKI, I., POLLEY, E. H., and ORREGO, R. F. Action potentials from individual elements in cat geniculate and striate cortex. *J. Neurophysiol. 17:* 454–474, 1954.
84. THOMAS, L. B., SCHMIDT, R. P., and WARD, A. A., JR. Observations on single units in chronic cortical epileptogenic foci and in normal or strychninized cortex. *EEG Clin. Neurophysiol. 7:* 478–480, 1955.
85. TOWE, A. L., and AMASSIAN, V. E. Patterns of activity in single cortical units following stimulation of the digits in monkeys. *J. Neurophysiol. 21:* 292–311, 1958.
86. VANASUPA, P., GOLDRING, S., and O'LEARY, J. L. Seizure discharges effected by intravenously administered convulsant drugs. *EEG Clin. Neurophysiol. 11:* 93–106, 1959.
87. WALKER, A. E., and JOHNSON, H. C. Normal and pathological after-discharge from frontal cortex. *Research Publ., A. Nerv. & Ment. Dis. 27:* 460–475, 1947.

88. Walker, A. E., Marshall, C., and Beresford, E. Electrocorticographic characteristics of the cerebrum in post-traumatic epilepsy. *Research Publ., A. Nerv. & Ment. Dis. 26:* 502–515, 1947.
89. Ward, A. A., Jr., and Mahnke, J. H. Standing potential characteristics of the epileptogenic focus. *Tr. Am. Neurol A.*, 93–95, 1960.
90. Whitlock, D. G., Arduini, A., and Moruzzi, G. Microelectrode analysis of pyramidal system during transition from sleep to wakefulness. *J. Neurophysiol. 16:* 414–429, 1953.

CHAPTER 5

Normal and Abnormal Sensory Patterns: Pain

I. ANATOMICAL, PHYSIOLOGICAL, AND PSYCHOLOGICAL FACTORS IN SENSATION OF PAIN*

GEORGE H. BISHOP

AS a basis for an understanding of abnormal patterns of sensation, the proposal here is first to relate the somesthetic sensations originating from peripheral stimulation to the physiology and anatomy of the paths over which the nerve impulses aroused are conducted. Aside from the interest in these relations as such, their recognition is essential in the diagnosis and treatment of neurological disease or abnormality. Sensation however is a many-faceted experience, and the question arises at once, which aspect of the sensations correlates most specifically with the central paths over which they are mediated. In the extremes, there are two quite different aspects of sensation. One is the recognition and discrimination of essential quality, usually recognized, for instance, as belonging in the categories of touch, pain, itch, and temperature. The other is the perception of the sensation, the interpretation of what a given instance of sensory stimu-

* This work was supported in part by a grant from the Supreme Council, 33rd Scottish Rite, Northern Masonic Jurisdiction, U.S.A., through the National Association for Mental Health; and in part by contract between Washington University and the Office of Naval Research.

lation means to the individual against the background of his past and current experience.

PERCEPTION OF SENSATION

There is obviously no sharp line of demarkation to be drawn between these two aspects of sensation; any sensation will be more or less completely interpreted as having meaning or significance in addition to its essential quality, and both these aspects of sensation involve consciousness. Of the anatomy and physiology of those parts of the central nervous system which serve as the morphological substrate of consciousness we know next to nothing. About the peripheral paths innervating this central substrate we now have considerable information. It is still seriously embarrassing, therefore, that the only final evidence of a sensory process in the paths whose characteristics we know has to come from the responses of a higher center whose complexities we cannot analyze and whose responses significant for our purpose are in terms of consciousness rather than in terms of the physiological activity corresponding to this.

It is evident from experimental testing of these relations that the best correlations between peripheral anatomical pathway and central conscious report are with the recognition and discrimination of the more elementary qualities of sensation, rather than with the interpretations of their meaning in the context of total experience. The first requirement in correlating the sensations and their pathways is then to induce sensations experimentally under conditions which emphasize this first aspect, and relegate the second, the more elaborate interpretation of their significance, to a status of minimal concern to the subject. This is the opposite emphasis one would desire if the object were to make the maximum and optimal use of the sensory information in a given situation. A second requirement is to ascertain in any instance which path mediates the impulses aroused, and where these paths terminate in the higher centers. Only then will we be able to correlate a given report with a given state of the apparatus which mediates it.

Many investigators over many years have dealt with the sensations in terms of specific sensory endings and central pathways, and the patterns of their excitation. Anyone so physiologically and anatomically oriented is liable to take for granted that the central mechanisms of conscious recognition are equally specific, categorical, and trustworthy as are the responses in terms of action currents in the paths leading to the higher centers. On the contrary, it has been increasingly and embarrassingly necessary to qualify, argue, and interpret the reports of conscious human subjects following peripheral excitation of their neurological mechanisms. A few introspective and neurologically compromising concessions are appropriate here. The first is that the highest centers of the nervous system are fallible, and sometimes capricious. The second concession is that the brain not only can make mistakes, but can add an enormous amount of significant, if complicating material to the information delivered by the peripheral nervous system. We have all learned too much about what our sensations may mean to us to give uncomplicated or unbiased answers as to what they feel like. Often this addition is naïve, even irrational, but it is obviously designed to be potentially useful to the organism. However, this includes more than the *immediate* response to sensory stimulation. There is added by the conscious centers the interpretation, often equivocal, of the material currently received, against the background of past and current experience in consciousness and perhaps below it. The final integration is what we get from the subject, often in response to even the most specific stimulation. This circumstance has been overlooked by many physiologists, and by some neurologists. But the only final evidence of what the subject experiences is what he reports. Under what circumstances then can we obtain the most simple and reliable reports as little as possible adorned by the subject's emotional or affective elaborations of what the sensation may mean to him or remind him of? This problem arises with peculiar cogency in dealing with anxious, sick, or suffering patients, and in testing for such a distressing sensation as pain.

Such a proposal represents an attempt to eliminate many subjective phenomena, in a discussion where paradoxically the conscious recognition of sensation is the key and essential datum. In this impossible impasse one can only compromise, by reducing the sensory response in consciousness to as simple and categorical a content as possible, in order to match this in fact with simple and categorical methods of testing. The result may not be erroneous, but it must surely be inadequate. The present question is, how far can we go with it?

How to Make Pain Simple

The simplest place to study the physiology and anatomy of painful sensation seems to be in the normal subject who isn't having any, except of course what the experimenter gives him, and it is still better if he is persuaded to give it to himself. He may then become interested chiefly in the external event, and state with a minimum of bias but with a maximum of discrimination what it "feels" like. If one wants to recognize the sensation resulting from a given stimulus, with a minimum of the embroidery of affective interpretation, the less he broods about it the better. The first necessity is to get his mind off his inner consciousness and directed toward the external situation. That is where he thinks his sensation is anyway, and the more he externalizes it the better. He will never tell you where it is in the brain, but he may tell you what it is like in consciousness.

To the extent that the elementary senses can be tested, this minimal subjective response becomes diagnostic of the state of the transmission system, of the afferent paths and their immediate central connections, and of the state of the excitable periphery. With due regard for central complicating factors, it becomes a method for analyzing pathology or abnormality, as well as for study of normal processes. It aims to obviate as much as possible those elaborations of subjective interpretation, which are added normally to the sensory message, without forgetting that in common experience these interpretations are of major importance in the competent response to the sensory environment.

DEFINITION OF PAIN; PAINFUL SENSATION AND PAINFUL EXPERIENCE

We learn the names for our sensations, by our own experience of them. We recognize first introspectively, and secondarily by agreement with the descriptions of others, similar sensations from similar stimuli, and we agree with each other, sometimes, as to what names we will apply to the sensations so aroused. It has long been agreed that there are at least four of these in the somesthetic system, the "modalities" of touch, pain, warmth, and cold, and within these there are further subdivisions, two types of pain and a number of their variants, at least three types of touch, and perhaps some, so far not clearly recognized, variants of temperature sense. Many of our casual sensations, however, are recognized readily as falling into these simpler categories, and these can be duplicated under controlled experimental conditions.

The "integers" of sensation are most appropriately recognized when aroused by moderate strength of stimulus to a minimal area with due consideration to the character of the energy applied to stimulate. The sensory quality of even such a "pure" sensation may then change significantly as the intensity or other parameters of the stimulus are increased, and may or may not be naïvely identified as the same sensation. Sharp becomes prick, and prick becomes pricking pain, the intensity and quality varying with the frequency or duration of stimulation, but without any evidence of a change in the type of end organs stimulated. We will define painful sensation for the purposes of this discussion as the simplest, most irreducible response in consciousness realizable by the average normal subject, which he designates as painful, and as distinct from other recognizable qualities, when stimuli are applied in the periphery which arouse no other sensation. This obviously implies that the subject is not frightened by the procedure, anxious about the result, helpless to avoid the sensation, or particularly disturbed by anything else. Having once recognized these integers of sensation, we will accept the subject's report that these unit sensations which he can be given experimentally under suitable conditions are also included in more complex patterns of sensory experience. We will insist that these experimentally induced painful sensations are effectively identifiable with certain sensations that every normal person has experienced in normal contacts with the environment, because normal subjects tell us that this is the case. We will emphasize a difference between this *elementary sensation* and a *painful experience,* the more elaborate state of consciousness that involves an emotional response, the threat of pain in disease or injury, anxiety as to what it may mean to the subject, and the associations in memory of the connotations of pain in past experience. Painful sensation is typically a component of certain kinds of painful experience. It may serve as the principal *initiator* of such experience, but does not necessarily arouse it. Pain may cause suffering, but we may suffer from other causes, and we may feel considerable pain as a sensation with a minimum of suffering or none.

Experimental Differentiations of Elementary Sensations

The simple sensations can be evoked by normal stimuli; but the electrical stimulation of nerve endings, or of nerve branches through the skin, or via needles inserted under it, can also evoke them. In this manner sensations are induced of sharp or blunt pressure, movement, temperature, etc., closely enough duplicating the effects of normal stimuli for recognition of identity. Their qualitative ranges may then be duplicated by manipulations of intensity, frequency, and duration of the electric stimulation. Complexes of such elementary sensations can also be induced when two or more different stimuli are manipulated in different proportions. Wetness, for instance, is chiefly the summation of tactile and temperature senses, optimally cool and exaggerated by moving contact, contributing a component of smoothness or slipperiness of touch. When the degree or character of either component of the stimulus is varied the recognition of wetness is lost at the extremes. Movement of the contact stimulus; variation of intensity, of frequency, or of area; and numbers of endings involved—all affect the quality of sensation. Repetitive touch is vibration, light moving touch gives tickle, heavier touch grades into pressure and finally into pressure pain. Two kinds of pain are often aroused from the same stimulus and are then difficult to discriminate. The sense organs and nerve terminals are not critically but only preferentially sensitive each to its own characteristic energy of activation, and stimuli to which one type of ending is of lowest threshold may activate others of a different modality when the stimulus is increased in intensity. Thus, high temperature adds pain to warmth, sharp tactile contact adds prick to touch, and electric current stimulates everything except possibly warmth, depending chiefly for relative sensitivities on the physical accessibility of the endings. On the other hand, unit cold spots, after removal of the epithelium and papillary layer of dermis, can be stimulated either electrically, by cooling, or by mechanical pressure to give the identical sensation of cool, without arousing any other sensations.

Varieties of Pain

In particular, there are two classes of painful sensation, distinguishable both by their qualities and by their origins due to peripheral stimulation. Each class includes variants associated with type or locus of sensory ending and with various parameters of the stimulus. The first class includes pricking pain aroused typically but not exclusively in endings close under the epithelium, and mediated over small myelinated fibers. The second is often referred to as burning or causalgic pain; its endings are typically located deeper in the dermis, and variously distributed in addition to subcutaneous tissue, muscle, periosteum, blood vessels, and internal organs. Its quality varies widely as elicited from different endings, but differs recognizably from pricking pain, as a dull hurt rather than a sharp ache. It has a common anatomical denominator of mediation over unmyelinated fibers in peripheral nerves. Its variants include pain typical of inflammation, of periosteal bruise, muscle ache, deep pressure, and probably headache. A useful differential criterion for these two classes of pain is that pricking pain induced by electrical stimulation of a nerve branch under the skin summates smoothly only at frequencies of 20 to 30 per second, while burning pain summates smoothly at less than 5 per second stimulation. Their experimental separation and reference to two size ranges in the nerve fiber spectrum as specific mediators can be accomplished by differential pressure block and by differential anesthesia of nerve trunks. By such means we may acquire a second criterion for characterizing sensations, the fiber size groups within which they are mediated.

Some Examples of Simple Sensations, Simply Differentiated

One direct way of isolating, however arbitrarily, the elementary sensations and their variants is through the testing of sensory endings or fibers where these can be dealt with in isolation. For example, there are sensory spots in the skin whose threshold is lower to either mechanical prick or to electrical stimulation than is the surrounding area. Their response elicits only pricking pain near threshold. Again, near-threshold repetitive stimulation by electric current of a certain branch of the radial nerve, activating only the largest fibers, will elicit only light touch in the thenar eminence of the palm, an abrupt tapping or vibratory sense at the two joints of the thumb, and "cotton wool" sensation of touch referable to hair follicle endings on the back of the hand. Or by employing either blunt pressure or an electrode of large area to permit low-current density through the skin, certain spots along the vessels of the back of the hand can be stimulated to give a dull aching pain with no prick. Pricking pain can be elicited equally uniquely by sharp pressure or via a needle electrode applied to the same area of skin. Similar deeply located endings are found more densely distributed under the skin, presumably in periosteum over the shin, giving a localized sensation, which when exaggerated becomes obviously the typical persisting and excruciating pain from a heavy blow over this region. These endings are chiefly those of unmyelinated fibers, since they remain partially active after nerve pressure block sufficient to abolish pricking pain. Pain of inflammation from a sterile boil due to subcutaneous turpentine injection is obtainable by blunt pressure too light to elicit any trace of prick. At the same time pricking pain from endings over the inflammatory area have their normal thresholds to sharp pressure or to electric current. Differential pressure block then abolishes prick leaving inflammatory pain, and differential anesthesia blocks inflammatory pain in a concentration leaving prick normal. The protopathic pain of Head and Rivers following nerve section can be blocked by anesthetics, leaving pricking pain in areas adjacent to the denervated area which are still normally innervated by an uncut branch of the nerve blocked. In such cases certain irreducible sensations can be isolated, and the fibers mediating them can be located in the nerve fiber size spectrum and their higher pathways identified by other procedures.

Experimental manipulations in animals and man serve further to correlate the sensations mediated with the sizes of nerve fibers involved, whether activated by normal methods of stimulation or by electric stimuli to superficial nerves. For instance, pressure from a cuff inflated to 250 mm. Hg or more progressively blocks larger fibers before smaller, while dilute anesthetics block the smaller before the larger, in excised nerves or in situ. From the order in which the *sensations* are blocked in normal subjects the *fibers* mediating them can be located in the nerve fiber size spectrum. Once these correlations have been determined, the paths over which the respective sensations are mediated can be followed by other means to their centers of termination in the central nervous system. These procedures have been reviewed recently (1) and will not be further elaborated here.

How Simple Sensations Become Complex

Such manipulations are deliberately designed to avoid the more comprehensive elaboration of interpretations, associations, and significations of the complex pattern of stimulation we usually receive in casual contact with the environment, and connoting perceptions in addition to simpler identification. They are also designed to minimize the contributions to interpretation from the random bombardment of consciousness by streams of impulses indicating the state of the body in general, or the attitude of the subject aside from his attention to the specific stimulus. This is not a normal way to react to the environment, and a certain amount of training of even normal subjects as well as of sick patients may be necessary to obtain reliable, that is, reproducible results. The aim here, however, is not to explore consciousness to determine what it can, or even usually does, make of a given pattern of stimulation, against its normal and variable background, but quite the opposite; what it makes of the pattern without the complications normally giving a variable meaning to sensory experience. However, we can never escape the fact that sensation involves consciousness, of many things other than the specific stimulus under test.

It may also be significant that only a fraction of the fibers in the central afferent paths relay to the higher centers directly. Most of them terminate in the brain stem with unknown effects on the higher centers by more indirect paths. The study of strictly "sensory" mechanisms in the context of the full afferent input is only in a restricted sense a study of sensation as such, as a psychological phenomenon.

Pain Sensation (Discrimination) and Painful Experience

As contrasted to single, elementary, and minimally distressing sensations, and the discrimination of recognizable combinations into more complex patterns, are those conceptual interpretations not so directly a part of the sensory message. These are capable of giving a rational or emotional significance to the information mediated, in addition to the identification or discrimination of basic quality. This is to make a distinction between sensation as such and the whole sensory experience; two extremes to be sure of a continuous range of increasing complexity, but recognizably separable at their extremes. Sensation is only a part of sensory experience, but the essential part when attending to peripheral mechanisms involved in initiating the experience. A sensory element here is simple in two ways; it is one that is irreducible into simpler components with respect to its peripheral activation, and it connotes an irreducible degree of significance of meaning. This has generally been recognized in the use of such dichotomies as pain and its affect, pain sensation and painful reaction, pain and suffering, etc. The whole resultant experience following a painful stimulus includes more than the immediate sensory response, and is liable to confuse the correlation between sensation and the pathway over which it is mediated.

THE CENTRAL SENSORY PATHS

There can be traced five afferent paths above the cord level in mammals, four of which and probably the fifth mediate sensation (Fig. 5-1). Two of these and possibly a third mediate sensations

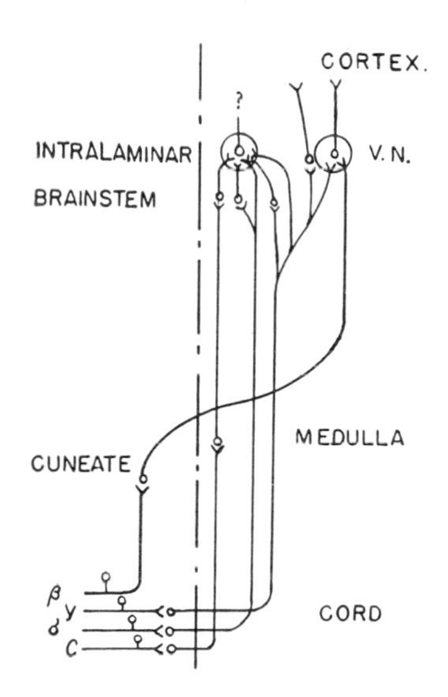

FIG. 5-1. Diagram of five afferent paths from the periphery to higher centers, four of which certainly, and the fifth probably, mediate sensations. The medial lemniscus rises from the dorsal column fibers (β-group of peripheral nerves), the remainder from the spinal lemniscus, of fibers crossing in the cord (γ, δ, and **C**). Terminations of the spinal lemniscus can be traced to the medulla (**C**), the medial brain stem, medial thalamus, and the ventral nucleus and its surroundings (γ and δ). The spinal lemniscus is present in animals below the mammal; the medial lemniscus occurs only in mammals. (Reprinted with permission from G. H. Bishop, Chap. V, *The Biology of the Skin*, edited by W. Montagna, Pergamon Press, Oxford, 1960.)

of pain, and a fourth may contribute to it. These are all crossed paths; some homolateral sensory fibers are also present, and probably a relatively few scattered fibers which are not confined to these bundles, but whose course and distribution are not accurately known. The evidence for these statements has been given elsewhere (1, 10) and need only be summarized here.

The organization of these sensory paths appears to be related to the phylogenetic history of the vertebrates, and to comprise the successive additions of new sensory components as overlays to the more primitive paths. These constitute new equipment required by the higher animals when they evolved into new environments. Parallel to this acquisition of more competent mechanisms for contact with an increasingly complex environment the vertebrates acquired more competent higher centers to deal with the information about those contacts. Thus, the esophageal head ganglion of Amphioxus chiefly integrating the special senses of the head and mouth-parts is dominated by the optic thalamus of the amphibian, and acquires connections from all the other sensory systems of the body. The primitive forebrain palium, extending posteriorly from the olfactory bulb and foreshadowing cortex, serves in the amphibian as an elaborator of olfactory sense. In reptiles, part of the palium as a *general* cortex acquires connections to and from the sensory thalamus. The olfactory region of its amphibian precursor develops into the piriform olfactory cortex of higher animals.

Parallel to this development, we find afferent paths, presumably sensory, terminating in the thalamus before the development of cortex, and relays of these paths to the single-layered cortex of the reptile before the development of the six-layered cortex of the mammal. In the latter we find again new sensory paths, terminating in specific cortical projection areas for the three major sensory systems of vision, hearing, and somesthetic senses, and from these relayed to other areas of the cortex. These projection areas serve as analyzers of *one component* only of the sensory periphery, that mediated in the somesthetic system by the cord dorsal column afferents. Meantime with respect to the remaining components of sensation (including in the somesthetic system the pain pathway), the old premammalian relation to the thalamus persists in mammals, and specific relays of these primitive thalamic sensory paths to cortex are not clearly identifiable. A comparison then is in order of the old, or paleospinothalamic, tract of the reptile with the classical neospinothalamic tract of the primates, and of these with the dorsal column–medial lemniscus–ventral nucleus projection to the somesthetic area of cortex appearing only in mammals.

Spinal Origins of the Sensory Paths

For this we may return to the periphery and trace the sensory fiber components, several or all of which are present in any peripheral nerve, as they become sorted out into the discrete paths to their various central destinations. This sorting out process consists of the repeated branching of the common bundle (not of each fiber, but of similar fibers from different regions of the periphery) carried into the cord by each spinal nerve. The first division occurs at the root entry zone where the larger fibers pass into the dorsal column and the smaller and unmyelinated fibers into the tract of Lissauer just ventral to the dorsal horn of gray matter. In terms of the sizes of fibers in peripheral nerves

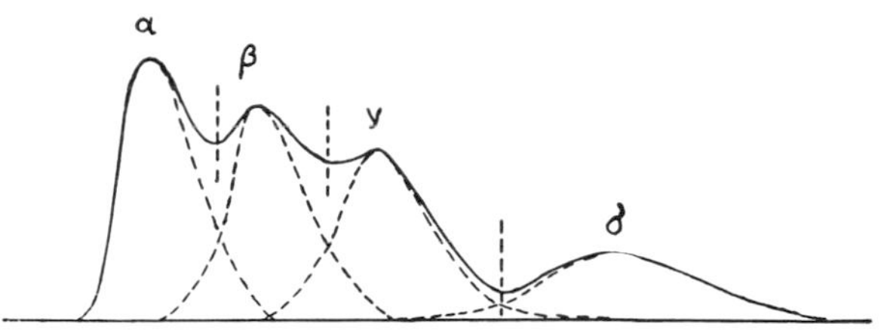

FIG. 5-2. Representation of overlap between fiber groups designated by their peak elevations in the conducted action current of peripheral nerve as α, β, γ, and δ. The C elevation (unmyelinated fibers) falls much later than delta. The most fundamental division lies between beta and gamma, innervating medial and spinal lemnisci respectively. The alpha group is not sensory, and is not present in superficial skin nerves. (Reprinted with permission from G. H. Bishop, Chap. V, *The Biology of the Skin*, edited by W. Montagna, Pergamon Press, Oxford, 1960.)

as displayed in the record of their action currents, the alpha and beta fibers pass into the dorsal column and the remainder—gamma, delta, and C—into the lateral (Fig. 5-2). From the dorsal column the alpha bundle terminates largely around the cells of Clarke's column in the cord and is relayed to the cerebellum. This is thus not a sensory component. The beta group passes upward, and some of its sensory fibers synapse in the cuneate and gracilis nuclei, from which they are relayed via the medial lemniscus to the ventrolateral nucleus of the opposite side. There the impulses are relayed again to the somesthetic area of cortex. This path mediates touch and certain proprioceptive impulses particularly concerned with contact and position of the body in space. It mediates neither pain nor temperature.

The smaller fibers postsynaptic to those of Lissauer's tract cross over in the cord and ascend in the anterolateral column. These include sensory components for touch, pain, itch, and the temperature senses of warmth and cold, in addition to many afferents which are not known to be sensory. This whole ascending bundle is known as the spinal lemniscus. The fibers are distributed continuously to the reticular formation of medulla, cerebellum, and brain steam, but the sensory components are concentrated into bundles passing to certain more specific regions.

The Central Distributions of Lateral Column Sensory Components

The first bundle to divide off from the common path is that of the unmyelinated fibers, which terminate in the medulla (4). Relays from this region to the thalamus are present, and these presumably mediate impulses for burning or causalgic pain. A second bundle separates to the upper brain stem where responses are recorded following stimulation of superficial nerves (3). They are presumably sensory, since they excite postsynaptic responses in the medial basal region of the thalamus. The fibers are myelinated, postsynaptic to those in the gamma and delta range of peripheral nerves and with similar conduction rates. Just below the level of the inferior colliculus the remainder of the sensory component of the spinal lemniscus, now designated as the spinothalamic tract, sheds a third bundle consisting of small fibers which pass medially and forward to terminate in certain of the medial nuclei of the thalamus (12, 13). They probably represent the mammalian heritage of the paleospinothalamic tract present in animals below the mammals, and, if so, must mediate the sensations of pricking pain and temperature, as did the old spinothalamic tract in lower animals not yet possessed of the more lateral path to the ventral nucleus. The latter path comprises the remainder of the sensory fibers of the lateral column, which terminate in the vicinity of the ventral nucleus. This tract mediates lateral column touch; whether any of its fibers mediate pain is still undetermined.

Concerning this point there are two items of interest, possibly of significance here. The first concerns the development of the two spinothalamic tracts, medial and lateral, in the course of mammalian evolution (12). Studied in the lower or more primitive mammals, the medial path predominates, with a relatively small component of fibers passing toward the ventral nucleus. As one ascends the mammalian scale the lateral classical spinothalamic tract becomes progressively more conspicuous, being more prominent in the primates and man, while the medial tract becomes relatively less conspicuous. In the lower mammals, whose medial tract carries the majority of sensory fibers reaching the thalamus from the lateral cord column, one can infer that pain and temperature are mediated by it. In higher mammals it is not known whether pain fibers pass into the neospinothalamic tract, although one could infer that they did not if this tract projected to the somesthetic cortical area where pain is not represented.

The second point concerns this lateral spinothalamic tract projection. Recent studies (15) indicate that it does not terminate in the ventrolateral nucleus proper, but at its margin, ventral and medial to it. Further experimental evidence points to its projection to another area of cortex, since extirpation including the secondary somesthetic area is reported to result in retrograde degeneration of cells in the area of termination of the spinothalamic tract. This simplifies matters by leaving the ventral nucleus proper and its projection to the cortex concerned only with dorsal column fibers via the medial lemniscus. It also raises the possibility that a component of pain might be mediated to the cortex over this lateral spinothalamic path, instead of exclusively by way of the paleospinothalamic path terminating medially. Nauta *et al.* (13) have inferred that this lateral path might add a component of sharpness to the more specifically painful sensation mediated elsewhere. The physiological experiments that might settle this question have not yet been reported.

In summary, we may order three of these sensory paths in terms of their directness of impingement on the cortex. This relation is also correlated with their phylogenetic ages. The unmyelinated fibers (causalgic pain) project to the medulla, and are relayed to thalamus, with no known projection to cortex.

This indirect relayed path through the reticular formation and the unmyelinated character of the fibers suggest that this path is the most primitive of the three; that is, its precursor presumably goes back in phylogeny to the most primitive vertebrates. The paleospinothalamic small myelinated fibers (pricking pain and temperature, and probably touch) project to the medial thalamus directly, but again with only diffuse cortical relations. The presence of such a path in vertebrates below mammals, even before the stage where cortex appears, attests to its relative antiquity of origin. The neospinothalamic tract, probably not primarily concerned with pain and temperature, appears only in mammals, and within this phylum increases in size and presumably in importance along the scale of development of the mammalian cortex. The medial lemniscus, also appearing only in mammals (8, 9), is the only path to whose specific projection a specific area of cortex can be assigned. The functions mediated appear to be peculiarly appropriate to a land animal with a highly developed locomotor system. This appears to be a highly specialized and differentiated system mediating a group of sensations of most acute discrimination. It conspicuously lacks the components of pain and temperature.

ABNORMAL VS. NORMAL PAIN PATTERNS

In relation to the subject under discussion, obviously an abnormal pattern is one that differs from the normal, or customary, or average. But we may further differentiate here between pain as an indicator of abnormality in other than nervous tissue when the latter is normal, and pain involving abnormality or damage in the nervous tissues over which it is mediated. Of course, an abnormality in tissue from which sensations arise may damage the adjacent or included nervous structures, as well as simply stimulate them. The pain associated with neoplastic growth must often be in this category; pressure may stimulate along the course of an otherwise normal nerve, where the abnormality consists of the abnormal mode and locus of stimulation. In such a case the response as referred to the periphery is evidence of damage more centrally. Again one need not take as abnormal the pain of inflammation, the mediation of which appears to be the normal function of certain nerve fibers. They give useful information of inflammation at the nerve terminals; the inflammatory process is the recognized and appropriate stimulus. But the inflammatory process may involve the nerve terminals themselves, when these may themselves react abnormally.

In patients, the arbitrary excitation of a simple response from a specific anatomical mechanism makes its elicitation useful in diagnosis of pathology, granted that one loses many of the less sterotyped qualities of complex sensations and their significance in experience. In sick, impaired, or conscious patients there may be not only a loss in effectiveness of the stimulus itself, but a clouding of the discrimination with respect to the more complex process of perception, or to qualitative interpretation, complicated by, and sometimes due to, anxiety as to what the sensation implies. Here it is usually possible to remove some of the confusion by focusing the subject's attention on the discrimination between two sensations, and in fact on the experimental procedure itself, rather than asking him for a description of his sensations as colored by what they threaten him with. The ultimate definition of pain is that it hurts, but the less it hurts in the sense of painful experience the better one can discriminate its essential quality as a sensation. The abnormality of a pain pattern may then be assessed in terms of intensity of response compared to the normal; for instance, in terms of threshold and of summation of repetitive stimuli, etc., and in terms of distortion of the quality of the sensation, or of its presence without a preceding normally adequate stimulus. It is also significant to determine which variety of pain is involved, and to relate this to fiber size as a criterion of the path over which the impulses are mediated to reach the higher centers.

We may first try to classify abnormalities related to pain, with respect to the locus of the abnormality. In a general sense all pain is abnormal to the extent that the normal condition is freedom from damage or disease. When a normal nervous system records abnormality in other tissues of the body, the patterns can hardly be considered abnormal; this is the normal function of pain mechanisms. But when the damage is to the nervous system itself its responses may be increased, reduced, or distorted as compared to results of the same stimulation in normal subjects. This category includes damage to the brain itself as the last link in sensory reception and the locus of its perceptual interpretation. Finally we may group those phantom or hallucinatory or primarily subjective pains for which no pathological tissue damage can be demonstrated, without, however, denying that an abnormality in the physiological substrate of perception may exist.

Illustrative samples of these three categories are listed here, with no pretense of covering the field. Rather, certain of these conditions may be referred to specific physiological losses or alterations, in terms of the normal properties and behavior of what have been called above the elementary sensations. The first fact to be noted is that these three categories are not mutually exclusive, but overlap complexly. Does inflammation in a tissue involve the nerve endings in the inflammatory process, or only receive from the inflamed surroundings a more effective stimulus than normal? Is congenital lack of pain sense physiological, anatomical, or subjective? To what extent are the mental aberrations of fever due to intoxication of tissues other than nervous, and to what extent to tissues of the brain itself? Is pain from a neuroma, presumably due to pressure from scar tissue contracting on the cut nerve fibers, a sign of abnormality of scarring, an abnormal mode of stimulus to otherwise healthy nerve? Or is the nerve itself damaged? Having attempted this classification, it will be simpler to ignore the boundaries imposed by semantic definitions and take the list as one which seems to progress more or less from the abnormal peripheral environment of nerve terminals upward toward abnormalities in the functioning of perception, i.e., of interpretation.

TABULATION OF SOME PAIN PATTERNS, ABNORMAL AND NORMAL

Section A

Pain due primarily to abnormal conditions or to disturbances in other than nervous tissue. The pain pattern may be normal for these conditions, though abnormal as compared to many more casually aroused sensations of pain.

1. Experimental procedures; arbitrary stimulation, response patterns under pressure block, asphyxia, drugs, anesthetics, etc.
2. Inflammation; possibly involving nerve terminals themselves.
3. Burns and other destructive lesions, neoplastic growth pressure.
4. Postoperative neuroma, stump causalgia, etc.

Section B

Pain involving defective or damaged nervous tissue.

1. Peripheral neuropathy; resultant disesthesia and disalgesia.
2. Protopathic pain following nerve section.
3. Tabetic pain.
4. Post-cordotomy pain.
5. The thalamic syndrome.
6. Central damage or ablation, hemidecortication, frontal lobotomy.

Section C

Abnormal or subjectively distorted interpretations of otherwise normal input, or of none. A physiological terra incognita.

1. Congenital absence of pain.
2. Hysteria.
3. Hypnosis.
4. Centrally acting drugs.
5. Subjective discomfort, pain, or distortions in neurotic and psychotic states, including painful experience and suffering involving minimal or no detectable pain sensation.

Except for the first item, section C will not be discussed further, but is included for contrast with those sections more amenable to physiological speculation. Here one must pass the ball to the psychiatrist, if with some misgivings whether he will more successfully bridge the stream of consciousness from its physiological bank to the hallucinatory. From Section C, it is only a step to subjective stress in general, the mental anguish of the divorce court, why babies cry, the mother-in-law syndrome, and various forms of pains in the neck, to emphasize that, in the analysis of pain, all is not gold that glitters.

THE PHYSIOLOGY OF CERTAIN ABNORMAL PAIN PATTERNS

Some of the patterns listed will be discussed, not primarily in terms of neurological diagnosis, for which the writer is by no means qualified, but in terms rather of the physiological interpretations that may be made of the changes from normal, assignable to specific experimental or pathological conditions.

Experimental Procedures Involving Pain

This section obviously includes the methods of inducing the sensations of pain experimentally in as isolated circumstances as possible (and to that extent abnormally), and of relating them to the anatomical and physiological substrates of their pathways. Some of the conclusions arrived at (1) will be briefly summarized here. Superficial pricking pain is mediated by smaller myelinated fibers, 6 μ and below in diameter, whose terminals in most of the body surface are grouped into pain "spots," with less sensitive regions between the more acute loci. Burning or causalgic pain and its variants are mediated by unmyelinated fibers, usually distributed less punctately. Their endings in skin lie deeper in the dermis in general than do those for pricking pain. Under cuff pressure block to arm or leg, pricking pain is lost before burning pain. On the contrary, during progressive block by anesthetics injected about small nerve trunks or branches, the order of blocking is reversed. The small myelinated fibers relay to the opposite lateral column of the cord, and postsynaptically their secondary neurons project in significant concentration to the medial thalamus and upper brain stem. The unmyelinated fibers similarly relay to the crossed lateral column and postsynaptically project to the medial medulla. Neither type of pain sensation is mediated via the dorsal column of the cord, nor is either projected through the ventrolateral nucleus of the thalamus to the somesthetic projection area of cortex. In the absence of pricking pain function, the responses of unmyelinated fibers show an exaggeration of painful sensation as compared to the intact normal.

Inflammatory Pain

Practically any tissue of the body is sensitive to inflammatory pain, with a marked lowering of threshold to mechanical distortion as a stimulus. The stretch due to inflammation itself may be an effective stimulus, though chemical irritation cannot be excluded. Wherever it has been tested for by pressure block or by differential anesthesia, it has proved to be mediated by unmyelinated fibers, with the qualification that inflammation involving the skin superficially also lowers the threshold to pricking pain. The two pain sensations are unmistakably different when excited separately by moderate stimuli. The unmyelinated endings are difficult to excite at all in many regions unless inflammation is present. For instance, electrical stimulation of subcutaneous tissue is ineffective below a strength that stimulates nerve branches. Pain caused by injection of 5 per cent NaCl into muscle is also due to stimulation of unmyelinated fiber endings, and from its similarity to muscle ache or the effect of pressure the latter may be inferred to be similarly accounted for. Only in muscle sheathes is myelinated fiber pain aroused.

Destructive Lesions

Severe burns result in anesthesia, obviously by destruction of the nerve supply. With less severe heating both types of pain must be induced, and if only the epithelium is destroyed, deeper endings of unmyelinated fibers are presumably chiefly responsible, probably involving an inflammatory process (2).

When nerve trunks or nerve roots are involved in neoplastic growth, pressure is presumably the effective stimulus to pain. It might be expected that pressure would block conduction, which in fact finally occurs. A localized area of skin is then denervated and insensitive to painful stimulation, although pain is referred to this denervated area. The stimulus for this must then be at the margin between the intact central fibers and the block. In addition, however, a region around the margin of the denervated area may be hyperalgesic. Either each stimulus applied here must set off a train of impulses when the propagated volley reaches the region of damage, which makes the area not yet blocked appear hyperexcitable; or else the pain aroused peripherally is similar to the "protopathic" pain of Head and Rivers, aroused at the margin of the denervated area following acute nerve section. In the case of nerve section this "protopathic" sensation is mediated by unmyelinated fibers. Hyperalgesia from nerve damage has not been investigated by differential block methods, but the character of the pain experienced suggests unmyelinated fiber involvement.

Scar and Amputation Pain

Postoperative causalgia certainly involves in some cases the contraction of scar tissue around growing nerve terminals, since resection of the scar may give relief. Such growing terminals are probably hypersensitive compared to normal nerve fibers (Tinel's sign) and react more like their normal terminals. For instance, after experimental removal of the epithelium and upper layer of dermis the regenerating nerve terminals show extreme hypersensitivity to sharp pressure or to electric current, long before the terminals have reached their normal loci just beneath the regenerated epithelium. One must infer that such growing nerve fiber tips act in some respects like sense organs. Their stimulation by single shocks results in a persistence of pain like that following strong shocks to sensory endings in normal skin, as contrasted to the brief sharp prick following similar single shock stimulation of nerve fibers beneath the undamaged skin. Postoperative scar causalgia has the general characteristics of burning or aching pain, implying that damaged unmyelinated fibers may become peculiarly irritable to pressure stimulation, although terminals of myelinated fibers are probably also involved as they are in regenerating skin. Similar causalgic pain is often associated with partial peripheral nerve lesions, where pressure, inflammation, or scar formation are all possible inciting causes. Beyond these simple inferences the more disturbing aspects of causalgia are beyond interpretation in terms of peripheral exciting cause; phantom limb, the severity of the experience as a whole, the apparent involvement of the autonomic nervous system, etc., must include complications of sensory interpretation and significance referred to previously as painful experience.

Peripheral Neuropathy

A simple form of this, below the level of frank pathology, results from stretching of or pressure on a nerve trunk, with resultant tingle or prickle referred to the peripheral distribution. A stimulus to the periphery sometimes excites an exacerbated shower of responses when the initial volley of impulses arrives at the affected locus. The abnormal sensation when walking after one's foot has gone to sleep and sensation is returning, the tingle appearing as sensation returns after cuff pressure nerve block, the results of a blow on the funny bone—all attest to the acute and chronic increase of excitability of nerve fibers, which compression may produce to the point of spontaneous firing, or to cause persistent firing by a brief peripheral stimulus. Since the large fibers of a nerve trunk are more susceptible than the smaller to acute pressure block, so they seem to be to other degrees of pressure. The nonpainful sensations mediated by larger fibers are pressure or stretch. On the other hand, inflammatory conditions along a nerve trunk may generate chiefly painful stimuli, referred to the peripheral distribution. The type of fibers involved may only be inferred from the sensations produced, and the involvement preferentially of unmyelinated fibers seems probable in some cases.

"Protopathic" Pain Following Denervation

The investigation by Head and Rivers of the effect of nerve section has given rise to a celebrated controversy, chiefly concerning the inference of two types of sensory mechanism invoked to account for the results. These they termed epicritic and protopathic with the obvious implications these terms carry. Epicritic sensation was primarily tactile or contact sense; protopathic sensation referred to pain, for example, that resulting from stimulation of a boundary zone surrounding a completely denervated area, a zone which fails to give pricking pain or touch. Without reviewing this controversy it seems that these authors were correct as to the involvement of two mechanisms, for painful and nonpainful sensations respectively, whatever the validity of their further speculative theories, although they did not differentiate two pain pathways. In one case of accidental nerve section examined by us the pricking pain of the normal surroundings proved to be that mediated by small myelinated fibers; the pain exclusively excited in the partially denervated margin was mediated via unmyelinated fibers. This was demonstrated by partial anesthetic block of the nerve, proximal to the level at which only one branch has been severed. The protopathic sensation of the border region was abolished while pricking pain in adjacent skin was still normal. The problem remains of accounting for the hyperalgesia of the unmyelinated fiber terminals in the affected region as compared to normal skin. It has been inferred that branching and growth of pain fibers innervate the margin of the denervated area from the normal surroundings, and ahead of regeneration of touch or other myelinated axons from the site of nerve section. If this is so, it must be that unmyelinated axons are those which precociously invade the area. The effect seems to be an example of the sensation resulting from a given stimulus being a function of the pattern of sensory endings activated, as discussed in the paper immediately following (Weddell). When normal innervation is regenerated, the severe "protopathic" character of the sensation aroused is lost. Since other situations occur in which such an exaggeration of unmyelinated pain fiber sensation occurs, the character of the abnormality will be discussed in further detail below.

Tabetic Pain

The pain of severe chronic tabes is assignable to a low-grade inflammatory lesion. The critical locus of damage is said to be at the root entry zone (14) and is assignable to pressure developed due to fibrosis. Chronic and slowly developing tabes thus furnishes a natural experiment in differential pressure block, extended in time, but duplicating in effects the results of acute experimental cuff compression. The first fibers to be affected are the largest, with loss of vibration and position senses. There follow reduction and final loss of pricking pain, sparing unmyelinated fiber function. With the progressive loss of other sensations, burning pain from peripheral stimulation is strongly exaggerated, and irritation of nerve fibers at the site of the lesion must be the cause of the "spontaneous" pain referred to the periphery. Either impulses from the periphery must be multiplied at the irritated site, or the reaction to stimulation of unmyelinated fibers is accentuated in the absence of other sensory components normally masking or depressing it centrally. The picture is comparable to that of many peripheral neuropathies, differing chiefly in that the lesion is central to the dorsal root ganglion. Differential pressure block at a stage completely blocking all remaining pricking pain leaves tabetic pain, spontaneous or induced by skin stimulation, completely unaffected.

Post-cordotomy Pain

For the relief of intractable pain, section of the ventrolateral column of the cord is frequently enough successful to be almost routinely employed in more severe cases. Failure to completely abolish pain in many cases is, however, still a perplexing problem. The sensory tracts appear to be more concentrated or better defined at the cervical level than below it, but in any case failure to cut all the fibers, some of which may stray from the main bundle, has been taken as the cause of painful residue.

Landau and Schwartz (10a) have found so far in one case of the residual pain, often following cordotomy, that epidural procaine anesthesia blocked this pain at a time and concentration which left intact the sensations mediated over the larger fibers of the dorsal column. This demonstrated that aberrant fibers not reached by the tract section were still intact, eliminating in this case scarring at the site of section as a possible source of pain stimuli. Differential block of unmyelinated fibers with sparing of small myelinated fibers was not demonstrated in this case, but might be possible by adjustment of anesthetic concentration. As a check on fiber sizes blocked in this case, plantar reflexes, dependent on the small (gamma) motor fibers innervating muscle spindles recovered in a temporal course about parallel to restoration of pain. Since these motor fibers are close to pricking pain in size, differential blocking of the critical reflexes by carefully graded anesthesia should serve as a check on the relative contributions of pricking pain and burning pain paths to post-cordotomy pain, even in cases where considerable reduction of pain in general has rendered equivocal a subjective discrimination between the two.

On the other hand, in some cases repeated cordotomies have been performed one above the other each followed by immediate relief, but with recurrence of "spontaneous" pain weeks or months later. It would appear that here glial scarring may be responsible, and in subjects prone to this, each transection of the pain pathway may result in a pressure lesion exciting fiber terminals above the cut.

In search of a more effective procedure, spinothalamic tract section at the mesencephalic level has been performed, but the results have been unfortunate. The persistence and recurrence of pain of a causalgic type have resulted, with no adequate explanation of its origin. Recent work on the anatomy of the central tracts indicates that the spinothalamic bundle divides at the mesencephalic level (13), the pain components passing medially to terminate in the medial thalamus. It is probable that some of these fibers, diverging from the classical spinothalamic course to the ventral nucleus of the thalamus, escape section at the mesencephalic level. In addition, it has recently been reported (4) that the main bundle of unmyelinated fibers leaves the spinothalamic path considerably below the mesencephalic level, and terminates in the medulla, to be relayed upward through the reticular formation. This path then must escape completely the mesencephalic section, and residual pain could still be assignable to peripheral activation of these fibers as before the section. The circumstance that the residual pain may be more severe than before operation suggests overaction of this unmyelinated component, due to elimination of the myelinated fiber sensations, as in the case of the protopathic pain following partial section of a peripheral nerve.

The Thalamic Syndrome

Following certain destructive lesions to the thalamus a typical pattern of sensory changes results, together with associated motor involvement assignable to inclusion in the lesion of the internal capsule or other adjacent tissue. There occur disturbance or loss of tactile and position senses and induction of spontaneous severe or paroxysmal pain of the causalgic type, all effects usually referred to the opposite side of the body. In terms of the physiology of the sensory paths presently under consideration, it is noteworthy that the sensory components most obviously depressed are those normally projected to the somesthetic area of cortex, whose path from the periphery is via the dorsal cord column, the medial lemniscus, and the ventrolateral nucleus of the thalamus. Pain is not mediated by this path. The pathway for pain is via the opposite lateral column and the spinothalamic tract, upward as far as the levels at which unmyelinated fibers diverge toward the medial medulla, and small myelinated fibers pass toward the medial thalamus. The typical lesion is infarction due to arterial occlusion, with results too diffuse to permit specification of definite loci of damage. The posterior region of the thalamus is commonly involved, though the medial brain stem and thalamus are often spared since they have a different blood supply from that of the more lateral portion. This tends to leave a path through medial thalamus to cortex less affected than that through the ventrolateral nucleus.

In these terms the thalamic syndrome might correspond to a lesion destructive with respect to the ventral nucleus and irritative with respect to the region of thalamus comprising the receptive field for pain pathways. Certain features of the condition call for qualification of so simple a dichotomy. The pain is often paroxysmal rather than continuous, and may be initiated by peripheral stimuli which would normally result in a less drastic sequela. The threshold for peripherally stimulated pain is higher than normal, though the pain response is strongly increased.

This aspect of the condition thus resembles that of tabes, where an increased threshold is in extreme cases assignable to loss of pricking pain fibers, requiring activation of unmyelinated fiber terminals to account for the pain.

It has been suggested that loss of other sensations in the case of the thalamic syndrome is in some way associated with the increased effectiveness of the pain mechanisms. The causalgic character of the pain experienced in the thalamic syndrome also implicates the unmyelinated fiber system, whose overaction in other conditions, e.g., protopathic pain of denervation and differential block of prick by pressure, is associated with the absence of pricking pain function.

Cortical Damage

There is no evidence for a specific and circumscribed projective locus in cortex for painful sensations comparable to the somesthetic area for certain other sensations. The obvious inference sometimes made, that consciousness of pain might be registered in the thalamus rather than in cortex, is permitted by the lack of any information pro or con about the pathway above the thalamus. However, these two anatomical structures are so initimately tied together as to justify thinking of them as one functional system. The dorsal column somesthetic paths then enter this by the cortical projection route, the lateral column paths by projection to the thalamus, with equivalent effectiveness of both. The medial thalamic nuclei implicated do not project directly to cortex; at least destruction of no area of cortex results in their retrograde degeneration (16). However, stimulation in these nuclei does result in electrical activity of cortex, rather diffusely distributed, and possibly transmitted by way of other thalamic nuclei. There are reports that injury or surgical removal of cortex in the region of the marginal and angular gyri is accompanied by dulling of the pain sense, and cortical damage elsewhere may also reduce it, as any cortical removal of sufficient magnitude may alter over-all cortical functioning.

The writer has seen one case of practically complete hemidecortication also involving one-half of the thalamus as demonstrated at autopsy (17). This patient recognized painful stimuli to the opposite side of the body, but with poor discrimination and a marked reduction of emotional affect. The only obvious explanation for this is that a relatively small fraction of sensory fibers, of the bundle which as a whole crosses in the cord, takes a homolateral course or recrosses at higher levels. The dulled character of the sensation is sufficiently accounted for by weak homolateral representation of the periphery in thalamus and cortex.

The most specific region of cortex where removal or under-cutting relieves pain is the frontal lobe, and this affects the reaction to the sensation rather than its recognition or discrimination. The question might be raised whether this effect is specific to the frontal lobe excision, or whether this region constitutes the largest area which can be spared without embarrassing damage to other essential cortical functions. A significant definition of the change is implied in the words of a patient with a long history of suffering preoperatively, who stated, after lobotomy, "It still hurts but I don't cry any more." This seems to designate the effect as chiefly on the painful experience rather than on the pain sensation, and re-enforces the inference that the cortex as a whole or cortex and thalamus together have as one major function the elaboration of the significance and the emotional evaluation of sensory information.

Congenital Absence of Pain

Only the first item in this section will be dealt with here, and this equivocally. There have been more than 30 cases reported of congenital absence of pain. Such subjects when experimentally stimulated show no evidence of avoidance or distress, and often undergo severe damage without recognizing the dangers of which painful sensations are normally the warning. Temperature sensations are reported to be normal. A biopsy of one such subject showed a normal size distribution of nerve fibers, and normal action currents were obtained from the excised nerve. His feet were deformed due to kicking rocks at the prompting of his playmates. A second boy, aged nine, had been carefully trained to avoid warm objects, but suffered blistered hands without apparent concern from washing them in too hot water. These subjects distinguish sharp from dull; one subject on being asked to find areas where an electric stimulus gave a clear sensation of sharpness found a distribution of such points on the arm which was approximately the distribution of pain spots on the normal subject. No known pathology accounts for the condition, but it is probably due to a central defect, with the thalamus as a possible locus. It does not resemble the effect of frontal lobotomy, after which the subject still recognizes painful sensations but with reduced affective reaction to them. One subject has been examined as a suspected case of congenital absence of pain. This subject, while identifying painful stimuli accurately, did seem abnormally tolerant of them. There may be such cases of partial insensitivity that are related to the extreme condition but which are sufficiently sensitive to escape notice.

This brief summary of the physiology of abnormal pain patterns can be neither all-inclusive nor neurologically adequate; the severity of the conditions and the variability of patterns of involvement in patients are extreme. In the present state of our ignorance of the physiology of the higher centers responsible for consciousness, these conditions can be physiologically defined only to the extent and with respect to the manner in which they involve the peripheral mechanisms of sensation. For this reason most of the subjects included in Section C on page 113 are beyond the scope of the present discussion. The examples cited may serve as the occasion for a few generalizations summarizing both normal and abnormal behavior of these neural mechanisms of sensation.

First, "spontaneous" pain, or increase above normal of painful response to stimulation, may be assigned to at least three conditions, in addition to the obvious and in a sense normal response to inflammation. One is compression or the equivalent irritation at the growing tips of regenerating nerve fibers, as in a neuroma, and probably in some post-cordotomy pains. A second is a similar compression as in neoplasmic impingement along the course of a nerve *tract*, or in certain neuropathies; that is, excitation by pressure at other loci than at nerve terminals may account for the constant pain experienced. Hyperalgesia, and hyperesthesia often reported by patients as painful, may be assigned to such damage along the course of a nerve. A stimulus at the periphery then excites high-frequency showers of impulses initiated at the damaged and hyperirritable region along the nerve trunk. A correspondingly potent sensory effect of increased frequency and numbers of impulses is readily demonstrated in the normal subject by increasing the frequency of electrical stimulation of the skin or, better, of a small nerve branch beneath it. The ability of nerve fibers to respond excessively due to pressure at other points than at their terminals is obvious in the tingling sensation following casual or accidental compression or stretch in normal subjects. A third condition is exhibited in the sparing and even overeffectiveness of unmyelinated fibers associated with the differential loss of myelinated pricking pain fiber functioning. This appears to be a fatcor in protopathic pain after nerve section, and in the exacerbation of pain after mesencephalic tract section. It probably occurs in the thalamic syndrome, and in other lesions giving evidence of differential block of large fibers with sparing of smaller, such as tabes, some peripheral neuropathies, and some post-cordotomy pain. The common causalgic quality of all these pain sensations is supporting evidence for the inference that unmyelinated fibers are the group most liable to remain functional after many types of nerve pathology.

An interesting characteristic in certain abnormal conditions is displayed after a partial loss of fibers occurs, whether or not the remainder mediate an exaggerated sensation. The random loss of part of the fibers in a nerve lesion should simplify the pattern of sensation following peripheral test stimuli, with a corresponding loss of information even though stimulus strength is increased to compensate. A similar loss of precision and accuracy of report of sensation occurs in association with cortical lesions, where partial loss or depression of *central* receptors is a reasonable inference. Pricking pain under these conditions is poorly localized and is more easily masked or ignored when normal areas are stimulated simultaneously. Recognition of figure writing in the palm is lost when touch is still present. Two-point discrimination is impaired, or requires a stronger stimulus (which, to be sure, improves this in the normal subject). The patient has difficulty in describing the sensation or recognizing the character of the contact arousing it. This presumably corresponds to the condition that much of the information resulting from normal contacts with the environment is due to the complexity of the pattern of normal innervation; most of our sensations, and particularly those giving us information about the environment, are complex and include more than one modality, as well as involving a high spatial density of endings and overlapping innervation of any one locus. The impaired patient then becomes a less than normally accurate reporter of sensations experienced because he receives a less detailed or inclusive report of the peripheral contact, even if the intensity of the contact is increased to compensate in total quantity of effect.

Still another characteristic of certain pathologically altered sensory patterns is due to the predominant effectiveness of pain in any sensory pattern, and the patient's attention is often oriented toward the expectation or the significance of the pain to which he is liable. Even in the normal subject, pain tends to mask the less threatening and less disturbing sensations, even when the latter are most acute if received without accompanying pain. In nerve branch direct electrical stimulation where the large and low-threshold fibers quite obviously mediate touch at low-stimulus intensities, stronger stimuli arousing pain cause touch to be masked quite effectively. No sensation of warmth is ever recognized following such electrical stimulation to nerves, though differential block with warmth as the stimulus indicates that there are fibers mediating this in the same size range as those for pricking pain. Temperature can be recognized after pressure block of all but unmyelinated fibers if the stimulus is a warm object, but not unequivocally following electrical stimulation of a partially blocked nerve. Here stimuli arouse most obviously only penetrating and difficultly tolerated pain. It may be that the quality of this pain sensation, often described as "burning," is actually assignable to an addition of temperature to pain, but it is difficult to confirm such an inference.

A counterpart of this masking of other sensations by predominant pain may be the opposite effect, in the common experience that finding the site of a poorly localized pain by exploring for it manually seems to alleviate its severity. Internal pains are notoriously poorly localized and are often referred to a part of the segmental nerve distribution where localization is more acute, namely to the skin or body periphery. The mustard plaster may owe some of its efficacy to such a localizing skin stimulus. Unmyelinated fiber pain is less accurately localized than is pricking pain, and pricking pain than touch. Exploration by pressure applied to a painful region, even though it may transiently increase the pain, seems to make it more bearable, probably due to localization in terms of touch. Localization and recognition of origin must fall in the category of interpretation which, in this account, has been relegated to the realm of painful experience. The assurance one thus obtains from further information about what is the matter is akin to putting oneself into the hands of the doctor, or, in extremis, of the psychiatrist.

THE PATH TO CONSCIOUSNESS; HOW DO WE KNOW WHETHER IT HURTS?

The foregoing account may be somewhat exasperating to the professional alleviator of pain. Fortunately for the physiologist, this is not his province. Unfortunately, however, the physiologist's business is largely unfinished business with respect to any activity above the brain stem. Both sensation and sensory experience as here defined occur in consciousness, the physiological substrate of which has so far eluded our comprehension. All sensations are experienced, but the experience seems to expand far beyond the range, and presumably beyond the normal paths that deliver to consciousness the impulses it interprets. Even at the threshold of perception, the consciousness of the modal sensations dealt with here obviously lies beyond those specific fiber paths over which we can follow the sensory message up the neuraxis.

It takes time to appreciate the meaning of this message, it takes more time to react to it, and still more time to react to it intelligently. There is every reason to believe that it also takes more neurons, and more extensive interconnections between them. In both these senses the elaboration of painful sensation to painful experience must require a spreading out, in both time and space, within the brain of the exciting message from the periphery. Among the many million cells in the human brain we have not yet found which are responsible for consciousness. The effect of ablation of any part of this structure indicates that many regions, if not all the neurons in them, may be involved. Possibly more are involved in an elaborated sensory experience than in the simpler identification of a sensation.

We may be sure that not all these neurons are involved equally in a given conscious state, that those involved will to some degree be selected, and others rejected, by the previous and concurrent patterns of sensory input, as well as by the residual traces of past experience. A similar selection and rejection may be accomplished by centrally acting drugs. Such a differential susceptibility of central patterns is foreshadowed in the periphery. Pain, for instance, is notoriously the first sensation to be lost in anesthesia, well before consciousness of other sensations is obliterated (though perhaps not before it is dulled). At least one path over which impulses within the pain range of fiber size are conducted upward is known to be preferentially blocked by general anesthetics. A region of upper brain stem and lower thalamus first studied by Magoun (11) and co-workers was investigated by Collins and O'Leary (3) as the terminus of the small-fiber path from peripheral nerves. Anesthesia blocks a postsynaptic response here well before the path to the ventral nucleus and somesthetic cortex is materially depressed. In fact the latter is peculiarly resistant to anesthetics, as least in its major features as recorded electrically. Stimulation of this path finds the response of the somesthetic cortex little altered at a degree of anesthesia that permits of surgery. The same is true for the visual area of cortex. Thus some considerable part of cortex is actively functional when consciousness is abolished. The particular response of this area of cortex to nerve stimulation is, however, not the only response of which it is capable, and differential effects of different drugs on different synaptic connections within the same cortical area have been demonstrated (5, 6, 7). Thus within one locus progressive depression must occur serially of one function after another. The difficulty is that this tells us nothing about the substrate of consciousness, further than to push it one stage farther from the periphery.

It is to be anticipated that not only differential responses of one region, but similar responses in different regions, may be affected one more than another by a given agent, and a more complex function rather than a simpler one. Presumably all "pain killers" are depressants somewhere, and possibly different agents are depressant of different functions in the complex of functions that must be involved in consciousness. To find where in the train of events, from periphery onward, pain impulses can be interfered with might be one way of approaching this problem. Testing depressant properties on different functions of a given area of cortex or thalamus, as well as of different regions, would be a similar physiological approach. Until such work has been accomplished the physiology of the path to consciousness deals chiefly with the peripheral mechanisms not immediately involved in its generation.

Consciousness is not simply a state of the brain; we must be conscious *of something*. The alleviation of pain *in an otherwise conscious subject* appears to be possible only by the differential limitation of one sensory path among many, whether in the periphery or in central structures. It would appear that the more peripherally one can block the pain pathway, the more comprehensively one can eliminate painful *sensation* and its sequelae. The more centrally one can depress activity following a pain stimulus, the more one will be operating on the apparatus of painful *experience*. The extremes of this way of looking at the problem are apparent in the two operations, of dorsal root section and of frontal lobotomy, the one blocking the input, the other limiting the final interpretation.

SUMMARY

In any sensory, that is, conscious response to a peripheral stimulus, we may identify a potentially simple sensation or combination of sensations as most immediate or of lowest denomination. We may enquire then in what respects the central apparatus of memory, habit, emotion, etc., has added to or qualified this lowest denominator, and extended it to a more elaborate and often confusing sensory experience.

As so defined, pain sensation is at one extreme of many ways of looking at distressing experience. At the opposite extreme one will find related to the painful stimulus the maximum of interpretation of the afferent message, however specific and limited or complex and variable. It is obvious that between these extremes there is no boundary, but a continuum of subjective experience. Any proposal to equate these extremes qualitatively or even to treat them as strictly comparable can lead and has lead to confusion. The sensory process is inextricably in consciousness; the afferent impulses are in neural structures functionally below this level, but propagate as such to an unknown complex of neurons where other than directly afferent paths take over.

To correlate the activity in peripheral sensory paths and the results of abnormalities there, with the effects following in consciousness, the simplest and most immediate response is the most useful. This is most consistently and constantly obtained from the normal subject under conditions leaving him free of apprehension, anxiety, etc., which may color the subject's report. The various sensations aroused may then be related by anatomical and physiological criteria to the specific central paths over which their impulses are mediated, and to the regions of the higher centers in which these paths terminate. Beyond this level we are unable at present to follow the course taken by the different sensory messages, except for certain limited inferences from the results of central lesions. As compared to the case of peripheral lesions these effects prove to be relatively nonspecific. It may be inferred that the involvement of the higher centers in sensory experience is correspondingly diffuse and pervasive.

Pain, as the most disturbing of the sensations, correspondingly predominates in consciousness not only with respect to recognition of other modalities in its presence, but in the elaboration of the extended sensory experience. Something of the affect of painful experience may then attach itself to other sensations, or even to situations, which arouse apprehension, fear, anxiety, and dislike in general. This is exemplified by the two meanings we attach to the word "feel"; we feel a sensation, and we feel pleasant or bad about it. The confusion between how a sensation feels as such, and how we feel about what it implies, appears to correspond to the relative specificity of the peripheral sensory mechanisms in contrast to the complexity and diffuse representation of the central machinery whose activity corresponds to the over-all conscious evaluation of the significance of a sensory message.

Because there is a common factor of discomfort and avoidance in many unpleasant experiences and in pain itself, the name of this sensation becomes attached naïvely to anything sufficiently obnoxious, to constitute one component of a pleasure-pain dichotomy. It is the proper task of the psychologist to unravel this skin of experience from its final fabrication in consciousness, and that of the physiologist to study the threads of activity that are woven into it. It is unfortunate that we are prone to use the same words in different languages, especially when objective and subjective functions are so inextricably implicated as they are in sensation, with so little knowledge of the actual relations of one to the other.

Not all afferent fiber paths are sensory, and not all potentially sensory messages reach consciousness. What messages do finally arrive in consciousness may not only be added to at higher levels, but conditioned by what fails to be consciously recognized as part of the specific message under consideration. The various sensations differ in the anatomical directness with which they are presented to the cortex; dorsal column senses to the cortical projection area, lateral column to circumscribed nuclei of the thalamus, upper brain stem, and even medulla, with relays of unknown complexity upward through the reticular system.

The majority of fibers of various sizes which leave the main bundles of the ascending paths and distribute continuously along the reticular formation are not known to be sensory at all.

However, there is ample evidence that activity in the reticular system may affect the activity of the cortex. There is no reason to suppose that the activity induced by afferent but not specifically sensory stimulation does not similarly condition the cortex to the more specifically sensory input.

The abnormal patterns of painful sensation include both reduction and accentuation, as well as distortion of the normal results of painful stimulation. The presence of abnormality of response may be assigned to several general classes of damage. One class is irritative, operating at the peripheral endings or along the nerve fiber pathway, and results in constant pain or in an abnormal intensity of effect from a given stimulus. Inflammation is the outstanding but not unique example. A second is exemplified by pressure, with a differential effect on fibers of different sizes. Such a condition may block large fibers, including pricking pain, and may at the same stage irritate the unmyelinated fibers, thus arousing causalgic pain. Following loss of pricking pain sensation, unmyelinated fiber pain appears to be exacerbated, as if pricking pain tended to mask it normally. A third type of damage is characteristic of central injury or ablation, accomplishing, for instance, changes in affect exemplified by those following frontal lobotomy. We must finally include those patterns of central activity for which we have little knowledge of locus or mechanism, but which distort the interpretation of the peripherally aroused sensations, or even generate centrally their subjective simulacra. In this dimension any afferent message may be reported as painful.

REFERENCES

1. Bishop, G. H. The relation of fiber size to sensory modality; phylogenetic implications of the afferent innervation of cortex. *J. Nerv. & Ment. Dis. 128:* 89, 1959.
2. Bull, J. P., and Leonard-Jones, J. E. Impairment of sensation in burns and its clinical application as a test of the depth of skin loss. *Clin. Sc. 8:* 155, 1949.
3. Collins, W. F., and O'Leary, J. L. Study of a somatic evoked response in midbrain reticular substance. *EEG Clin. Neurophysiol. 6:* 619, 1954.

4. COLLINS, W. F., and RANDT, C. T. Evoked central nervous system activity relating to peripheral unmyelinated or C fibers in the cat. *J. Neurophysiol. 21:* 343, 1958.
5. GOLDRING, S., METCALF, J. S., HUANG, S. H., SHIELDS, J., and O'LEARY, J. L. Pharmacological selectivity manifested by agents acting upon the cortical dendritic spike and its slow aftereffects. *J. Nerv. & Ment. Dis. 128:* 1, 1959.
6. GOLDRING, S., and O'LEARY, J. L. Pharmacological dissolution of evoked cortical potentials. Symposium on Physiology and Drug Actions. *Fed. Proc. 19:* 612–618, 1960.
7. GRUNDFEST, H. An electrophysiological basis for neuropharmacology. Symposium on Neuropharmacology. *Federation Proc. 17:* 1006, 1958.
8. HERRICK, C. J. *The Brain of the Tiger Salamander.* University of Chicago Press, Chicago, 1948.
9. HERRICK, C. J., and BISHOP, G. H. A comparative survey of the spinal lemniscus system. In *Reticular Formation of the Brain,* Edited by H. H. Jasper. Little, Brown & Co., Boston, 1959.
10. LANDAU, W., and BISHOP, G. H. Pain from dermal, periosteal and fascial endings and from inflammation. *AMA Arch. Neurol. & Psychiat. 69:* 1, 1953.
10a. LANDAU, W., and SCHWARTZ, H. A. Personal Communication.
11. MAGOUN, H. W. An ascending reticular activating system in the brainstem. *AMA Arch. Neurol. & Psychiat. 67:* 145, 1952.
12. MEHLER, W. R. The mammalian "pain tract" in phylogeny. *Anat. Rec. 127:* 332, 1957.
13. MEHLER, W. R., FEFERMAN, M. E., and NAUTA, W. J. H. Ascending axonal degeneration following antrolateral cordotomy. An experimental study in the monkey. *Brain 83:* 718–750, 1960.
14. OBERSTEINER, H., and REDLICH, E. Ueber das Wesen und Pathogenese der tabischen Hinterstrangs Degeneration. *Arb. aus der Hirnanat. Inst. 2:* 158, 1894 and *3:* 192, 1895. Cited in H. Merritt, *Textbook of Neurology,* p. 124. Lea and Febiger, Philadelphia, 1955.
15. ROSE, J. E., and MOUNTCASTLE, V. B. Vol. I, Chap. 17, p. 418, *Handbook of Physiology.* American Physiol. Society, Washington, 1959.
16. ROSE, J. E. Personal Communication.
17. WEISS, S., LEVY, I., SMITH, D., and O'LEARY, J. L. Loss of right hemisphere due to natural causes. *EEG Clin. Neurophysiol. 8:* 682, 1956.

II. "ACTIVITY PATTERN" HYPOTHESIS FOR SENSATION OF PAIN

A. G. M. WEDDELL

Pain is a concept. It is also, of course, an abstract noun which is usually regarded as having two polar connotations.

On the one hand there is "pain" which results from the stimulus of injury or disease; on the other hand, there is "pain" which is evoked by memory or imaginative thought. These extreme connotations may be directly related; for example, pain can be evoked by the memory of a bodily injury, but often they are apparently completely unrelated.

In what follows, the kind of pain with which we shall be most concerned is that referred to by an individual whose body surface has been stimulated. It is not possible to study pain of this kind in isolation. To introduce the subject in its proper perspective, a description will be given of what is currently known of the anatomy and physiology of common sensibility.

THE NEUROHISTOLOGY OF THE INTEGUMENT

1. *Nerve Terminals*

In our laboratory we first concentrated our attention on the neurohistological framework available for transducing various stimuli into nerve impulses and for conveying them to the central nervous system. Only later did we carry out experiments calculated to determine what relationship this framework had to the mechanism of common sensation, i.e., to evoked reports of touch, warmth, cold, and pain. Skin and exposed mucous membranes are the tissues which have received most of our attention, and their pattern of innervation will now be described.

In hairy skin which covers the greater part of the human body, there are commonly only two morphologically distinct types of nerve termination (13): circumscribed or "focal" endings which take the form of basket-like networks of fine nerve filaments in hair follicles, and diffuse arborizations of fine filaments which pervade the dermis and epidermis. These diffuse filaments, however, are most numerous at the junction between the dermis and epidermis and more particularly where the epidermis is thin. They are commonly called "free" nerve endings, a term which will be used in this discussion, but its use does not imply that the filaments are necessarily lying freely in tissue spaces. Both the number of terminal filaments (free and related to hairs) and the number of axons from which they arise vary from place to place in hairy skin. Recently we have made charts of the tactile acuity of hairy skin covering the body and find that it varies widely from place to place, forming a complex pattern. This pattern, however, varies little from person to person, and we have been able to confirm, from skin biopsies, that in areas where the tactile acuity is high, the number of nerves per unit area of skin is also high and vice versa. Unfortunately, this observation, although highly suggestive, cannot yet be expressed quantitatively, owing to the complications introduced by the plexiform arrangement of the sensory cutaneous nerves, of which a description will be given shortly.

In nonhairy skin (palms of the hands, soles of the feet, and parts of the backs of the fingers and toes), the hair follicle nerve terminals are replaced by encapsulated end-organs, having a distinctive morphology, termed Meissner's corpuscles. From the functional point of view, these have many properties in common with hairs. There are also free nerve endings arranged just as they are in hairy skin. But, some of the most superficial free nerve endings, related to the cells of the germinal layer of the epidermis, are distributed over not more than one square milli meter of skin surface; they are served by large axons and they are surmounted by distinct swellings which resemble so-called Merkel's disks. The possible significance of these terminals will be referred to shortly. Thus, in nonhairy skin as in hairy skin there are morphologically only two distinct classes of termination, circumscribed and diffuse receptors.

In exposed mucous membranes, specifically the lips, nipples and parts of the areolae, glans penis, foreskin, glans clitoris, and anal mucous membrane are seen a profusion of nerve end-bulbs. These have only Schwann cell capsules and are of every shape and size. Their neural elements may consist of a simple club or axonal coil, but more usually they form complex arborizations of axons of various diameters. The axons serving these terminals vary in diameter, and one or more commonly emerge from the bulb and may continue for some distance before terminating in another coil, tangle, or circumscribed arborization of fine filaments. Some of these nerve terminations resemble so-called "Krause" end-bulbs, but to classify them on a morphological basis in man would be an impossible task, for one variety shades almost imperceptibly into another. Free nerve endings pervade these tissues just as they pervade the skin.

Thus, in the exposed mucous membranes which have been cited, from the morphological standpoint, the nerves end either diffusely or in a relatively circumscribed manner (4, 23, 25).

2. *The Axons Serving the Nerve Terminals*

Hairs, Meissner's corpuscles, and a large number of mucous membrane end-bulbs (especially in the lip) are served by *more* than one axon. Moreover, these axons with few exceptions are myelinated and are among the largest fibers which serve the skin. Axons leaving most hairs and Meissner's corpuscles, acquire their myelin sheaths when they leave these end-organs. Axons serving mucous membrane end-bulbs, however, may acquire myelin sheaths some distance after leaving their terminations. By contrast, free nerve endings are served by axons having a wide range of diameters from the largest myelinated to the finest nonmyelinated fibers, although most of them are served by smaller axons than those serving circumscribed receptors. The fibers serving free nerve endings characteristically increase in diameter as they are traced proximally. Thus, a myelinated stem axon may be served by a relatively long nonmyelinated preterminal segment. It is also noteworthy that the free filaments from neighboring stem axons intertwine and interweave intimately and extensively. Thus, any area of skin is supplied by overlapping free endings of a number of different stem fibers (18).

3. *The Lability of Peripheral Sensory Nerves*

The description which has just been given is both qualitatively accurate and consistent when applied to most healthy young adults in relatively sedentary occupations in temperate climates. Under certain conditions and in selected individuals, however, end-bulbs are seen in *hairy* skin. This is particularly noticeable in skin which is diseased, has been injured, or which is being subjected to severe wear and tear in the course of everyday life. In nonhairy skin it has been shown that the size and shape of Meissner's corpuscles vary both with the amount of manual work which is carried out and with the age of the individual concerned. The end-bulbs in hairy skin (and this applies also to some clusters of "Merkel's" disks in non-hairy skin) have certain distinguishing characteristics. Their axonal morphology is usually bizarre. The sheath surrounding them is only composed of Schwann cells and collagen, and the axon or axons serving them are usually swollen and irregular in diameter. Moreover, a careful examination of nerves in small cutaneous bundles (particularly from individuals in which these end-bulbs are numerous), which have been carefully fixed, handled, and stained with silver, shows that a larger proportion of nerve fibers than usual (1 in 10–20) are exhibiting classical histological signs of either degeneration or regeneration. This is so even after account has been taken of the fact that in middle-aged adults the number of fibers affected in this way is considerably greater than in children. In children, the number of fibers affected is of the order of 1 in 1000 and in middle-aged persons between 1 in 100–500 (21).

Because histological techniques which display tissue neural elements specifically are apt to give rise to artifacts, the validity of these observations has recently been checked as follows.

Closely adjacent pieces of fresh human adult skin were prepared for examination (*a*) under the light microscope after being stained in silver by a new technique developed by Dr. Keith Richardson (11), this is not only specific for axis cylinders but also results in the minimum of tissue shrinkage and distortion; (*b*) under the electron microscope after fixation in either osmium tetroxide or potassium permanganate and embedding in either "methacrylate" or "araldite."

Bundles containing degenerating axons were common to both specimens, and the appearance of the affected fibers could be compared and contrasted. The electronmicrographs showed unmistakable evidence of degenerative and regenerative changes, and we were able to confirm that the pictures seen by light microscopy were not artifacts but could be interpreted at their face value.

We have also demonstrated the labile nature of integumental nerve fibers by examining the conjunctiva.

4. *The Innervation of the Conjunctiva*

In a study of the innervation of the human conjunctiva in both living subjects and in material taken from patients shortly after death, we have shown that in children and young persons the majority of nerves end freely, but with advancing years, more and more end-bulbs make their appearance. These end-bulbs take a wide variety of forms, many of them resembling those seen in hairy skin either following injury or in the course of disease.

By comparing our pictures with the descriptions and pictures given by Cajal of the changes in the proximal stumps of divided nerves, it became clear that conjunctival end-bulbs (as well as those seen in hairy skin) were but stages in a cycle of degeneration and regeneration of peripheral nerves. A "sterile" end-bulb forms when an axon is prevented from reaching its destination, a hazard which starts in childhood and becomes increasingly evident in the middle and later decades of life. It is also clear that in a few individuals, *conjunctival* end-bulbs are more common than in others, irrespective of age (10).

5. *The Innervation of the Cornea*

The cornea is the only integumental tissue which we have examined which contains only free nerve endings served by nonmyelinated axons which become myelinated axons when they leave the cornea. At no time have we seen end-bulbs in normal corneas. In pathological conditions, myelinated axons creep into the cornea from the limbus, and end-bulbs are then occasionally encountered at the margin of the cornea (29, 31).

6. *Summary—Sensory Nerve Terminals in the Integument*

The superficial layers of the exposed integument of the human body contain numerous nerve fibers and terminals, but these are most numerous in areas of acute tactile sensibility. From the morphological point of view, the terminals can be divided into two broad categories.

(A) CIRCUMSCRIBED OR "FOCAL" RECEPTORS. These are hair follicle terminals in more than 90 per cent of the skin covering the body surface, Meissner's corpuscles and Merkel's discs in palmar and plantar skin, and a bewildering variety of end-bulbs in exposed mucous membranes, i.e., lips, nipples and parts of the areolae, glans penis, foreskin, glans clitoris, and anal mucous membrane. Hairs and Meissner's corpuscles are served by a number of stem axons, and this is also the case for a great many mucous membrane end-bulbs. In the conjunctiva, there are in youth few if any circumscribed nerve terminals. In later life, end-bulbs are found in irregular numbers and irregularly distributed. These do not have the relatively stable appearance which is characteristic of those found in skin and in the mucous membranes cited. More particularly, however, the axons which serve conjunctival end-bulbs often have collaterals which can be traced to "free" nerve endings in other positions in the conjunctiva. This is never seen in relation to Meissner's corpuscles or to hairs, but only in relation to end-bulbs and other terminals with overt signs of impending dissolution. No circumscribed receptors are seen in the cornea.

(B) DIFFUSE RECEPTORS. These are arborizations of fine filaments which pervade the integument covering the whole of the body. Filaments from neighboring stem axons interweave intimately with each other so that an area of skin is always served by a number of filaments from neighboring stem axons.

(c) LABILITY. There is clear-cut evidence that integumental nerve fibers and terminals are labile and subject to degenerative and regenerative changes. This turnover is variable but increases with age and with the amount of wear and tear to which the integument is subjected. In this respect, the nerves can conveniently be compared with small blood vessels. Disease, trauma, and severe wear and tear sometimes result in the appearance of end-bulbs in hairy skin. When present, these resemble conjunctival end-bulbs.

7. *The Patterned Arrangements of the Axons Serving the Nerve Terminals*

One of the most striking facts about the innervation of skin and the other tissues which go to make up the integument of the body is the complicated pattern formed by the preterminal axons. This plexiform meshwork of nerves is termed the cutaneous plexus and may form two or more distinct layers in a richly innervated piece of skin. Even in whole and cleared mounts of thin skin in which nerve fibers are specifically and optimally stained, it has proved impossible to trace with certainty all the ramifications of a single axon from the point where it enters the cutaneous plexus. This is chiefly due to the complexity of the arrangements which are found. For example, one preterminal branch which is only a few microns in diameter may leave a hair follicle and enter the plexus after traveling no more than a millimeter from the follicle. Here it will join another preterminal branch at its junction with another branch, which serves them both. The two fibers proceed in different directions, but side by side with other axons of comparable size and formed in the same way. Thus, there is no way of telling which branch serves another hair and which is the mother branch leading to the stem axon. We now know, as the result of degeneration and electrophysiological experiments in animals (which will be described shortly), that a single stem axon may supply over 100 hairs, and that these hairs may be scattered over several square centimeters of skin. It is therefore not surprising that the direct approach, i.e., attempting to map daughter axons a few microns in diameter by tracing them under high magnification ($\times$ 1000) throughout areas which may cover several square centimeters, lead us into confusion and eventually to despair.

Clearly the problem was one which could only be analyzed indirectly by the use of experimental animals following partial destruction of cutaneous nerves and the analysis by electrophysiological means of the peripheral distribution of bundles as well as of single cutaneous nerve fibers.

The choice of animal was easy in our case, for we had by this time learned how to stain nerve fibers in the rabbit ear specifically and evenly throughout the whole of its extent. Moreover, in preliminary experiments, in which a small number of nerves serving the skin had been divided three to five days previously, it became clear that the hairs were served by a number of separate and distinct nerve fibers. Just how many was not certain, but even the smallest hairs appeared to have at least two separate axons serving them (which remained discrete for as far as they could be traced). Furthermore, it was also apparent that the hairs in the rabbit ear are served solely by myelinated axons, thus rendering our contemplated electrophysiological approach immeasurably easier. Before proceeding further with our peripheral analysis, however, it was necessary to establish (*a*) whether or not a hair can properly be regarded as a sensory unit, (*b*) the number and arrangement of the hairs in the rabbit ear, and (*c*) the number of dorsal roots available to serve the hairs.

8. *Hairs in the Rabbit Ear*

Because we had seen that hairs were served by more than one nerve fiber, it was clear that merely counting the number of hairs in the ear skin and comparing this with the number of myelinated nerve fibers entering the ear would not give us the data necessary to analyze the role of hairs as sense organs. Moreover, we quickly found that in some parts of the ear single follicles gave rise to two hairs. Further, the number of hairs, each derived from a separate follicle, which emerged from a single orifice in the skin varied from one to seven. The diameters of the hair shafts and size of the follicles from which they emerged also varied. Large follicles were commonly, but by no means always, associated with single hairs of large diameter, which were the sole occupants of the orifices from which they emerged. There was, in addition, a striking variation in the patterned arrangement of the orifices from which the hairs emerged. Other variables which must also play a part in determining the precise reaction of an individual hair to a given mechanical stimulus (and thus to the number and frequency of the impulses passing along the various nerves supplying the follicle) include its length, its degree of stiffness as well as the physical properties of the skin (for example, its elasticity) in the region where the hair emerges. Most of these factors were too complicated for us to express in the form of measurements, but, nonetheless, they are clearly most important. We only found it possible to determine the number of hairs, the number of orifices from which the hairs emerged, and the number of groups into which these orifices were gathered, in a series of rabbit ears.

The number of hairs in the ear skin of Dutch rabbits when no follicular growth is taking place is of the order of 100,000. The number of follicles is some 4 per cent less than this. The number of orifices from which hairs emerge is of the order of 40,000, and the number of groups into which the orifices are gathered is of the order of 13,000. The number of hairs in the skin of the front of the ear is about half that over the back, but the number of orifices and groups of orifices are about the same on both sides of the ear. The average area occupied by a group of orifices is 0.25 sq. mm., and the average linear distance between hair stumps is 0.35 mm. Thus, the hairs are so arranged that the chance of a single follicle or group of follicles being stimulated by any commonly occurring natural contact stimulus is negligible. Furthermore, the size of the hairs, their density, and the arrangement of the orifices from which they emerge form complicated nonrecurrent patterns which are similar from rabbit to rabbit, but which make the relationship of a given hair to those surrounding it unique.

These findings emphasize the fact that counting the number

of hairs in the skin of the rabbit ear and comparing the figure obtained with the number of sensory myelinated axons entering the ear is not of much value in the analysis of the sensory information available when hairs in the skin of the ear are stimulated naturally. In other words, we are now of the opinion that a single hair in the rabbit ear cannot properly be regarded as a sensory unit (22).

9. *The Number of Nerves Supplying Hairs in the Rabbit Ear*

At first sight it appeared to be quite a straightforward task to determine the number of myelinated axons of spinal and cranial origin entering the rabbit ear; on the contrary, it proved very difficult! The reasons for this were threefold. In the first place, the major (spinal) sensory nerves carried fibers destined for neck and auricular muscles and received fibers from the face, back of the neck, and scalp. The second difficulty was due to the free interchange of fibers at the root of the ear between the two main spinal nerve trunks serving the ear. The third difficulty lay in the free interchange of fibers between fasciculi comprising the nerve bundles. However, by making fiber counts at a number of different levels from a series of serial sections, and by carrying out degeneration experiments in animals having nerve trunks in which the level of the major interchange of axons was favorable for this purpose, these difficulties were overcome. We found that no significant amount of axon multiplication by branching took place between the dorsal roots and the base of the ear. We also determined that the number of myelinated axons available to innervate hairs in the rabbit ear was certainly not in excess of 6500. Indeed, since some myelinated axons serve free nerve endings, the operative figure was judged to be not in excess of 6000 (24).

10. *Pattern of Innervation of Hairs*

(A) HISTOLOGICAL. The small number just quoted was a surprise to us, but it stimulated us to analyze the pattern of innervation of hairs more precisely. In the first place, we examined the anatomy of the nerve trunks entering the base of the ear. We found that the great auricular nerve contained between 18 and 22 fasciculi and the lesser occipital between 12 and 15. Together these nerves contained approximately 6000 dorsal root myelinated axons. In addition, each of the fasciculi entering the base of the ear contained a variable number of myelinated axons, the diameters of which were representative of those appearing in the two chief nerve trunks (i.e., the great auricular and lesser occipital) as a whole. It was also noteworthy that an interchange of axons was continually taking place between the fasciculi forming these nerve trunks throughout their course to a greater or lesser degree.

Each of the fasciculi entering the base of the ear we found eventually terminated in the cutaneous plexus in which the individual axons started to divide, and then to subdivide a large number of times before ending. About three-quarters of the myelinated axons of all diameters in the nerve trunks served hair follicles. Axons in fasciculi at the base of the ear served widely differing areas of skin, some of which extended to the front of the ear. There was, however, no linear relationship between the number of axons in a given fasciculus and the area of skin which it served.

We found that the smallest hair follicles were served by at least two separate stem nerve fibers. Large follicles had between six and ten and the largest between 20 and 30 axons, each of which gave rise to a separate group of terminals. These end in two series lying in two different tissue layers, one within the other, parallel to, and encircling the shaft respectively.

We found, further, that excision of a single fasciculus at the base of the ear caused a large number of axons to degenerate within a relatively restricted area of skin, although some axons within the heavily affected area always escaped. At the same time, we were surprised to see a few degenerating axons related to hair follicles of all sizes scattered everywhere in the skin covering the dorsum of the ear, despite the precautions taken to avoid damage to neighboring fasciculi at the time of operation.

By contrast, if a single fasciculus of comparable size was excised at the level of the vertebral column, degenerating axons were seen in every fasciculus of the two nerve trunks at the base of the ear and also in the cutaneous plexus throughout the dorsum of the ear.

(B) ELECTROPHYSIOLOGICAL. On the dorsum of the ear the receptive field of each fasciculus dissected free either from the great auricular or lesser occipital nerve at the base of the ear, could be clearly defined by recording evoked action potentials brushing the clipped hair stumps. In one case, we mapped the areas served by 18 fasciculi in a single ear and found that a small zone of skin was served by six separate fasciculi, i.e., six separate dorsal roots. In another series of experiments we mapped the areas at the base of the ear served by 67 fasciculi in 12 rabbits. These were measured and scaled for comparison with a "standard" ear. Since the number of hairs does not vary with the size of the ear, we were able to calculate that the sum of the total areas served by the average number of fasciculi entering the ear was over four times greater than the area of skin covering the ear. Thus, if each hair or group of hairs emerging from a single orifice were served by an *equal* number of dorsal roots, *each* would be served by four or more roots. Other important findings were that large compound action potential spikes of simple wave form were recorded from fasciculi near the tip of the ear by stimulation of hair stumps at the center of the active area, while smaller spikes were evoked by stimulating near the periphery. By contrast, large, small, *and* complex compound action potential spikes were recorded from fasciculi at the base of the ear by stimulation of hair stumps both at the center and at the periphery of the active area. These findings prompted us to sample comparable fasciculi dissected close to the vertebral column. They were found to serve areas amounting to as much as half the dorsal surface of the ear. Surprisingly enough, however, the areas served by comparable fasciculi extending between the dorsal root and the spinal cord approximated in size to the smaller areas outlined when sampling fasciculi at the base of the ear. From this last series of observations it is clear two major regroupings of the myelinated sensory axons must take place during their passage from the periphery to the spinal cord (28).

11. *The Innervation of Hairs in the Human Ear*

It was, of course, not possible to determine the pattern of innervation of hairs in human ear skin, but to compare the neurohistological arrangements in normal skin from both sources and to make some sort of estimate as to the number of myelinated nerves leaving the human ear which were available to innervate the hairs.

This we did, and were surprised to find that, despite the fact that hair shafts in this region are so inconspicuous, the hair follicles are as numerous and as lavishly innervated as they are in the rabbit. There is a comparable cutaneous plexus, and the number of myelinated axons available to innervate the hairs is of the same order as in the rabbit. It seems likely, then, that the kind of information delivered to the central nervous system by stimulating hairs in the skin of the human ear is comparable with that found in the rabbit. This is interesting for the head of a pin placed on the dorsum of the human ear can be precisely localized.

We are now in a position to integrate some of the observations which we have made on the innervation of hairs in rabbit and human ear skin. Hairs vary in size, and are arranged in a complicated and continuously variable pattern which ensures that, in the case of the ear, almost any kind of contact stimulus must strike a number of hair follicle groups. The stimulus will thus activate, simultaneously or sequentially, some or all of the individual groups of follicular terminal nerve filaments. Since these end in two series lying in two different tissue layers, one within the other, parallel to, and encircling the shaft respectively, the group of terminals transduced will depend greatly upon the nature and direction of the stimulus which is applied. These terminals, in turn, will activate a variable number of dorsal root preterminal axons, the precise number depending upon the size and number of follicles activated by the stimulus.

Since, on the average, 80 hairs are served by a single dorsal root axon, it follows that, once a nerve impulse from a hair reaches the parent axon, it is no longer specifically related to the particular hair from which it arose. Indeed, it might have arisen from any one of a large number of widely separated hairs. However, each hair follicle is innervated on the average by four or five dorsal root axons. Thus, trains of impulses are likely to pass up four to five stem axons from each of the follicles stimulated. Although the fibers carrying the action potentials are dispersed at random in the nerve trunks, they become re-orientated between the dorsal root ganglion and the spinal cord, so that the image transduced in the periphery is, to some extent at least, reformed at this, the first level of integration. These anatomical arrangements alone make it possible to understand why punctate stimuli in the spinal animal can evoke reflex responses patterned in relation to the site of stimulation.

However, this arrangement alone cannot account for the ability of a human subject to locate the precise position of a stimulated hair on the back of the ear, since, by analogy with the rabbit, each of the four to five impulses could have come from any of over 350 hairs in quite different parts of the ear. From our histological observations, however, it is clear that the closer a particular hair is to its parent dorsal root axon, the quicker an impulse coming from it will reach the spinal cord. For this reason, the temporal pattern of the action potentials evoked is likely to be unique, since the hairs served by a single dorsal root axon are all situated at varying distances from the parent nerve fiber at the end of preterminal nerve fibers, whose diameters decrease in the cutaneous plexus as they approach their termination. Furthermore, the diameters of the parent axons serving hairs themselves vary in diameter over a wide range. Thus, localization is likely to depend both upon the spatial *and* the temporal relationship of the impulses which reach the central nervous system. If this is the case, then a relatively small number of dorsal root axons will be able to convey a very large number of uniquely patterned action potential sequences. There is here, then, a system for the transmission of information containing enough detail to allow of a precise response even in relation to a punctate stimulus.

In view of these arrangements, it is of course impossible to regard either a single nerve fiber or a single nerve ending related to a single hair as a primary sensory unit, for under no natural circumstances is either such a single nerve ending or such a single nerve fiber ever stimulated unless it displays a very much lower threshold to stimulation than any of its neighboring terminals. Moreover, it is possible to occupy each and every dorsal root axon serving the hairs with action potentials evoked by selectively stimulating hairs situated in an area occupying less than one-quarter of the total skin surface of the ear. This can only mean that information relative to contact with hairs cannot be related directly and exclusively to the number of parent axons supplying them.

These, then, are the anatomical arrangements whereby hairs in the ear are able to transduce contact stimuli and code the information into a spatiotemporal pattern of impulses for decoding in the central nervous system.

Histological evidence is steadily accumulating which indicates that hairs in skin from other parts of the body are served by nerve fibers which form patterns comparable with those in skin from the ear, and the same is true for the Meissner's corpuscles in nonhairy skin. Indeed, it seems likely that all "focal" receptors will prove to be served by nerve fibers having comparable patterned arrangements but of variable complexity. There is physiological evidence that hair follicle endings and Meissner's corpuscles are stimulated by deformation but not by heat exchange, and some of the mucous membrane end-bulbs (lips) also appear to be specialized in this way. Finally, on grounds of size alone, it is clear that the majority of nerve fibers serving hairs and Meissner's corpuscles join the dorsal columns of the spinal cord, and it must be that when these are stimulated, reports of sensations described as either "epicritic" or discriminative touch are recorded. On morphological grounds alone, then, it is clear that the skin does not contain a mosaic of independent touch transducers having private and exclusive lines of communication with the central nervous system. On the contrary, the following train of events must be assumed to occur. Effective touch stimuli are transduced by "focal" receptors and so initiate trains of impulses which ultimately reach the central nervous system as unique space/time patterns of action potentials. These impulse patterns then traverse relays to reach the brain, where they are integrated with other impulse patterns; the result is analyzed and finally categorized in terms of a report in words to the examiner.

12. *The Patterned Arrangement of Free Nerve Endings*

It was no easy task to determine the pattern of innervation of hairs in the rabbit ear, even though they are circumscribed and served by myelinated nerve fibers. We found it quite impossible, with the techniques at our disposal, to analyze the patterned arrangement of the free nerve endings in the skin. For one thing, on morphological grounds, it is not possible to distinguish one terminal from another except by virtue of its location; moreover, the filaments of which each is composed are so fine that the use of relatively thin sections and high magnifications are necessary in order to see them. This fact alone rules out the possibility of tracing their course accurately, for they may travel for more than a centimeter before ending. Histochemical techniques are of some value in distinguishing between autonomic efferent endings and others, but so far no method has been developed which enables a closer analysis to be made. Because of this it was necessary to find a region in the integument served exclusively by free nerve endings having only somatic sensory functions. The cornea at once suggested itself. We ourselves have shown that few if any autonomic nerves reach the cornea, which is avascular and, from the histological standpoint, a very much simpler tissue than skin (31a).

The pattern of innervation of the cornea proved possible to analyze in experimental animals; moreover, its pattern of innervation in man is strictly comparable with that seen in a wide range of animal species including those commonly used in the laboratory.

Briefly, it is now known that, in the cat for example, the free nerve endings served by a single stem axon are spread over a *variable* area, but which on the average amounts to as much as a quadrant of the cornea and adjacent bulbar conjunctiva. The filaments from different stem axons interweave and intertwine extensively, and any given zone of cornea is served by an overlapping meshwork of filaments, the largest number of which are served by the nearest stem axons, but a significant number of which come from stem axons sited at different distances, many being much further away. Terminal filaments are found at all levels in the epithelium and the substantia propria but (reminiscent of skin) are most numerous just below the basal layer of the epithelium. Most of the stem axons serving these terminal arborizations leave the cornea at the limbus, but before reaching them, the preterminal axons join one another to form bundles in which they pursue a bewilderingly complicated course. In other words, they form a plexiform meshwork of nerve fibers which is in every way comparable with the cutaneous nerve plexus. A stem axon at the limbus thus serves a number of terminal arborizations which occupy variable areas of the cornea. At the limbus the nonmyelinated stem axons join myelinated stem axons which enter into yet another plexiform meshwork formed by ciliary nerve fibers serving other parts of the eyeball. From here they find their way into the long ciliary nerves which in due course join the ophthalmic division of the fifth nerve to reach the trigeminal nerve ganglion and brain stem. From this description, it is clear that once again there is no question of the cornea being served by a mosaic of nerve terminals, each having a private and exclusive line to the central nervous system. On the contrary, in the cat, numerous overlapping, interweaving terminals, each occupying as much as a quadrant of cornea, form a dense meshwork which pervades the cornea. These are served by relatively very many fewer myelinated stem axons, but so arranged that to denervate the cornea completely it is necessary to perform an almost total keratotomy at the limbus (19).

In the cornea, as in the skin, any naturally occurring stimulus must activate a large proportion of the total number of sensory root ganglion axons serving it.

Now, despite the fact that it is not possible to analyze the arrangement of free nerve endings in human skin, as we have done in the cat cornea, all the evidence which is available suggests that they are in fact arranged in a comparable manner. They certainly are in the case of more primitive creatures such as Amphioxus (5).

EXPERIMENTAL OBSERVATIONS ON COMMON SENSIBILITY

With this anatomical framework in mind, we felt that it was permissible to approach the problem of common sensibility from a new angle, and to formulate experiments to test the hypothesis that some free nerve endings may be specific but not strictly modality-specific, and that it is in part the different patterns of activity evoked from endings having collectively a wide range of specificities by different stimuli which are analyzed by the brain and expressed in terms which are usually referred to as the "modalities" of common sensation.

1. *Corneal Sensibility*

It was and is still commonly believed that stimulation of the cornea by any means whatever only leads to reports of pain. This belief is probably based on the experimental observations of von Frey (3a, 3b), who, among others believed that pain was a quite specific sensory modality and that it was served exclusively by free nerve endings. The experimental data which he published, purporting to demonstrate that pain is the only kind of sensation reported when the cornea is stimulated, now appears to be uncritical, and the results far from convincing. At the time common sense, however, suggested that his conclusion was right, and although a few workers refused to accept this, their protests went unheard. Once, however, the seed of doubt had been sown regarding modality specificity, it was relatively easy to design new experiments to test von Frey's conclusions. In the first place, we found that von Frey had not taken precautions to ensure that heat exchange took place between the cornea and the object used to test for the existence of temperature sensibility. Furthermore, on his own admission, he chose to ignore a report of touch made by one of his subjects. von Frey and most of the early workers on common sensibility seemed convinced that warm endings and cold endings in the integument were not specifically affected by heat exchange, but rather that an object which was by common consent considered to be either warm or cold was an effective stimulus notwithstanding the resting temperature of the body surface. Likewise, because a fine stiff hair could evoke reports of touch when applied to the *skin,* he believed that this was an adequate stimulus object with which to stimulate the *cornea.*

To be brief, it was easy to demonstrate that reports of touch, warmth, cold, and pain could all be evoked when suitable stimulus objects were applied to the cornea in a controlled manner. Our experiments also made it clear that by altering the nature of the stimulus objects and by encouraging the subject to discuss what was felt following the application of stimuli from such objects, *a whole range of sensory experience* could be evoked, depending upon the precise nature of the stimulus and to the extent of the vocabulary of the subject stimulated (6).

2. *Action Potentials Evoked by Stimulation of the Cat Cornea*

From the preceding, it is quite clear that the free nerve endings in the cornea do not exclusively transduce stimuli which evoke reports of pain. But this does not rule out the possibility that in the cornea there are four "physiologically" specific types of overlapping free nerve terminations, stimulated respectively by touch, warmth, cold, and pain, each type having private and exclusive lines of communication with the central nervous system. Since this could only be tested in the cornea of experimental animals, we chose the cat because it had already been shown that it is possible to map the size of sensory units in the cornea in this animal by leading action potentials from long ciliary nerves. We found that stimulation of the cornea (using stimulus objects comparable with those which evoke reports of warmth, cold, touch, and pain in man) evoke action potentials which pass along in myelinated axons of the long ciliary nerves. Moreover, many of the endings served by single myelinated axons are each stimulated alike by deformation (touch), positive and negative heat exchange (warmth and cold), and injury (nociception). Some endings are stimulated by approximately equal rates of heat exchange in either direction, others preferentially by positive and still others preferentially by negative heat exchange. No action potentials are evoked from corneas the temperatures and surroundings of which are being uniformly raised and lowered above and below the body temperature of the animal respectively. The effective thermal stimulus is clearly not absolute temperature, but heat exchange. In some cases we came across endings which were not activated by positive heat exchange and others which were not activated by negative heat exchange, although deformation and injury were effective stimuli in every one of these cases. The temporal patterns of the activity induced by the selected stimuli are quite characteristic though different in detail from animal to animal. Deformation (touch) evokes short-lasting high-frequency outbursts of activity. Heat exchange (warmth and cold) evokes outbursts (after short latent periods) which slowly increase in frequency, reach peaks, and then decline. Injury (nociception) evokes more or less long-lasting high-frequency outbursts of activity. Thus, in the case of the cat, it is clear that the sensory nerve terminals in the cornea can be regarded as specific transducers but not always, in respect of touch, warmth, cold, and noxious stimuli separately. Whether or not the same is true in man we do not know, but, in view of the anatomical arrangements which are so similar in man to those in the cat, it seems to us that it is possible and perhaps even probable. Indeed, our observations as a whole suggest that it is not only unnecessary to invoke the notion of strict modality specificity in relation to the corneal nerve terminals responsible for corneal sensibility but also contrary to the evidence which is available. In the cat, the terminals as a whole vary widely in respect of their availability to stimuli of particular kinds, but the over-all pattern of spatial and temporal activity evoked by a given stimulus is nevertheless quite specific. In man, it could be that it is patterns of this kind which are eventually decoded to give the particular reports evoked by the stimuli used (7).

3. *Free Nerve Endings and Cutaneous Sensibility*

There are certain experimental observations which become much easier to explain if it is assumed that while individual free nerve endings respond "specifically," the availability of such endings to stimuli of deformation, heat exchange, and injury varies over a wide range.

For example, the insertion of a fine quartz needle into and even through the skin never evokes a report of either warmth or cold although a wide variety of other sensations are reported. Nevertheless, a fine cold copper wire placed on the lip is usually reported correctly as cold touch, although the same wire when hot is either reported as touch or as a painful sting. In other words, it must be assumed that mechanical stimulation of either warmth or cold endings is not an effective method of transducing them and that only heat exchange will do. It must further be assumed that cold endings lie more superficially in the skin than warmth endings.

It seems to us that these findings, collectively, can be most readily explained if it is assumed that the sensations reported are the result of the recognition of the particular patterns of activity which are being evoked from a series of terminals having different thresholds of specificity, each of which is only being activated in the relation of the amount of specific stimulus energy reaching it. Quartz needles, having negligible heat capacity, are unable to evoke a slow rise and fall in activity from the temperature sensitive free nerve endings in their neighborhood, which it appears is part of the code which evokes reports of either warmth or cold from the cornea. On the other hand, a cold copper wire could evoke activity of this kind in terminals close to the skin surface, for there already exists a thermal gradient from the depths to the surface of the skin which it can be assumed is fairly readily increased. By contrast, a point source of warmth will have to reverse this gradient before more deeply situated endings are activated. To achieve this requires that considerable energy be transferred from a point, indeed, sufficient to cause the "cold" endings to fire at such a speed that a report of pain is evoked before sufficient heat transfer to the deeper layers of skin is achieved.

In support of this hypothesis is an experiment reported by Ebbecke (2). He found that if an arm is immersed in cold water, equilibrium is reached after some minutes, as judged by the fact that the water no longer feels cold. At this time, the circulation to the arm is occluded, and it is removed from the water, dried, and has skin thermometers strapped to it. The subject usually reports no thermal sensations from the arm as the result of these manipulations, but as soon as the blood flow is restored, the arm is reported as feeling intensely cold, despite the fact that the skin temperature is seen to be rising rapidly.

These findings are, it seems to us, most easily explained on the basis that the pattern of activity being signalled from the skin when the blood flow is restored will be comparable with that obtained by simply cooling a large area of skin surface relative to its depths, for it is the gradient which is responsible for the pattern evoked, not the absolute temperature of the skin surface. This experiment also suggests that cold sensibility may well be related in part to the active firing of superficial endings, and warmth to the active firing of deep endings, but that this is not the whole story. Reports of cold and warmth, it seems, depend *primarily* upon temperature gradients in the skin which evoke characteristic patterns of activity from a *series* of endings lying at different depths from the skin surface. This implies that a particular report may well depend as much upon the fact that some endings cease firing as upon the fact that others at a different depth start to fire. Indeed, if this is not the case, it is difficult to understand why direct stimulation by a quartz needle never evokes a report of warmth or cold.

On the other hand, Bishop (1a) has evidence for the existence of specific "cold" spots which cannot be denied, but it seems to us that such spots are so few in number in the forearm that they must be regarded as statistical incidents rather than primary sensory units underlying cold sensibility. The same thing must surely be true of "warmth" spots which are rare entities indeed; yet the warmth of the sun shining on one's forearms is easily detected even during an English winter. In other words, provided a customary and recognizable matrix of impulse patterns reaches the "brain" it will evoke the customary report by whatever means it is evoked.

If heat is transferred to skin at a steadily increasing rate, a series of reports are evoked, which can be divided into a number of categories: (*a*) innominate, (*b*) faint warm, (*c*) warm, (*d*) very warm, (*e*) stinging, burning or hot, (*f*) pain, (*g*) intolerable pain. Furthermore, reports of (*a*) innominate, (*h*) faint cool, and (*j*) cool or cold are made when the skin is radiating to a black body. The categories are not sharply demarcated but merge insensibly from one into another as the surface temperature rises or falls. They have been arranged in a series of relatively arbitrary headings culled from tape records purely for descriptive purposes. Each of the headings is related to a *series* of rates of heat transfer scattered about a mode, but the rates on either side of the mode are related to adjacent headings. In other words, there are no abrupt changes suggesting that different sets of endings are becoming involved. We have also shown, that subjects in a state of "thermal neutrality" at a room temperature of 18 C° had surface skin temperatures ranging from 20° to 35° C. Thus, reports of thermal sensations cannot be directly related to the absolute temperature of the skin surface.

If the rate of heat transfer to an area of skin remains constant we find that, on increasing the area of skin stimulated, there is an increase in the "intensity" of the sensation evoked and vice versa. However, the word "intensity" of sensation cannot be confined to a single so-called primary sensory mode (warmth or cold) when using heat exchange as a stimulus. Rather, we feel that the sensory quality reported is directly related to the number of nerve fibers activated and to the patterned frequency at which the fibers discharge, i.e., to the total pattern of impulse frequency.

"Threshold" in respect of radiant heat exchange at the skin surface is a misleading word, since it can refer to the minimal rate capable of evoking a sensation in at least three of the four commonly recognized primary modalities, i.e., warmth, cold, and pain as well as of other sensations unrelated to these modalities and for which no adequate words exist. This suggested to us that the *modality status* of the sensation reported as the result of heat exchange (a "pure" physical stimulus) should really be referred to the *way in which the stimulus affects the skin* and not to the specific physical nature of the stimulus itself.

4. *Cutaneous Pain*

We are now in a position to discuss the problem of pain as defined in the opening paragraphs of this discussion and to see where it leads us.

The experiments just described suggest that, within the proposed framework which we used, pain is reported when the amount of action potential activity evoked from the skin reaches a critical pattern and that this pattern can be achieved either by temporal or spatial summation (1). In our experiments, this pattern of activity appears to be one which in the experience of the subject is judged to be just short of that which threatens damage to the skin. By altering the framework within which such an experiment is conducted, the subject can be deceived as to the imminence of damage. For example, a pattern of activity sufficient to evoke excruciating pain can be obtained by immersing a cold foot in a tub of hot water which is, however, far below the temperature necessary to cause tissue damage. Clearly then, reports of pain can be evoked in the normal subject in the absence of tissue damage if the framework of the experiment is suitably designed.

In the experiments described above, when the patterns of neural activity was increased beyond this arbitrary level by increasing the amount of heat exchange, a reflex withdrawal occurred and the subject reported that the pain was intolerable. As already stated, there was no suggestion in the experiment that more than one set of nerve terminals (having a range of thresholds and serving nerve fibers of relatively low conduction velocity) was involved in transducing stimuli which gave rise to a wide range of reports extending from cold, cool, through innominate to warmth, hot, pain, and intolerable pain. Is pain, then, a warning signal depending solely upon the number of action potentials from free nerve endings entering the anterolateral columns of the spinal cord (or spinal nucleus of the fifth cranial nerve) from a given area of integument in unit time?

Within the framework of our experiments, this seemed to be the case, but the framework which we chose was narrow and designed to test a new hypothesis: that reports of pain evoked by stimulation of the integument are not due solely to the stimulation of a specific set of receptors having high thresholds and reserved for this purpose, but rather to a particular form of activity evoked from receptors with both low and high thresholds some of which, when otherwise appropriately stimulated, evoke reports of touch, warmth, and cold. This concept is different from that currently accepted. In particular, it suggests that the recognition of stimuli depends as much on the central nervous system as it does on the peripheral nervous system. Yet it argues the existence of a peripheral nervous system capable of delivering for analysis an almost infinite variety of specific and reproducible patterns to the door of the central nervous system. If this hypothesis is correct, it allows far more room for flexibility of sensory interpretation than has hitherto been supposed. For example, pain need no longer be regarded as the inevitable consequence of the stimulation of a particular set of terminals which transmit impulses along private lines in private pathways to the brain, which they can proceed to belabor to exhaustion. On the contrary, the sensory cutaneous nerves can now be seen to be part of an elaborate communication system, so arranged that despite the relatively few lines of communication it has with the brain and the skin, and despite imperfections in the structure and operation of some of the lines an adequate neural framework is always available for encoding an almost limitless amount of information from a wide range of stimuli and delivering this in a recognizable form from the body surface to the central nervous system for analysis and interpretation.

"Pain," on the basis of this hypothesis then, is reported when particular patterns of activity are recognized. These are patterns which, in the *experience of the individual himself* usually signal conditions that threaten or are causing tissue and/or bodily injury. On the other hand, pain may be reported when a particular pattern of activity is recognized which the individual has been either *taught or conditioned to believe* is evoked by a stimulus threatening tissue and/or bodily injury.

ABNORMAL SENSORY PATTERNS

1. *"Unpleasant" Cutaneous Pain*

It has been known for a long time that following section of a peripheral nerve, abnormal sensations are reported when the margin of the area of sensory loss is stimulated. We have examined this phenomenon in detail by both sensory testing and the neurohistological examination of biopsy material in numerous cases over many years. In addition, we have examined excised painful skin scars after testing them in the same way. As a result, it is possible to make certain generalizations.

We find that, in some cases, within 48 hours or so of nerve damage (particularly those involving areas of acute tactile sensibility), merely brushing the margin bounding the area of sensory loss gives rise to reports of pain having a most "disagreeable" quality. The pain can be described as protopathic in nature, but is remarkable in that it can be evoked by a light brush stroke.

Histologically, such zones contain short newly formed filaments surmounted by large growth cones lying in the most superficial layers of the dermis. These nerve filaments are new formations which have grown in from surrounding undamaged nerves toward the denervated zone (20, 27). They are isolated from one another and do not intertwine and interdigitate with neighboring filaments, as is the case in the unaffected surrounding skin. In time the fibers become longer, the growth cones disappear, and with them the ability to evoke pain of "unpleasant" quality by *stroking* the skin with a brush. Nevertheless, pinprick will still evoke the same kind of pain, as long as the terminals remain isolated from one another. The "unpleasant" quality disappears when biopsies show that the filaments are interweaving freely with one another and that there are no longer any isolated terminal axons.

In the course of reinnervation of skin and in certain partially reinnervated cutaneous scars, pain of the same "unpleasant" protopathic quality can be evoked by pinprick, and it is in these zones that isolated terminal filaments are seen histologically (27).

Reports of pain having a similar "unpleasant" quality can also be evoked by pinprick in the forearm of subjects in which the circulation has been occluded by a sphygmomanometer cuff placed around the arm. It is only reported after the cuff has been in position for 15–20 minutes, and the onset of sensory loss is clearly demonstrable. The alteration in quality of the sensations evoked by pinprick at this time can be interpreted as being due to the blocking of fibers capable of conducting impulses to the central nervous system, the fall out being spatially random such that it leads to an *apparent* isolation of the endings which are still responding (26).

In support of this interpretation is a paper by Livingstone (9) giving details of a patient with multiple injuries in which an area of skin on the hand had become reinnervated by fibers from separate nerve trunks. Pinpricks gave rise to sensations in this zone which were indistinguishable from those obtained by pricking within the equivalent area on the contralateral side of the body. However, when one of the nerve trunks supplying the affected area was blocked with local anesthetic, pinprick at once gave rise to pain of an "unpleasant" protopathic quality.

2. *"Unpleasant" Cutaneous "Touch"*

Cutaneous scars, particularly in regions of acute tactile sensibility, will often give rise to reports of a most "unpleasant" sensation when touched. They are not painful in the ordinary sense of the word; in fact they are usually described as being more akin to a light touch than anything else, but the subjects find it quite impossible to describe them more precisely because they are not like anything they have ever felt before. Indeed, the sensation is so "unpleasant" that, if the scar is touched repeatedly, it makes them feel sick and faint. Moreover, their pupils may dilate, and other signs of vagovagal syncope arise.

Histologically, such scars are always found to contain isolated terminal axons, but in these cases a number of them are of relatively large diameter, and are found to be serving either bizarre axonal end-formations, or to be the only stem axons serving hair follicles. If such sensations *have* to be categorized, we suggest that they are examples of "unpleasant" touch and are the result of presenting a particular type of abnormal activity pattern to the central nervous system. These sensations are almost invariably labeled "pain" because of the manifestations of activity in the autonomic nervous system which occur when they are evoked, but patients usually accept this simple label grudgingly and not without qualification if they are given a chance to talk about their experiences.

Comparable reports of "unpleasant" pain and/or touch can be evoked from patients with certain forms of "peripheral neuritis" in certain stages of their disease, and also from the skin in otherwise healthy subjects who have suffered direct blows on the skin in regions where such blows may have injured peripheral nerves.

This phenomenon may also follow the wearing of clothing with unusually tight constricting bands around the hips or limbs.

All the examples which have just been given are, in our opinion, paresthesias due to a disturbance in the pattern of neural activity reaching the spinal cord from the periphery following stimulation. In view of the evidence presented, it is unlikely that they are due to an *excessive* number of potentials reaching the cord from terminals in a given area, or even from a single terminal. Moreover, patients do not complain of an excessive quantity but of the "unpleasant" quality of the sensations evoked. They appear to dislike most their inability to describe the sensations they experience adequately, either to the examiner or to themselves. In the case of "unpleasant" pain evoked by pinprick, they also complain of the lack of graduation in the sensation evoked; the pin either evokes no pain or a sudden and most unpleasant prick.

Patterns of this kind clearly indicate that the sensory nervous system serving the affected area is severely impaired, and are, in this respect, valuable warning signals.

3. *Protopathic and Epicritic Sensibility*

Our histological observations have made it clear that, by and large, the nerve fibers serving focal terminals in the integument pass to the dorsal columns of the spinal cord, whereas those serving the "free" nerve endings pass to the anterolateral columns. This observation, together with the experimental and clinical observations just reported, suggests that Head's theory of "protopathic" and "epicritic" sensibility (4a) could be reformulated without rejecting the words be coined. These words are useful concepts in clinical neurology, and it would be foolish as well as unnecessary to try to replace them. The Brown-Séquard syndrome indicates quite clearly that the dorsal columns of the spinal cord are associated with proprioception and discriminative touch, whereas the anterolateral columns are associated with crude touch, temperature, and pain sensibility. As far as touch is concerned then the dorsal columns might be considered as carrying "epicritic" messages and the anterolateral columns "protopathic" messages, but the latter are not reported in the form which Head regarded as completely characteristic. Nevertheless, his belief that there were two sensory peripheral nervous systems is certainly correct, but we do not consider, as he did, that both are involved with each of the so-called primary modalities of common sensibility. Head's explanation, we suggest, was a logical piece of deduction, but an elipsis, based on both clinical and experimental observations and upon the notion that each sensory terminal was "modality" specific and had a private and exclusive line of communication with the brain. This is now known not to be the case. In fact, the peripheral arrangements are such that any given area of skin is served by many stem axons whose terminals overlap extensively (15, 16, 17). If, however, these become isolated from one another, then stimulation of a single axon evokes a sensation having some of the features Head regarded a characteristically "protopathic." In this sense, "protopathic" is synonymous with incomplete innervation by either "focal" *or* diffuse terminals and the delivery of too little information to the brain via either the dorsal *or* anterolateral columns of the spinal cord. Thus, we suggest that the term "protopathic" (without qualification) should be used (as indeed it usually is) merely to imply that incomplete sensory information is reaching the brain, if it is to remain meaningful. In other words, that the terms "protopathic" and "epicritic" should no longer be used to imply a belief in Head's original hypothesis which Trotter and Davies demolished many years ago (14).

4. *The Interaction between Impulses Entering the Dorsal and Anterolateral Columns of the Spinal Cord*

So far, it has been assumed that evoked sensory impulses enter the spinal cord and pass along two major pathways to the brain where they give rise to perceptions which, under the conditions of the experiments we have conducted, are issued as reports. But other factors have to be evaluated when considering the problem of pain as a whole. The peripheral receptor network which we have described is clearly highly complex, but once sensory nerve impulses enter the central nervous system, things become even more complex. For example, if the framework of our experiments is altered, then additional factors are found to be capable of modifying the reports given and the reactions made in response to the stimuli we give. To be specific, there is now good evidence that impulses entering the dorsal columns of the spinal cord can produce either excitatory or inhibitory activity in the anterolateral columns and that these effects can be achieved merely by altering the pattern of impulses presented to the dorsal columns. Ebbecke (3) has shown that the tickle component aroused by stimulating hairs in such a way as to simulate an insect crawling on the skin can be abolished if the hairs are first stimulated in a slow wiping rhythm. Furthermore, he has shown that large spreading areas of raised or lowered threshold for tickle can be induced in the skin by relatively prolonged stimulation of the hairs in an appropriate manner (fast, irregular, or slow regular patterns) in a restricted area. Moreover, such spread cannot be blocked by the injection of a confining ring of local anesthetic into the skin around the area. This tickle component, however, can no longer be evoked immediately and for some time (perhaps indefinitely) after section of the anterolateral columns of the spinal cord or descending nucleus of the fifth cranial nerve.

This seems to us to be a good example of the way in which an alteration in the pattern of impulses entering the spinal cord from one and the same set of nerves can alter the sensory report evoked and the potential or actual state of reflex exitability of the spinal cord, since tickle evokes a desire to scratch which has to be consciously inhibited if the tickle is not to be abolished.

5. *Efferent Activity of Dorsal Root Axons*

Our concept of the functional activity of the peripheral nervous system is still further complicated by the fact that Woolf, *et al.* (30) has now brought forward indisputable evidence that impulses can and do pass antidromically from the spinal cord along sensory dorsal root nerve fibers into the skin. These impulses, through the mediation of chemical substances at free nerve endings, certainly affect the cutaneous blood vessels and the reaction of the skin to injury. The sensory nerves which end in free nerve terminals in the skin, then, are apparently not only capable of transmitting impulses to the central nervous system from the skin, but also vice versa. If this same system of nerves is responsible in the skin for the nocifensor reactions demonstrated by Lewis (8) this might certainly be the case. On the other hand, these efferent dorsal root nerves may affect the sensory response of the skin by modulating the activity of its sensory nerve terminals to stimulation. If impulses can pass in both directions over the dorsal roots, it is clearly highly probable that under certain circumstances impulses originating in the periphery can be blocked before or soon after they enter the central nervous system. Indeed, it is now known that in the cat impulses passing along the auditory nerve can be blocked at the first synaptic junction, by stimuli arising elsewhere in the brain. Thus, there now appears to be evidence that the term psychosomatic has a physiological basis and is not just a useful concept. Further, it appears to be probable that noxious stimuli which evoke patterns of activity commonly reported as pain may under certain circumstances fail to produce the usual response owing to the blockage or alteration of the pattern of impulses evoked *before* they pass up the spinal cord.

6. *Pain and the Dorsal Columns of the Spinal Cord*

So far, our experiments have suggested that pain, as usually understood, is a warning signal and most commonly follows massive stimulation of free nerve terminals for a relatively extended period of time, and that the impulse pattern which is evoked passes to the anterolateral columns of the spinal cord. Nevertheless, it has been demonstrated that abnormal patterns of activity arising from endings of all types in the integument are regarded as "unpleasant." Whether or not they are painful is to some extent a semantic problem, but there is good evidence which suggests that somatic pain, *as commonly understood,* is primarily associated with activity in the anterolateral columns rather than in the dorsal columns of the spinal cord.

It is often stated that stimulation of the dorsal columns of the spinal cord at operation under local anesthesia gives rise to profound pain and a fall in blood pressure. In a series of cases, Dr. Henry Schwartz (12) has been examining this question more carefully, and it now seems that it is probably incorrect to infer that profound pain is evoked when the dorsal columns of the spinal cord are stimulated, but rather than the patient reports a violent shock-like sensation which, on analysis, proves to be most "unpleasant," but which the patient says cannot be called painful in the recognized sense of this term. It is more like an electric shock, for it tingles rather than hurts. Indeed, it has been compared to the feeling which ensues when the ulnar nerve is struck at the elbow, except that it is much stronger and therefore more "unpleasant." This, we submit, is another example of an abnormal pattern of activity within the sensory system being regarded as "unpleasant." It is even possible to suggest, in this particular case, that the abnormality is of a purely temporal rather than of a (more commonly observed) tempero-spatial nature.

7. *Congenital Absence of Pain Sensibility (Sometimes Called Asymbolia for Pain)*

This finding is, we believe an important one, for it helps to some extent to explain why it is that the small group of persons with a congenital *absence* of pain sensibility are otherwise to all intents and purposes normal from the neurological aspect. In view of Dr. Schwartz's findings, it is no longer necessary to assume that more than one of their afferent sensory pathways is affected although it is impossible to say whereabouts the lesion is situated (if in fact an *anatomical* lesion exists). Careful examination revealed that in three cases examined personally temperature sensibility was completely absent, although by making use of certain cues, such as wetness, they deceived even competent examiners on this point. They were in one sense completely "epicritic creatures," and the value of the "protopathic" senses as warning signals could be very fully appreciated when these people were carefully examined. For example, they all had one or more grossly deformed or "Charcot" joints, and, but for antibiotics, would have had a very short life span, as such cases did in the past, owing to the unavoidable injuries they had sustained by burns and other noxious and tissue-damaging agents.

On the other hand, it is remarkable what training can do for such persons, providing the disability is recognized early enough. For example, they often become overheated in the summer, but with training this can be recognized by the increase in pulse rate and a tendency to a pounding in their heads. Abdominal discomfort manifests itself in nausea and a tendency toward rigidity of the abdominal wall, both of which a child soon learns to recognize. Above all they can and should learn to recognize early that the shock-like tingling which accompanies blows on certain major peripheral nerve trunks (especially the ulnar nerve at the elbow and the lateral popliteal nerve at the neck of the fibula) is a warning signal indicating that they are indulging in potentially dangerous activity. This may enable them, in the course of everyday life, to avoid those forms of physical activity which tend to cause comparable sensations elsewhere, however insignificant they may be quantitatively. This is the more important since such persons do not instinctively regard the shock-like tingling which accompanies a blow on the ulnar nerve as "unpleasant." Indeed, it is remarkable how careless of their bodies such persons are, particularly when young. They clearly have no in-built warning system which enables them to avoid injuries resulting from excessive changes in the physical characteristics of their environment.

8. *Dissociated Anesthesia*

It has been reported on many occasions that dissociated anesthesia is not an uncommon finding in syringomyelia and in other diseases i.e., leprosy resulting in partial loss of cutaneous sensibility. In particular, it is said that completely normal temperature sensibility may be present in the complete absence of pain sensibility and vice versa.

If these statements are accepted at their face value, it is hard to subscribe to the "pattern" hypothesis which we have just erected without qualification. Moreover, it can be so easily argued that the new hypothesis is unlikely to be applicable, for it has its experimental roots in the analysis of *corneal* sensibility in the light of electrophysiological experiments in the *cat*.

On the other hand, as has already been pointed out, what seemed to be obvious common sense to an eminent physiologist such as von Frey (3a, 3b) lead him to the use of experimental methods on the cornea which were ill designed to obtain an unbiased scientific answer.

This we submit is just what has happened in many cases of dissociated anesthesia. The usual methods of testing are ill adapted to obtain an unbiased scientific answer in these cases. It will be remembered that as the result of analyzing reports from subjects on the sensations evoked by transferring heat to the skin at steadily increasing rates we were forced to conclude that the modality status of the sensation reported did not depend so much on the nature of the stimulus object used as upon the effect of the stimulus on the nerve terminals present in the skin.

With this particularly in mind we have now examined a large number of patients who, as the result of syringomyelia, leprosy, and other diseases affecting the somatic sensory pathways, have been reported to us as having dissociated anesthesia. In almost every instance we have been able to show that the dissociation was only apparent and primarily related to the particular stimulus objects which were being used.

For example, reports resulting from isolated pinpricks which did not refer to pain were being compared with reports of hot and cold resulting from the application of test tubes filled with hot (42° C) and cold (4° C) water either being placed in the subject's hands or being rubbed over large areas of skin covering the extremities. If the subjects were able to distinguish the warm tube from the cold but reported that pinpricks were no longer painful, then this was a case of dissociated anesthesia. This conclusion was, of course, true within the framework of the tests carried out, but pinching a piece of skin firmly between finger and thumb almost invariably evoked a report of pain. On the few occasions when it did not, then we were able to convince ourselves that the patients were in fact unable to distinguish warmth from cold provided additional sensory cues such as wetness and air convection currents were eliminated which had hitherto made this possible.

Likewise we found, in subjects who were said to be able to feel warmth and not cold, that the heat exchange values being used in respect to warmth were far in excess of those for cold. Indeed, we have not yet come across a case of true dissociation of pain and thermal sensibility although this *is* possible on the basis of the "pattern" hypothesis.

On the other hand, dorsal column touch can be sharply dissociated from anterolateral column activity, and in cases with hemisection of the cord we believe that there is a complete sensory dissociation at least for a time in adults.

As a result of the investigations reported above, we are even more strongly of the opinion that the chief purpose served by the anterolateral columns of the spinal cord is one of protection.

Impulses from free nerve endings in the periphery are, through its agency, able to inform the "brain" of the nature of the environmental conditions surrounding the organism, which then reacts both reflexly and according to its experience.

These impulses can also be stopped from entering the cord by its agency, and it is even capable of initiating activity in the skin and other tissues by the liberation of chemical substances at the free nerve endings. Thus, we have come to regard the anterolateral columns of the cord as having many attributes in common with the reticular formation of the brain stem.

9. *Chronic Pain*

There is another factor which we believe to be connected with pain of a chronic variety which deserves consideration, but it remains in the nature of extrapolation from clinical observations and experiments in animals, for it is not yet susceptible to strict experimental verification. In patients with long-lasting chronic pain, most attempts to relieve the condition fail, and there are records of unfortunate persons who sustained a gunshot wound which gave rise to "causalgia-like" pain. To relieve this, they have suffered first a sympathectomy, then local amputation, followed by amputation of the whole limb, a rhizotomy, a unilateral cordotomy, a bilateral high cervical cordotomy, and finally a lobotomy, before obtaining any kind of permanent relief from pain. And this was merely relief of an indirect kind, for lobotomy only enables the patient to avoid concentrating on his disability and to regard it with some degree of detachment.

This sort of pain is still sometimes labeled "psychogenic," but this is no explanation since all pain is psychogenic in that it is dependent upon an intact "mind" and every possible peripheral factor needs careful consideration in such a case before assuming that the cause of the phenomenon must lie centrally.

In the first place these pains usually arise spontaneously, gradually increase in severity, and continue almost without remission from the time of their onset. The subject usually protects the painful part assiduously, owing to the extreme ease with which the pain can be increased by either deformation or heat exchange, and for this reason he tends to avoid active and early treatment of any kind. We suggest that "facilitation" is a most potent factor in the generation of the pain in such cases.

The "abnormal" activity pattern we suggest becomes laid down firmly as a preferential circuit activating a series of neuron pools which evoke the sensation of pain. This is the more likely if the hypothesis concerning the relative nonmodality-specificity of some free nerve endings is accepted because it is now certain that the anterolateral columns of the cord consist of a polysynaptic system of internucial neurons which are in a state of almost constant activity and discharging in various combinations in response to impulses arising from many different sources (convergence). Such a system will normally present remarkable fluidity and continual adaptation to varying input patterns. It will only repeatedly react in the same way following facilitation or conditioning. If this notion is correct, then it would seem reasonable that the sooner impulse patterns giving rise to reports of severe and continuous pains are blocked, the better.

In view of this somewhat theoretical generalization it is of more than passing interest that in some cases of chronic pain (neuromas) good clinical results follow such forms of treatment as local vibration or direct blows from a hammer. Painful nodules in skin and muscle may also respond well to vigorous massage. In these particular cases, the form of treatment adopted not only alters the pattern of activity entering the nervous system during treatment but there is histological evidence that in time it also tends to alter the neurohistological picture in the region concerned. Presumably it causes fine nerve filaments which have been caught up in scar tissue and which are very sensitive to deformation to be damaged and to degenerate. Pain does not follow regeneration if the neuromata are kept mobile by regular massage vibration or mild percussion.

THE ROLE OF THE "MIND" IN RELATION TO PAIN SENSIBILITY

Although pain and abnormal sensory patterns are of diagnostic value to the physician, it is important to try to see them in a biological setting rather than in a purely human setting to avoid the danger of regarding (without adequate evidence) the abstract noun "pain" as being synonymous with a specific neurological mechanism. If the hypothesis we have made is correct, it suggests that pains resulting from minimal pathology but which incapacitate so many persons should be capable of relegation to their proper role for explaining their cause and using counter-innervation to "prove" it and mechanisms already available in the nervous system brought into play to suppress them.

In the opening paragraphs of this discussion, it was stated that "pain" is an abstract noun having two polar connotations, and that the one with which we should be most concerned is that which results from the stimulus of injury or disease. In what has gone before, an attempt has been made to analyze, as far as is possible, the origin, course, and destination of the nerve impulses passing from the integument to the spinal cord which evoke reports of pain.

We have seen that, in general, pain is reported when an "excessive" number of impulses (both per unit time and over a period of time) arise from one or a number of free nerve terminals (or the axons serving them) and enter the anterolateral columns of the spinal cord. On the other hand, some of the most unpleasant "pains" are associated with the firing in this way of relatively few terminals, but those which can be assumed to evoke an unusual pattern in the spinal cord (isolation of terminals). In other words, pain is reported as the result of a particular pattern of activity which impinges on the spinal cord. Pain may be pleasant or unpleasant, tolerable or intolerable, but the closer the pattern gets to evoking a reflex withdrawal response, the more the subject complains of its severity; and vice versa, the closer it gets to warm or to brief contact the less it is regarded as pain.

It is also clear that action potentials from focal receptors which enter the dorsal colmuns (or impulses arising therein) of the spinal cord can give rise to "unpleasant" sensations under certain circumstances, in particular, when the collective pattern evoked in them (hairs supplied by single axons or stimulation of the dorsal columns at operation) is abnormal or unusual. These reports do not refer to "pain" in its commonly accepted sense; nevertheless, the sensations evoked give rise to phenomena commonly associated with "pain," and even the victims of such sensations find it hard to choose a more appropriate word to describe their experiences.

The work of Ebbecke and others, on the other hand, makes it clear that activity is evoked in the anterolateral columns of the spinal cord by impulses entering the dorsal columns and that the nature of the activity evoked depends upon the pattern of impulses entering the dorsal columns. Thus, the "unpleasant" quality of the sensations evoked by some impulses which enter the dorsal columns may produce this effect by activating the anterolateral columns of the spinal cord unusually strongly.

In general, then, even within a fairly narrow experimental framework, it seems that there is only a rather loose relationship between the word "pain" and the peripheral activity which must be evoked to obtain such a report.

If the new hypothesis concerning integumental pain is acceptable, it is perhaps permissible to extrapolate from integumental pain to pain in general. If so, then a number of observations related to different fields become easier to understand, and moreover it becomes possible to tackle the clinical problem of pain from a new angle.

For example, although it is not correct to employ the term "pain" in animal experiments, it is permissible to use stimuli which both in man and in animals evoke nociceptive responses (and which in man are reported as pain) to gather relevant data. The experiments of Pavlov are, of course, classical in this respect. He was able to demonstrate that it is possible to condition dogs to nociceptive stimuli such as electric shocks of gradually increasing intensity if they are repeatedly associated with rewards. It has also been shown that, after periods of conditioning in this way, cats and dogs are not only undisturbed by the nociceptive experience but even show a reversal of the normal avoidance response, since they will deliberately press levers to receive a stimulus in the absence of a reward. Hebb (4b) and others (4c) have also shown that dogs brought up in isolation do not respond to nociceptive stimuli (as do their litter mates) when they first enter normal surroundings, but have to *learn* (unfortunately slowly) that such stimuli, far from being interesting, may be lethal.

These experiments not only suggest that nociceptive stimuli below a certain intensity level are effective warning signals only when interpreted as such, but that in many cases a learning process is necessary before a correct adaptation is made. Massive stimuli almost certainly produce their effect through in-built local reflex patterns before the animal is old enough to become aware of them. All of which argues the importance of education in the early years of life from birth at least until puberty.

In this connection it is of interest that in man pain (usually below a certain intensity level) is often regarded as stimulating and invigorating rather than unpleasant and to be avoided. This is seen in an extreme form in sexual masochists who cannot achieve orgasm unless bodily pain accompanies intercourse. Other experiments in dogs suggest that it is possible by extreme forms of conditioning to get an animal to suppress nociceptive impulses in such a way that they neither reach consciousness nor evoke any responses from the autonomic nervous system. In man, this can readily be done under hypnotism, and it is also clear that techniques which lead to so-called "brain-washing" in man can achieve the same end. If common sensibility is dependent upon patterns of activity being decoded in the central nervous system, then it is possible to see how such patterns can be modified and suppressed at any level by activity generated within the nervous system itself. In other words, by taking appropriate "thought," it should be possible to suppress pain from an arthritic joint rather than to resort to such therapy as rhizotomy or cordotomy, for these themselves introduce all the problems of unbalanced input patterns, and every neurosurgeon is aware that in tic douloureux the absence of sensation following *section* of the central root of the fifth nerve may cause more complaints than the "pain" which disappeared as the result of the operation.

It seems to us that if conditioned reflexes in animals can be established in relation to noxious stimuli the same should be possible in man, and, in fact, Moran in *The Anatomy of Courage*

(9a) cites the case of Russian Cossacks in World War I who suffered amputations without anesthetics because they had been conditioned not to feel pain resulting from the surgery necessary to deal with war wounds. In a less dramatic category come examples of persons who show almost complete indifference to pain (noxious stimuli) at times of strong emotional excitement such as combat or when engaged in tasks of a highly absorbing kind. Indeed, if the "mind" is completely absorbed by almost anything, "pain" can be virtually ignored.

So far, we have concentrated on the inhibition of stimuli which normally evoke reports of pain since this is clearly an important field which needs further investigation. But presumably "pain" as a concept is useful if it leads an individual to avoid serious injury or to seek advice when sick, but beyond this, sensitiveness to, or overemphasis on, pain is to be discouraged. Pavlov (10a), who believed strongly in the physiological importance of words, has written as follows:

> Obviously for man speech provides conditioned stimuli which are just as real as any other stimuli, speech on account of the whole preceding life of the adult is connected up with the internal and external stimuli which reach the cortex, signalling all of them and replacing all of them, and therefore it can call forth all those reactions of the organism which are normally determined by the actual stimuli themselves. We can therefore regard "suggestion" as the most simple form of a typical conditioned reflex in man . . . . The fact that it is possible to suggest to a hypnotised subject almost anything, however little it may correspond to the physical reality, and evoke a reaction in opposition to the actual reality . . . can be compared with the fact observed in the paradoxical phase of transition in the dog, that weak stimuli have a greater effect than strong ones. It is highly probable that it plays an important part in normal men too, who are often apt to be more influenced by words than by the actual facts of the surrounding reality.

Here, then, is a possible connection between mental and physical pain, and this is why overemphasis on the word "pain" cannot be too strongly deprecated.

Aristotle regarded pain as a passion of the soul and the antithesis of pleasure. Perhaps it would be wise for us also to realize that there is much to this notion although it is manifestly not the whole story, for otherwise there could be no such thing as congenital absence of pain.

REFERENCES

1. Benjamin, F. B. Spatial summation of pain. *Proc. Soc. Exper. Biol. & Med. 101:* 380–382, 1959.

1a. Bishop, G. H. Responses to electrical stimulation of single sensory units of skin. *J. Neurophysiol. 6:* 361–382, 1943.

2. Ebbecke, U. Über die Temperaturempfindungen in ihrer Abhängigkeit von der Hautdurchblutung und von den Reflexzentren. *Pflüg. Arch. ges Physiol. 169:* 395–462, 1917.

3. Ebbecke, U. Zentralnervöse Irradiation, Konvergenz und Fusion in ihrer Anwendung auf Reflex-und Sinnes-Physiologie. *Pflüg. Arch. Bd. 264:* 1–16, 1957.

3a. von Frey, M. Beiträge zur Physiologie des Schmerz-sinnes'. Parts I & II. *Ber. sächs. Ges. Wiss. 1894a:* 185–196, *1894b:* 283–296, 1894.

3b. von Frey, M. Die Sensibilität der Hornhaut und Bindehaut des menschlichen Auges. *Dtsch. med. Wschr. 48:* 212, 1922.

4. Hagen, E., Knoche, H., Sinclair, D. C., and Weddell, G. The role of specialized nerve terminals in cutaneous sensibility. *Proc. Roy. Soc. B. 141:* 279–287, 1953.

4a. Head, H., Rivers, W. H. R., and Sherren, J. The afferent nervous system from a new aspect. *Brain 28:* 99–115, 1905.

4b. Hebb, D. O. On the nature of fear. *Psychol. Rev. 53:* 259–276, 1946.

4c. Hymovitch, B. The effects of experimental variations on problem solving in the Rat. *J. Comp. Physiol. Psychol. 45:* 313–321, 1952.

5. Lele, P. P., Palmer, E., and Weddell, G. Observations on the Innervation of the integument of the Amphioxus (Branchiostoma). *Quart. J. Micro. Sc. 99:* 421–440, 1958.

6. Lele, P. P., and Weddell, G. The relationship between neurohistology and corneal sensibility. *Brain. 79:* 119–154, 1956.

7. Lele, P. P., and Weddell, G. Sensory nerves of the cornea and

cutaneous sensibility. *Exper. Neurol. 1:* 334–359, 1959.

8. LEWIS, T. Observations upon the vascular axon reflex in human skin as exhibited by a case of urticaria with remarks upon the nocifenser nerve hypothesis. *Clin. Sc. 4:* 365–384, 1942.
9. LIVINGSTONE, W. K. Evidence of active invasion of denervated areas by sensory fibers from neighbouring nerves in man. *J. Neurosurg. 4:* 140–145, 1947.

9a. MORAN (LORD). *The Anatomy of Courage.* Constable, London, 1945.

10. OPPENHEIMER, D. R., PALMER, E., and WEDDELL, G. Nerve endings in the conjunctiva. *J. Anat.* (Lond.). *92:* 321–352, 1958.

10a. PAVLOV, I. From KEELE, K. D., *Anatomy of Pain,* p. 187, Blackwell, Oxford, 1957.

11. RICHARDSON, K. C. Studies on the structure of autonomic nerves in the small intestine, correlating the silver-impregnated image in light microscopy with the permanganate-fixed ultrastructure in electronmicroscopy. *J. Anat.* (Lond.), *94:* 457–472, 1960.
12. SCHWARTZ, HENRY G. Personal communication, 1960.
13. SINCLAIR, D. C., WEDDELL, G., and ZANDER, E. The relationship of cutaneous sensibility to neurohistology in the human pinna. *J. Anat.* (Lond.). *86:* 402–411, 1952.
14. TROTTER, W., and DAVIES, H. M. Experimental studies in the innervation of the skin. *J. Physiol.* (Lond.). *38:* 134–246, 1908–9.
15. WEDDELL, G. The clinical significance of the pattern of cutaneous innervation. *Proc. Roy. Soc. Med. 34:* 776, 1941.
16. WEDDELL, G. The multiple innervation of sensory spots in the skin. *J. Anat.* (Lond.). *75:* Pt. 4, p. 441, 1941.
17. WEDDELL, G. The pattern of cutaneous innervation in relation to cutaneous sensibility. *J. Anat.* (Lond.). *75:* 346–367, 1941.
18. WEDDELL, G. Cutaneous sensibility Chapter 3, in *Modern Trends in Dermatology* (2nd series), edited by R. M. B. MacKenna. Butterworth, London, pp. 46–56, 1954.
19. WEDDELL, G. Studies related to the mechanism of common sensibility, in *Biology of Skin,* Vol. 1. Cutaneous Innervation. Pergamon Press, Oxford, 1960.
20. WEDDELL, G., GUTTMANN, L., and GUTMANN, E. The local extension of nerve fibers into denervated areas of skin. *J. Neurol. & Psychiat., 4:* 206–225, 1941.
21. WEDDELL, G., JAMISON, D., and PALMER, E. Recent investigations into the sensory and neurohistological changes in leprosy. Chap-

ter VII in *Leprosy in Theory & Practice,* edited by R. G. Cochrane. John Wright & Sons, Bristol, 1958.

22. WEDDELL, G., and PALLIE, W. Studies on the innervation of skin; II. The number, size and distribution of hair, hair follicles and orifices from which the hairs emerge in the rabbit ear. *J. Anat.* (Lond.). *89:* 176–188, 1955.
23. WEDDELL, G., PALLIE, W., and PALMER, E. The morphology of peripheral nerve terminations in the skin. *Quart. J. Micro. Sc. 95:* 389–397, 1954.
24. WEDDELL, G., PALLIE, W., and PALMER, E. Studies on the innervation of skin; I. The origin, course and number of sensory nerves supplying the rabbit ear. *J. Anat.* (Lond.). *89:* 162–174, 1955.
25. WEDDELL, G., PALMER, E., and PALLIE, W. Nerve endings in mammalian skin. *Biol. Rev. 30:* 159–195, 1955.
26. WEDDELL, G., and SINCLAIR, D. D. Pins and needles. Observations on some of the sensations aroused in a limb by the application of pressure. *J. Neurol., Neurosurg. & Psychiat. 10:* 26, 1947.
27. WEDDELL, G., SINCLAIR, D. D., and FEINDEL, W. H. An anatomical basis for alterations in quality of pain sensibility. *J. Neurophysiol. 2:* 99–109, 1948.
28. WEDDELL, G., TAYLOR, D. A., and WILLIAMS, C. M. Studies on the innervation of skin; III. The patterned arrangement of the spinal sensory nerves to the rabbit ear. *J. Anat.* (Lond.). *89:* 317–342, 1955.
29. WEDDELL, G., and ZANDER, E. A critical evaluation of methods used to demonstrate tissue neural elements illustrated by reference to the cornea. *J. Anat.* (Lond.). *84:* 168–195, 1950.
30. WOLF, HAROLD G., CHAPMAN, L. F., and GOODELL, HELEN. Structures and processes involved in the sensation of itch, pp. 161–188, in *Biology of Skin,* edited by W. Montagna. Pergamon Press, Oxford, 1960.
31. ZANDER, E., and WEDDELL, G. Observations on the innervation of the cornea. *J. Anat.* (Lond.). *85:* 68–99, 1951.

31a. ZANDER, E., and WEDDELL, G. Reaction of corneal nerve fibres to injury. *Brit. J. Ophthal. 35:* 61–88, 1951.

CHAPTER 6

Influences of Afferent Neurons on Efferent Neurons

I. EFFECTS OF DEAFFERENTATION ON BRAIN FUNCTION AND BEHAVIOR*

JACK H. MENDELSON and FRANK R. ERVIN

AMONG the criteria used to define life, the ability to respond to stimuli from the external environment is always cited. Response to stimuli requires that the organism possess some biophysical matrix for receiving and transmitting stimuli, and the complexity of behavioral response is frequently correlated with the degree of development and elaboration of sensory systems. The course of phylogenetic and ontogenetic development is closely associated with the appearance of increasingly refined and elaborate mechanisms for receiving, transmitting, and integrating stimuli from the organism's internal and external environment. The course of social and cultural development is firmly bound to man's increasing ability to communicate sensory experience. It is not surprising, therefore, that sense and sensing have been a major focus of discourse among philosophers and natural scientists since the beginning of recorded history.

* This study was aided by grant NONR 1866 (41) from the Office of Naval Research.

At the opening of the *Metaphysics*, Aristotle (4) states:

> All men by nature desire to know. An indication of this is the delight we take in our senses; for even apart from their usefulness they are loved for themselves; and above all others the sense of sight. For not only with a view to action, but even when we are not going to do anything, we prefer seeing [one might say] to everything else. The reason is that this, most of all the senses, makes us know and brings to light many differences between things.

The early philosophic issues of "how and what" man senses catalyzed the development of logic and scientific method which have yielded our contemporary concepts of perception. These same early questions of "how and what" man senses contributed to the development of ancient and modern theological theories of "why" man has certain unique sensory experiences. In the Old Testament, Job cries to the apparition in the whirlwind: "I have heard of thee by the hearing of the ear; but now mine eye seeth thee." It is of interest, however, that the general concept of "sensing" is conspicuously absent in ancient theological writings. For example, there is no word in Biblical Hebrew for sense or sensation and the appearance of this term in the New Testament is the product of Greek translation.

Returning, however, to unique forms of sensory experience, i.e., visions induced by isolation and solitary contemplation which appear in the literature of almost all folklores of magic and religion, we are introduced to accounts of possible abnormalities of perception and behavior induced by the impoverishment of environmental sensory stimuli. More complete anecdotal documentation that reduction or stereotyping of sensory input may be associated with aberrant patterns of behavior is recorded in the accounts of isolated explorers (13, 20, 66, 78), shipwrecked sailors (36, 84), and prisoners kept in solitary confinement (18, 56, 69). Questions raised concerning effects of solitary confinement on political prisoners and prisoners of war in relationship to propaganda susceptibility resulted in the initiation of the human isolation studies in Montreal (10). These studies have stimulated research in many other centers. However, long before the study of such applied problems, a large body of experimental and theoretical knowledge had been accumulated on the effects of reduced sensory input on central nervous system physiology and function. We should like to review and integrate some data from relevant anatomical, biochemical, neurophysiological, and psychological studies and attempt to offer some further data and hypotheses to this rapidly expanding area of inquiry. Since studies of the visual system have been most frequently reported in this literature, we will confine the material in this paper for the most part to aspects of visual deafferentation.

ANATOMICAL STUDIES

Isolation from sensory experience produces different behavioral responses in the immature and mature organism, and similarly the neuroanatomical changes following deafferentation differ. It has been known since the early work of Gudden (39) that transneuronal changes occur readily in growing animals after surgical deafferentation. Until recent years little attention had been directed to the value of experimental manipulation of afferent stimuli even though a sizable body of evidence had accumulated in regard to transsynaptic changes following interruption of afferent fibers. Studies by Ströebe (86), Kam (52), Durante (30), and Hoche (49) at the turn of the century documented alterations in the staining characteristics and morphology of cells whose major afferent innervation was interrupted. Although these investigators relied on histological techniques which could not show fiber terminations with precision, their reports are of value because of the attention to human neuropathologic material. Such studies showed, for example, degeneration of the globus pallidus following lesions of the caudate nucleus and motor cortex, degeneration of cerebellum following loss of cerebral hemispheres, changes in the mammillary bodies following damage to the hippocampus and fornix, and changes in the pontine nuclei following their deafferentation. Less conclusive were the studies initiated by Warrington in 1899 (92) in regard to changes in the spinal cord, particularly in the ventral roots and ventral horn cells following dorsal root section. Though his work has been supported by the subsequent studies of Dunn (29) in the frog, Tamaki (87) in the rat, and by some studies of Gagel (35), they were not verified in the more recent study by Cook, Walker, and Barr (26) on adult cats and rabbits.

Probably the most striking and best-studied instance of transneuronal degeneration is that seen in the geniculate body following damage to the eye or optic nerve. Following Minkowski's work (68), this phenomenon was utilized by Clark and his collaborators (24) over a period of years for a detailed study of cell and fiber relationships in the visual system. They indicated that in the primate geniculate with its rigid lamination, its point-to-point representation of the retina, and its absence of either internuncial fibers or interlaminar terminal processes transneuronal changes were seen rapidly and intensely. However, in the dog, cat, and rabbit, where integration of visual stimuli is apparently extensively carried out at precortical levels, and where there are multisynaptic connections to geniculate cells, transneuronal changes take place only after much longer periods of time. For example, in the study of Cook, Walker, and Barr cited above, the earliest change seen was a decrease in size ("area") of geniculate cells. This was not apparent at 32 days, but by 63 days had shown a "25 per cent decrease." The other changes that they noted were an increase in the size of the nucleus at 32 days, normal size at 63 days, and a total decrease of 15 per cent by 90 days. In addition, there was a change in the profile area of the nucleolus not apparent until 210 days after lesion. There was also a progressive decrease in Nissl substance, which followed a pattern different from the Nissl changes seen in chromatolysis. These findings have been confirmed by Torvik (89) in his study of changes in the inferior olive and pontine nuclei in kittens. In his experience these changes appeared four to five days after lesion. He pointed out that retrograde degeneration is associated with loss of nerve cells while, in contrast, transection of afferent fibers is followed by reduction of nerve cell size, loss of Nissl substance, and shrinkage of the affected area (due to resorption of afferent fibers). Torvik found the earliest changes to be in the nucleus and made the interesting suggestion that these alterations may be mediated via glial cells. He based this suggestion on the findings of Scheibel (quoted by Torvik, *op. cit.*) that there are nerve fibers which terminate on oligodendroglia which in turn make contact with other nerve cells. He also described similar cell changes in parts of the lateral reticular nucleus of the medulla, and in the external cuneate nucleus. Earlier work relating to this area has been reviewed thoroughly by Becker (9) and by Jakob (50).

W. E. LeGros Clark (*op. cit.*) hypothesized that the laminar structure of the primate geniculate might be related to color vision, and raised three monkeys in monochromatic red light. A conspicuous selective laminar atrophy occurred in two of the monkeys, but paradoxically this occurred only in lamina one, the cell layer receiving afferents exclusively from the contralateral eye. This work has not been followed up.

Riesen (75) has reported almost complete disappearance of ganglion cells in two chimpanzees kept in the darkness for one and one-third and two and one-half years. A third animal kept in the dark for seven months and examined after two years in the light was reported as "normal." Two other animals kept in the dark for eight months by Chow (23) were reported to show no change in the density of ganglion cells or in cell density in the lateral geniculate. Similarly, a study by Goodman (38), who kept rabbits in the dark for six months and produced a behavioral visual deficit, was reported as showing no changes in the visual system although the combined thickness of the optic fibers, ganglion cells, and internal plexiform layers were smaller in experimental than control retinas. In addition, the density of cells in the superior colliculi and in the striate cortex was slightly greater in experimental than control animals, as was also the lamina molecularis of the striate cortex. Although these changes were quite slight they were used by Weisenkrantz (94) to support his own more detailed findings. He raised cats on a schedule found by Riesen, Kurke, and Mellinger (76) to produce marked performance deficits on visual tasks. At the end of 17 weeks he found a decrease in thickness of the inner plexiform layer, and about a 20 per cent decrease in the density of the Müller fibers in the experimental retinas. No differences were found in the relative thickness of the nuclear layer, and there were no significant differences between the absolute thicknesses of the retinas. He argues from these results that the learning deficit reported after isolation is secondary to changes in the peripheral sensory apparatus.

Although Becker (*op. cit.*) makes a reasonable case for both anterograde and retrograde transneuronal degeneration of a first and second order, direct evidence of changes in the cortex following deafferentation is scarce. Such a study carried out by Haddara (40) in mice reported no changes.

Though many details regarding structural changes following deafferentation are lacking, the following points seem pertinent. (*1*) Adequate connection with afferent fibers is important for maintaining the integrity of neural cells. (*2*) Removal of such afferent connections produces consistent and early changes which are striking in the developing organism and most easily seen in neural structures with a single major afferent supply (e.g., the geniculate, the inferior olive). (*3*) The changes induced by deafferentation are initially a reduction in the size of the nucleus and nucleolus, and secondarily a reduction in the amount of Nissl substance. However, preceding these changes in the cell body there may be changes in dendrite and/or axon structure.

The neuronal nucleus, nucleolus, and Nissl substance are composed in part of nucleic acids, and it may be suggested that changes observed in morphological appearance following deafferentation are an advanced indication of a derangement in nucleic acid synthesis and metabolism. Thus, alteration of the microscopic anatomy of the central nervous system following deafferentation raises many questions concerning the neurochemical processes involved.

NEUROCHEMICAL STUDIES

As early as 1898 the effects of visual stimulation on cytoplasmic constituents of retinal cells were studied with analin dye techniques (1, 6, 11). In 1902 A. J. Carlsson (21) reported a reduction of the chromophil substance of retinal ganglion cells following retinal stimulation. These very early studies were among the first attempts to correlate changes of the chemical composition of nerve cells with their functional activity. It remained, however, for the introduction of modern biochemical and biophysical techniques to provide methods for assessing the effects of stimulus input on specific chemical constituents of single cells or small cellular aggregates. Hamberger and Hyden (41, 42, 43) employed ultraviolet microspectrography in their studies of the effects of stimulation on purine and pyrimidine bases in the neurons of the auditory system. Their data showed a decrease of nucleic acid concentration in cells of the cochlear ganglion and

Table 6-1. Pentose Nucleoprotein (PNP) of Retinal Ganglion Cells.

WEIGHT IN 10^{-9} mg/μ^3

8 MONTH OLD RABBIT	MEAN	S.D.	P
STIMULATED >6 HOURS	0.490	0.100	
DARK ADAPTED 10 MINUTES	0.230	0.118	<0.001
DARK ADAPTED 3 HOURS	0.050	0.029	<0.001
DARK ADAPTED 3 HOURS THEN STIMULATED 3 HOURS	0.240	0.034	<0.001

from Brattgård

vestibular ganglion following intense stimulation. An extensive study of the effects of visual stimulation on ganglion cells of the retina was carried out in 1952 by Brattgård (14) using a modification of the x-ray microradiography technique (15) described by Engstrom and Lindstrom (32). Brattgård summarized his findings in adult rabbit retina as follows:

> The PNP fraction of the ganglion cells, which was relatively large with adequate stimulation, was appreciably decreased with a complete absence of such stimulation. When the previously unstimulated retinas were exposed to stimulation, the PNP fraction of the nerve cells increased. A complete lack of stimulation for the periods in question led to no demonstrable change in the size of the protein fraction in these cells.

Table 6-1 presents the PNP data and demonstrates the statistically significant differences between the control groups of rabbits stimulated for more than six hours and three other groups listed below. Ultraviolet micrographs of a ganglion cell from a three-hour dark-adapted eight-month-old rabbit when compared with a normally stimulated control show a striking degree of difference in density of nuclear and cytoplasmic nucleic acids when photographed at 2570 Å (Fig. 6-1). These U.V. microspectrography findings are consistent with changes of the

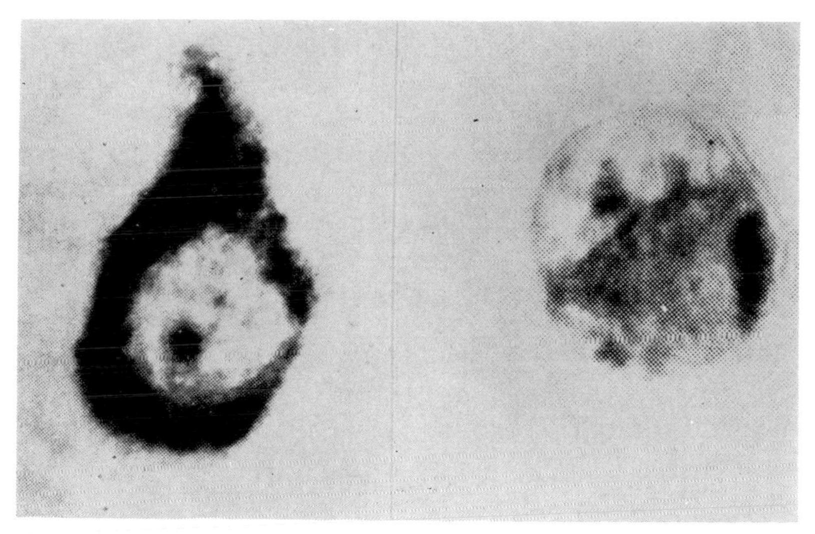

FIG. 6-1. Retinal ganglion cells in 8-month-old rabbits. (*Left*) Control, stimulated less than 6 hrs. (*Right*) Experimental, dark adapted 3 hrs. 2570 Å, × 2000. (From Brattgård, 14.)

PNP fraction of the ganglion cells. More recent studies by Einarsen (31) have corroborated these changes in the nucleoprotein fraction of retinal ganglion cells following light deprivation. The findings of protein alterations of the retina during visual stimulus deprivation by Brattgård have been supplemented by the recent study of Wase and Christensen on phospholipid metabolism in whole brain (93). Data presented by Wase and Christensen showed that phospholipid turnover in whole mouse brain, as measured with techniques employing P^{32} incorporation was significantly lower ($p < 0.01$) in single isolated adult animals kept in totally dark and sound-attenuated cages for 31 days when compared with group isolated and nonisolated controls. Unfortunately, these authors presented no data regarding regional fractionation of P^{32} incorporation in different areas of the brain, and it would be most interesting to see this study repeated with more detailed examination of protein metabolism in areas of the brain subserving visual and auditory function.

The biochemical studies discussed so far have dealt with findings in the adult animal. A separate and most important issue is

Table 6-2. The Influence of Adequate Stimulation on the Development of Retinal Ganglion Cells from Birth to the Adult Stage

(WEIGHT IN 10^{-9} mg/μ^3, MEAN VALUE ± S.D.)

	TOTAL DRY WEIGHT	PNP FRACTION	PROTEIN FRACTION
RABBITS LIVING IN DAYLIGHT 10 WEEKS	0.78±0.057	0.47±0.055	0.31±0.027
RABBITS BORN IN AND LIVING IN DARKNESS 10 WEEKS	0.16±0.042	0.00±0.029	0.16±0.027
RABBITS BORN IN AND LIVING IN DARKNESS 10 WEEKS, THEN LIVING IN DAYLIGHT 3 WEEKS	0.58±0.085	0.22±0.099	0.36±0.082
RABBITS LIVING IN DAYLIGHT 11 DAYS	0.42±0.055	0.21±0.049	0.22±0.015

from Brattgård

the significance of afferent input to the biochemistry of the developing nervous system. Boell and Shen (12) demonstrated in 1950 that the removal of one eye of Amblystoma prior to development of the optic nerve resulted in hypoplasia of the midbrain on the involved side. In addition, cholinesterase activity was markedly reduced. Brattgård (14) also studied the effects of visual deprivation on the chemical composition of retinal ganglion cells during early postnatal development. He examined the retinas of dark-reared rabbits with the techniques described above, and his findings are summarized in Table 6-2.

Brattgård summarized these data as follows:

> In nerve cells that have never been exposed to adequate stimulation, the nucleoprotein fraction will be lacking and the size of the protein fraction smaller than those of control cells. If nerve cells,

which from birth and a period thereafter have never been stimulated, are then adequately stimulated, both the nucleoprotein and the protein fraction will increase. This increase will vary quantitatively in different cells of the same kind. In addition, the variation will be greater in the case of the dark-adapted animals than of the controls.

He also added:

The lack of adequate stimulation during the early post-natal period therefore leads not only to incomplete development of the nerve cells, but also to disturbances in their metabolism and chemical composition.

Table 6-3. Retinal Enzyme Activities of Dark-Reared Rabbits

ENZYME	AGE AT WHICH SIGNIFICANT DIFFERENCES ($P < .01$) WERE PRESENT	DIRECTION OF CHANGE	AGE AT WHICH NO SIGNIFICANT DIFFERENCES OCCURRED
DEHYDROGENASES			
ISOCITRIC	120	DECREASE	26, 60
GLUCOSE-6-P	26, 60	INCREASE	120
LACTIC	60, 120	DECREASE	26
MALIC	26, 60, 120	DECREASE	
PHOSPHATASE			
ACID	26, 60, 120	DECREASE	

from Schimke

There are further data to support this hypothesis from the studies of Hellstrom and Zetterstrom (45) and Schimke (80).

Hellstrom and Zetterstrom studied the SH-groups in retinas of kittens reared in total darkness from birth and compared these with animals reared in normal light. They found, with histochemical techniques, that SH-groups were present in high quantitative amounts at birth. There was a significant decrease of SH-groups in the retinas of animals that were dark-reared as well as a delay in development of the electroretinogram, unit potential. Schimke studied enzyme activity in whole retina and whole brain of albino rabbits reared in total darkness from birth and compared the data with normal light-reared controls. He found significant changes in retinal enzymes after varying periods of light deprivation as summarized in Table 6-3. These differences in enzyme activity were observed only in retina and did not occur in whole brain and were not associated with or appear to be caused by changes in water, total protein, or lipid content. Unfortunately since Schimke's investigations were confined to the total retina and whole brain, no information was obtained relative to enzyme changes in different regional areas or cellular layers.

Although gross histological changes may be produced in the visual system following deafferentation, the biochemical and biophysical techniques employed in the studies discussed above indicate that subtle changes occur in the structure and chemistry of nerve cells before they can be demonstrated by classical neuropathological tissue examination. Thus, we now have opportunities to move closer to the goal of understanding some relationships between certain aspects of sensory function of the nervous system and behavior as well as sensory function and development. If we consider some parallel developments in research on the neurochemical mechanisms of motor function, it appears that much progress in this area occurred because of the development of techniques for evoking motor response with increasingly refined inputs of appropriate physiological parameters. It may be reasonable to expect that modification of parameters of sensory input may provide a technique for learning more about the neurochemistry of sensory transmission and integration in the central nervous system. Similarly, modification of the sensory environment of the developing organism may provide a method for controlled examination of the evolution of certain neurochemical processes during growth and maturation.

NEUROPHYSIOLOGICAL STUDIES

Electrophysiologic investigation of the effects of deafferentation has been chiefly concerned with the question of "spontaneous" *vs.* "evoked" CNS activity. A study by Lissman, for example (60), reported cessation of movement following loss of sensory input in the dogfish and concluded that there was no spontaneous neural activity. Bremer's classic study (16) of brain stem transection was generally interpreted as evidence that sensory deafferentation produced sleep. The later observations of Moruzzi and Magoun (70), however, showed the importance of the mesencephalic reticular formation in determining sleep-wakefulness cycles. It is increasingly apparent that the interplay of a number of intrinsic systems (i.e., the reticular formation, hypothalamus, intralaminar thalamus, rhinencephalon, caudate and lateral thalamus) determines the instantaneous organization of the electrical activity of the brain at least as much as the activity of primary sensory pathways. Preliminary work in clarifying the role of the reticular formation in the organization and timing of sensory input has been summarized by Lindsley (58). Little work has been done to date to elucidate the effects of changing magnitude or pattern of primary sensory inflow on cerebral organization. It seems a reasonable hypothesis that it is the loss of the organizing influence of incoming stimuli on spontaneous cerebral activity which underlies the observed behavioral effects.

Neural tissue is clearly capable of spontaneous activity (91). The activity of isolated cortical slabs (19) is not rhythmic like intact cortex, and may be electrically silent unless stimulated. However, this preparation, though deafferented (and de-efferented), is difficult to interpret for our present purposes. Of more interest, indeed the physiologic analogue of transneuronal degeneration, is the denervated neuron studied by Cannon who demonstrated that such cells show a persistent alteration in sensitivity of response to humoral agents (especially acetylcholine and epinephrine). Drake and Stavraky (28) extended this study to the afferent arc and showed that interruption of the posterior root produced hypo- and later hypersensitivity of the anterior horn cells to epinephrine, acetylcholine, strychnine, and other drugs. These findings, similar to the changes in staining characteristics noted earlier, suggest some permanent alteration of metabolic and physcochemical organization of the affected cell.

A similar interpretation can be made of the work of Posternak *et al.* (73). Sectioning of both optic nerves or ablation of the ipsilateral geniculate raised the amplitude and increased the recovery cycle of visual cortical responses to electrical stimulation of geniculate radiations. (They interpreted this acute change in sensitivity as evidence for interruption of inhibitory or occlusive activity from the retina.)

In summary, many critical experiments in this area are lacking. However, the effects of decreased sensory input on human and animal behavior provide some suggestions for further electrophysiologic studies.*

ANIMAL BEHAVIOR STUDIES

Growing animals have been subjected to restriction of sensory experience in various ways. For example, attempts to differentiate "innate" as opposed to "learned" behavior have utilized social isolation with more or less stereotyping of environment. A review of the effects of early experience on behavior of mammals and birds has been presented by Beach and Jaynes (8). The sterility of the artificial "innate-learned" dichotomy is shown by the most careful of such studies from the American Museum of Natural History (79) (cf. also 81 for discussion). Kittens were isolated from the litter at various ages for time intervals of four days to 18 months. Behavioral deficits which appeared on their return to the group were caused equally by inexperience of the isolate, and progressive change of the intact social group. Of pertinence for our consideration was the persistent alteration of behavior in isolates raised to maturity. Such animals were awkward in coordination, showed little spontaneous searching, but were easily excitable and combative. They failed to copulate with estrus females. No formal perceptual or learning studies were carried out on these cats, but puppies similarly raised have been studied by Thompson and Heron (88) and Melzack *et al.* (63, 64). Such dogs returned to a normal environment showed marked hyperactivity and impairment in delayed reaction tasks

* An excellent article has been published demonstrating that sensory deprivation of the forebrain by brain stem lesions results in striking behavioral abnormalities. SPRAGUE, J. M., CHAMBERS, W. W., and STELLAR, E. Attentive affective, and adaptive behavior in the cat. *Science 133:* 165–173, 1961.

and in such simple problem solving as circumventing a barrier to obtain visible food. They were unable to learn to avoid painful experiences, repeatedly burning themselves on a candle flame, bumping their heads on radiators, etc., to the point of physical jeopardy.

Among the first investigations concerned specifically with sensory function was that of Riesen (75) on dark-reared chimpanzees. These animals after return to a normal environment showed severe impairment of visual-motor performance tasks and of social behavior. The careful extension of these studies by Dr. Riesen and his collaborators (76, 77) has detailed the time course of changes and of recovery, the details of functional deficit, and the anatomical consequences of light deprivation. We previously cited the reservations of Weisenkrantz (94) that structural changes in the peripheral apparatus could account for the impaired visual performance. These apply also to the earlier studies of Siegel (82, 83), who raised winged doves to maturity in translucent hoods and found impairment in discrimination of a circle and triangle. Such reservations seem less pertinent to the study of Nissen, Chow, and Semmes (71), who deprived a young chimpanzee of tactual and manipulative experience for 31 months. On testing he was inferior to normally raised controls in tests of tactual motor coordination although not in visual discrimination. Earlier studies in this area have also been conducted and reviewed by Carmichael (22).

These studies suggest that, for the maturing organism, experience is necessary for the adequate organization of the sensory system, perhaps for the forming of the "S-S" connections which Hebb (44) postulated must precede "S-R" learning. Both this process and the behavioral consequences of sensory isolation are different in the mature organism. Studies of the latter process are at present restricted to man.

HUMAN BEHAVIOR STUDIES

Studies of human subjects during reduction or stereotyping of sensory stimuli have shown that transient though severe abnormalities of behavior may occur in a variety of experimental situations (46, 57, 85, 95). These studies which have been conducted during the last decade have been described under the very general and somewhat inadequate generic titles of sensory deprivation or sensory isolation. We shall not attempt a critique of the methodology of the investigations reported in the literature except to point out that many interacting variables other than stimulus deprivation are of major importance. These factors have been adequately reviewed elsewhere (54, 55). One of the most consistent findings, however, in many "deprivation" studies has been the experience of visual imagery by some subjects. These phenomena have been described as hallucinations, illusions, fantasies, and hypnagogic states. Since we have been focusing upon the visual system there are a number of interesting facets to consider relative to the visual imagery of subjects who have experienced experimental visual deprivation and patients who have had acute or chronic loss of vision. Considering the latter category first, a number of opthalmologic surgeons (17, 72, 74) have reported the occurrence of psychotic-like episodes characterized by visual hallucinations in patients afflicted with cataracts. Furthermore, it was observed that postoperative cataract patients tended to have acute psychotic episodes following surgery when both eyes were covered with patches, and it was suggested (59) that visual deprivation was a crucial etiological factor. When bilateral eye patching was modified to patching of only the one eye operated upon a significant remission of symptoms occurred. These clinical observations received relatively little attention until the group of investigators at McGill University began the systematic study in 1954 of the effects of stimulus reduction upon behavioral and cognitive processes in man (10). Since that time a large number of investigations have been carried out with a variety of technical and methodological approaches but most could be placed in one of three possible categories. (*1*) Attempts to reduce the absolute level of afferent input as exemplified by the studies conducted by Lilly (57). (*2*) Attempts to reduce patterning of afferent input as exemplified by the studies of Bexton and his associates (10) and in later studies by Vernon and Hoffman (90) and Goldberger and Holt (37). (3) Attempts to produce a monotonous structuring of afferent input as exemplified by the reports of Wexler *et al.* (95), Mendelson *et al.* (65), and Davis, McCourt, and Solomon (27).

It was suggested by a number of investigators (5, 67) that use of isolation or deprivation techniques might provide a means of understanding and subsequently treating the causes of visual imagery frequently but by no means universally observed in certain types of psychotic illness. This suggestion may be considered to be a logical consequence of the pharmacological approach to the study of psychosis via the utilization of the so-called psychonimetic drugs. In fact, a number of investigators (33, 62) have presented data to support the hypothesis that drugs such as LSD act directly upon neuronal and synaptic mechanisms in the visual system. While these studies are of great interest the links between experimental evidence obtained to date and the behavioral events related to abnormalities of visual perception observed in mental illness are still quite vague.

A more circumscribed and what appeared to be a potentially better controlled area of investigation was the study of the relationships between visual deprivation and sleep-wakefulness behavior. A number of hypotheses were discussed concerning the effects of deafferentation on sleep-wakefulness cycle at the First conference of the Macy Foundation in 1950 on *Problems of Consciousness* (2). The influence of deafferentation on sleep-wakefulness cycles as reflected by the electrical activity of the brain was presented by Kleitman (53) as: "The deafferented brain is the sleeping brain." This statement was tempered by Fremont-Smith's addition (34):

For the purpose of this discussion we should, perhaps, broaden the term "afferent impulse" to mean any afferent impulse to those cells from which we are measuring brain waves. This would include afferent impulses arising within the central nervous system as well as those coming from outside, or, as what probably normally takes place, a mixture of those coming from inside the brain and from outside. I am assuming then that the reticular formation may be a source of "intranervous afferent" impulses.

However, Hoagland followed with the quandry (48): "Would the brain by itself, if it could be shelled out, let us say, and had no afferent connections whatever, be a brain that would be essentially a sleeping brain? That is the question I am still puzzled about."

This question remains unanswered in man, but attempts have been made to assess sleep-wakefulness activity during periods of reduced or monotonously structured environmental input.

Lilly (57) approached this problem by attempting to reduce the absolute level of visual-auditory-tactile stimuli experienced by the human subject. His technique involved placing a subject who wore a blacked-out headmask in a state of neutral buoyancy, in a tank of slowly flowing water maintained at 34.5° C. Lilly reported subjective experiences which suggested that long periods of sleep did not occur in this deprivation situation. Although Lilly's subjects said they were awake and alert during most of the experiment, no objective data on sleep-wakefulness behavior was reported. Heron (47) studied periodic EEG tracings during an experiment in which patterned visual and auditory stimuli were removed. Although he reported data concerning alpha frequency and per cent time alpha he presented no assessment of sleep-wakefulness behavior. We will discuss Heron's findings relative to the alpha rhythm later in this paper. During the early experiments conducted at Boston City Hospital involving the monotonous stereotyping of visual and auditory stimuli (95) it appeared that there was some change in the sleep-wakefulness behavior of subjects. These impressions, however, were based on gross observations of behavior and could not be interpreted as wholly valid. In order to assess more adequately the effects of visual and auditory deafferentation in an experimental setting which was roughly analogous to that described by Heron, a consecutive series of EEG tracings were made on a group of volunteer subjects during a six-hour experimental period.

The subjects studied were adult male college students who were recruited through the offer of pay per hour. All of the subjects selected had been in the experimental situation at least one previous time so that they were all familiar with procedure and the novel environment. It was considered important to utilize "trained" subjects since novice subjects might experience feelings of apprehension or anxiety, which alone might affect sleep-wakefulness patterns. The subjects were seated in a sound-attenuated room in a comfortable Barcalounger-type reclining chair. Their eyes were covered with translucent occluders which permitted entry of light but which precluded the experience of any pattern vision. Earphones were placed on the subject's head and a comfortable level of white noise was played continuously throughout the experiment. Bottles containing cold milk or water were attached to the side of the chair and from which the subject could take fluid at any time via glass feeding tubes placed close to his mouth. A urinal was placed by the side of the chair so that the subject could void at any time he wished. All experiments were conducted during the early morning of the experimental day and were designed to last six hours. The subject was not told the exact duration of time of the experiment. Prior to the experiment, the subjects were instructed to obtain a full night's sleep and to eat their usual breakfast. After the subject was comfortably seated in the chair autoclaved, platinum needle electrodes were inserted into his scalp in the frontal, temporal, parietal, and occipital regions. The information given to each subject just before the experiment was as follows: "This is an experiment to measure your brain waves while you are seated comfortably with your eyes covered and a soft sound is played through earphones. We would like you to remain seated during the entire experiment. Someone will be outside of the room at all times but you will not see them and they will not speak with you, even if you ask them questions. This experiment is to last most of the day, and will end when I terminate it. Cold water and milk can be sipped by you at any time through these tubes. If you wish to urinate, a urinal is available on the table next to the chair. We would like you to talk and tell us what your thoughts and feelings are while you are sitting here. The time is now______. We are ready to begin." Baseline EEG recordings were made at the beginning of each experiment with subject's eyes open and eyes closed. The subject's eyes were then covered with the translucent occluders, the white noise was turned on, and a similar series of EEG recordings were then made. Following this, EEG recordings were made at 15-minute intervals during the course of the entire experiment, and all the subject's verbalizations were recorded on a voice-activated tape recorder. Observations of the subject's fluid intake, motor behavior, and urination were also recorded via observations through a one-way mirror-pane screen. After the experiment was concluded a series of post-experimental EEG's were obtained in a parallel manner to those made at the beginning of the experiment. Sleep-wakefulness activity was classified in five categories according to the criteria of Loomis, Harvey, and Hobart (61).

(*1*) Awake —predominant activity, 9–11 per sec.
(*2*) Drowsiness —flattening of activity, occ. runs of 5–7 per sec.
(*3*) Light sleep —4–6 per sec. with occ. 14–16 per sec. spindles in vertex leads
(*4*) Moderate sleep—irregular slow waves 1–3 per sec. mixed with intermediate slow waves 4–8 per sec.
(*5*) Deep sleep —½–2 sec. high-voltage activity

The results of this experiment showed a variety of sleep-wakefulness patterns of the group of subjects studied with no single pattern being dominant. Sleep-wakefulness activity ranged from a subject who slept almost continuously throughout the entire experiment (Fig. 6-2) to a subject who was awake most of the time (Fig. 6-3). All subjects experienced some period of sleep or drowsiness during the experiment, and none reported an increasing feeling of wakefulness of exhilaration as noted in Lilly's experiment. One subject reported experiences of visual imagery. The relationship between verbalized imagery and sleep-wakefulness behavior is seen in Figure 6-4. Imagery appeared to occur at transitional phases of either entering into or awaking from sleep and was reported during both drowsiness and fully awake periods. These findings suggest that imagery experienced during deafferentation may be hypnagogic and associated with drowsi-

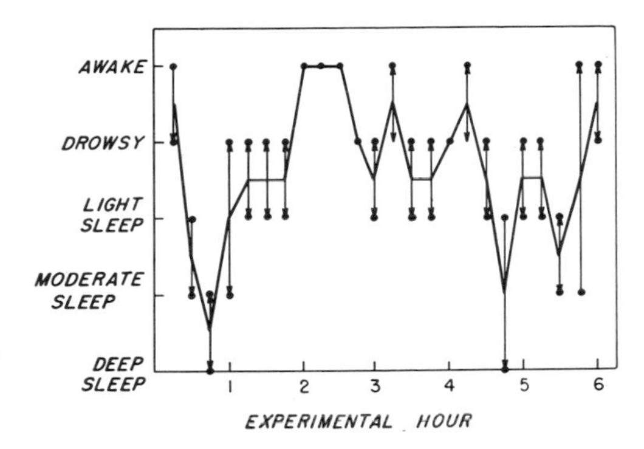

FIG. 6-2. Sleep-wakefulness pattern. Subject IV. *Arrows* indicate direction of change between 2 levels.

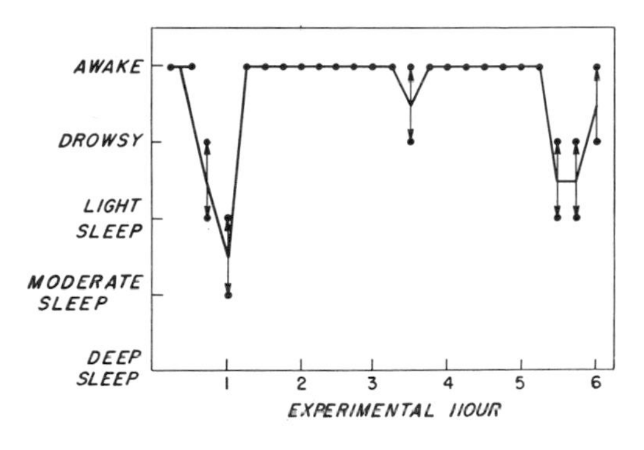

FIG. 6-3. Sleep-wakefulness pattern. Subject III. *Arrows* indicate direction of change between 2 levels.

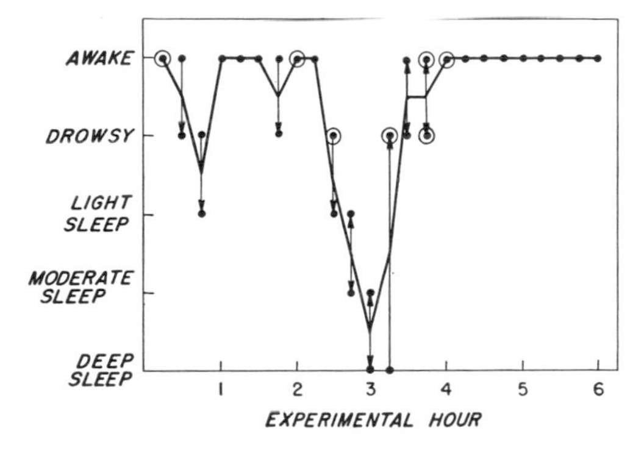

FIG. 6-4. Sleep-wakefulness pattern and imagery. Subject VI. *Arrows* indicate direction of change between 2 levels. *Dotted circles* indicate occurrence of imagery.

ness (Fig. 6-5) or hallucinatory and associated with a fully awake EEG pattern (Fig. 6-6). When the subject experienced imagery while awake no suppression of alpha activity was observed (Table 6-4). Furthermore, no relationship between type of imagery and alpha frequency or per cent time alpha was

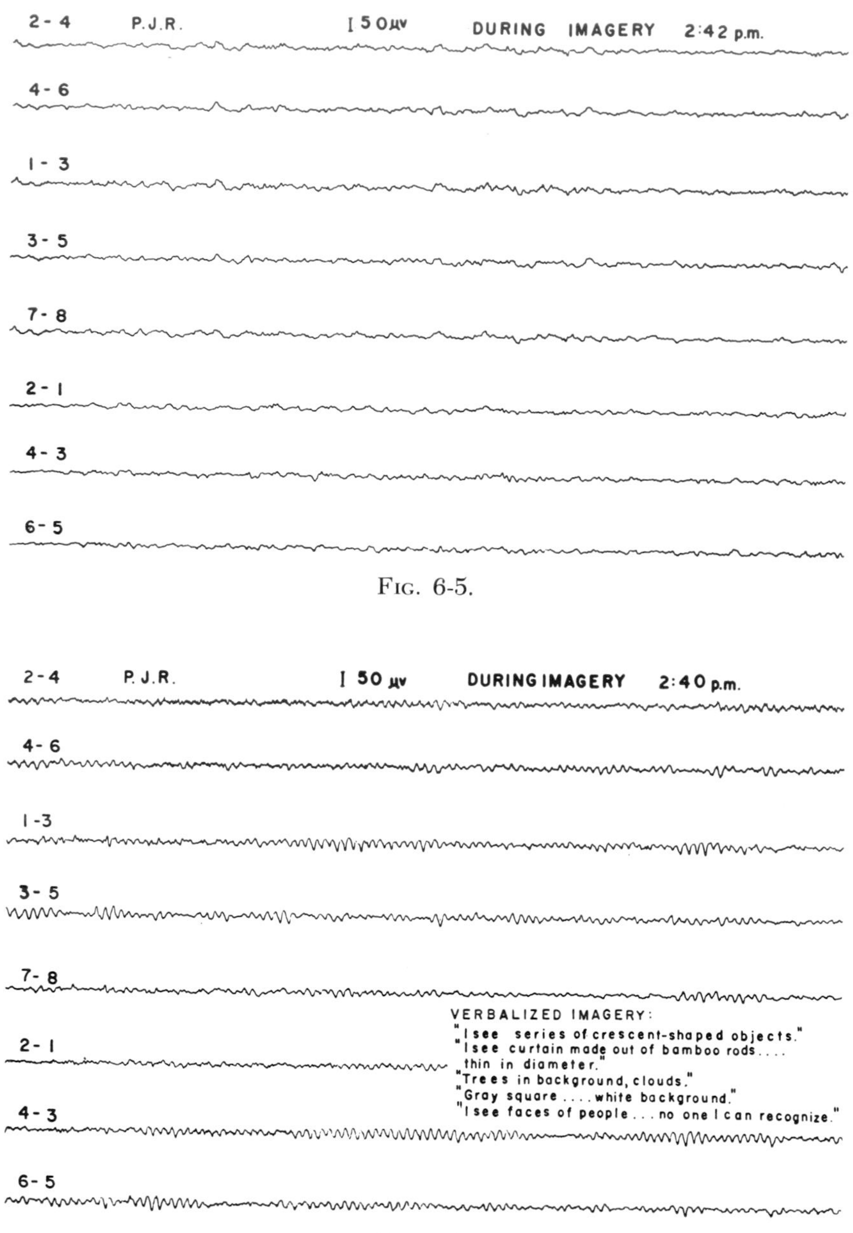
2-4
P.J.R.
I 50 μv
DURING IMAGERY 2:42 p.m.
4-6
1-3
3-5
7-8
2-1
4-3
6-5
2-4
P.J.R.
I 50 μv
DURING IMAGERY 2:40 p.m.
4-6
1-3
3-5
7-8
VERBALIZED IMAGERY:
"I see series of crescent-shaped objects."
"I see curtain made out of bamboo rods.... thin in diameter."
"Trees in background, clouds."
"Gray square.... white background."
"I see faces of people... no one I can recognize."
2-1
4-3
6-5

FIG. 6-5.

FIG. 6-6.

noted. This finding is in agreement with reports of Barrott (7), who found the amount of alpha could not be employed as a measure of imagery. The lack of change in alpha activity is at variance with findings of Heron who reported greatly reduced

Table 6-4. Subject VI

	Experimental Time		Alpha Frequency	% Time Alpha
PRE	CONTROL	EYES OPEN	10.5	7
		EYES CLOSED	9.9	29
	OCCLUDERS AND WHITE NOISE	EYES OPEN	10.4	20
		EYES CLOSED	10.6	40
EXPERIMENT	OCCLUDERS AND WHITE NOISE	START	10.3	15
		MIDDLE	10.1	26
		END	10.1	19
		HALLUCINATIONS	10.2 - 10.6	13-43
POST	OCCLUDERS AND WHITE NOISE	EYES OPEN	10.0	37
		EYES CLOSED	10.1	34
	CONTROL	EYES OPEN	10.2	5
		EYES CLOSED	10.2	50

amplitude of EEG tracings obtained during periods when subjects were hallucinating. Heron also reported that after 16 hours subjects showed a shift to slower frequencies and that a return to pre experimental baseline frequencies was delayed for several hours after the subject left the experiment. Our data show no significant change in alpha frequency (Table 6-5), or per cent

Table 6-5. Alpha Frequency

	PRE-EXPERIMENT				POST-EXPERIMENT			
SUBJECT	CONTROL		OCCLUDERS AND WHITE NOISE				CONTROL	
	OPEN	CLOSED	OPEN	CLOSED	OPEN	CLOSED	OPEN	CLOSED
I	9.6	10.0	9.8	10.2	10.1	9.8	9.7	9.8
II	NONE	10.9	10.5	NONE	10.1	NONE	10.0	10.0
III	9.4	9.1	9.0	9.1	9.1	9.0	9.0	9.1
IV	NONE	10.8	11.0	NONE	10.1	10.0	NONE	10.4
V	NONE	11.0	11.1	11.0	10.9	11.0	NONE	11.5
VI	10.5	9.9	10.4	10.6	10.0	10.1	10.2	10.2

time alpha (Table 6-6) during the course or at the end of the six-hour experiment. It can be seen, however, that the difference

Table 6-6. Per Cent Time Alpha

	PRE-EXPERIMENT				POST-EXPERIMENT			
SUBJECT	CONTROL		OCCLUDERS AND WHITE NOISE				CONTROL	
	OPEN	CLOSED	OPEN	CLOSED	OPEN	CLOSED	OPEN	CLOSED
I	36	79	69	81	67	82	18	83
II	NONE	39	14	NONE	17	2	3	3
III	13	86	35	77	56	82	16	85
IV	NONE	57	45	NONE	46	52	NONE	49
V	NONE	35	55	20	21	20	NONE	9
VI	7	29	20	40	37	34	5	50

in per cent time alpha between eyes open and eyes closed was diminished with visual occluders and white noise (Figs. 6-7, 6-8). This phenomenon is not surprising since in 1934 Adrian and Mathews (3) pointed out that pattern in the visual field

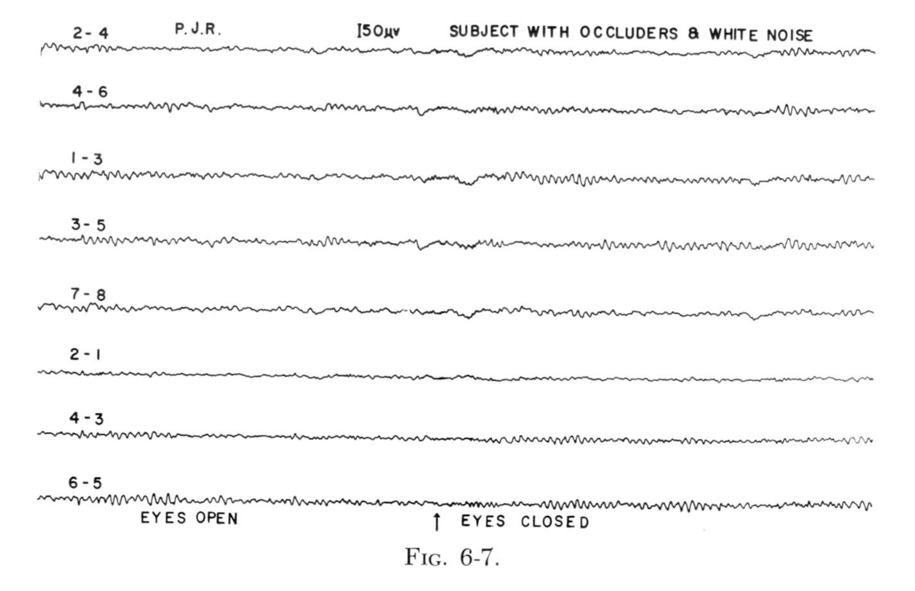

Fig. 6-7.

was an effective factor in alpha inhibition. Finally, although subjects verbalized a wide variety of thought processes which ranged from self-initiated complex problem-solving tasks in mathematics and philosophy to random pleasant and unpleasant daydreams, no significant correlation with alpha activity was found. While more sensitive techniques of recording and analysis of the EEG may provide important data in the future, no relationship between the alpha rhythm, visual imagery, and stereotyping of visual and auditory stimulus input was found in this study.*

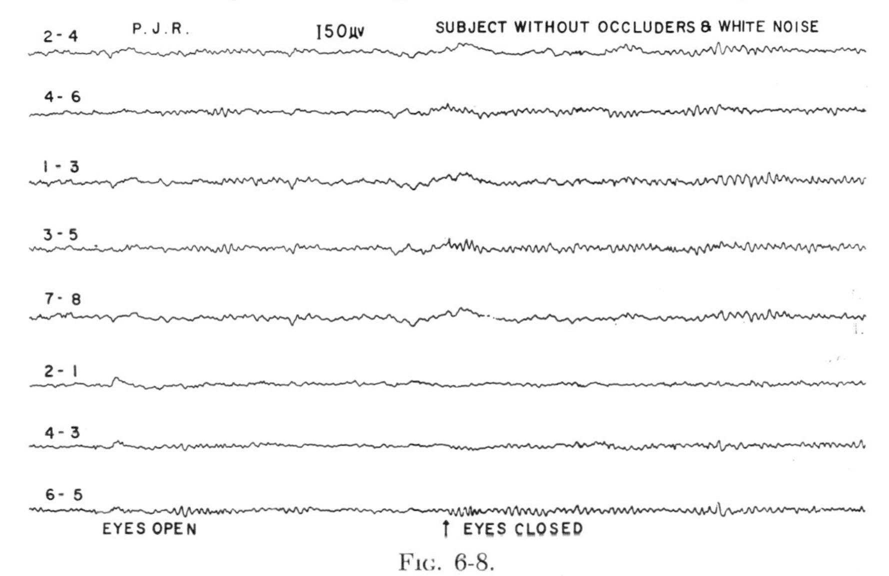

FIG. 6-8.

COMMENTARY

Although the catalogue of data is not complete, it appears that deafferentation produces morphological, biochemical, and electrophysiological changes in neural tissue. Associated with these neurobiological effects are behavioral alterations which are dependent upon the sensory modality involved and the level of maturity or development of the central nervous system. Because both the specific sensory modality and the age at which deafferentation occurs are important determinants of the effects of deafferentation, it is suggested that experimental deafferentation under controlled laboratory conditions as well as clinical observations in congenital deafness or blindness can provide a useful approach for studying certain aspects of central nervous system

* Acknowledgment: The authors thank Dr. P. H. Leiderman for his assistance in completing this study.

function and behavior. If we re-examine the major findings from studies of the effects of sensory deprivation upon the central nervous system, the following pertinent features stand out.

First, the metabolic and structural integrity of neural aggregates of the central nervous system is quite sensitive to disruption of major afferent axons, particularly in growing animals. This observation is classic in the primate visual system with its single important input system, but seems to apply generally where conclusive data are available. Second, stimulus (e.g., light) deprivation alone leads to similar changes in growing animals. Of particular importance to note is that the most obvious chemical changes involve RNA metabolism which is important both in protein synthesis and in the mechanisms of the body's other information-preserving systems (genes and antibodies). Third, absence of patterning of sensory experience without actual removal of the stimulus (as in the studies of Melzack *et al.*), leads to serious impairments of learning ability, activity level, and perception. As yet, no electrophysiologic or biochemical data accompany these experiments, but one might propose a number of direct observations to be made in such animals.

Riesen (75) has pointed out: " . . . The speed with which certain particular combinations of sensory inputs can be incorporated into behavior depends upon the degree of prior exposure to such combinations." This is consistent with Hebb's emphasis on the importance of building "simple" perceptions from experience, e.g., a triangle is first recognized by an adult who has recovered from blindness as a series of connected angles which must be counted to distinguish it from a square. Further, it has recently been shown by Kalin (51) that a pattern-recognizing system cannot be made up of randomly connected elements, but that certain minimal structural restraints (primarily metric conserving) are necessary. Analysis of published information on the anatomy and physiology of the visual cortex suggests that these restraints are in fact met. It is of interest in this regard to note that Conel's (25) developmental studies of human cerebral cortex demonstrate that primary sensory cortex (visual, auditory, and somatosensory) has less dendritic arborization and therefore fewer cellular interconnections at birth than primary motor cortex or archicortex although many more than "association" cortex. The dendritic density increases with age and precedes the increase in the sensory association areas (Figs. 6-9, 6-10), suggesting that the organization of the primary cortex is a necessary condition for association area development. Since we have found no comparable anatomic data in the literature for congenitally blind or deaf individuals, the developmental sequence reported by Conel may be genetically determined (as Kalin argues).

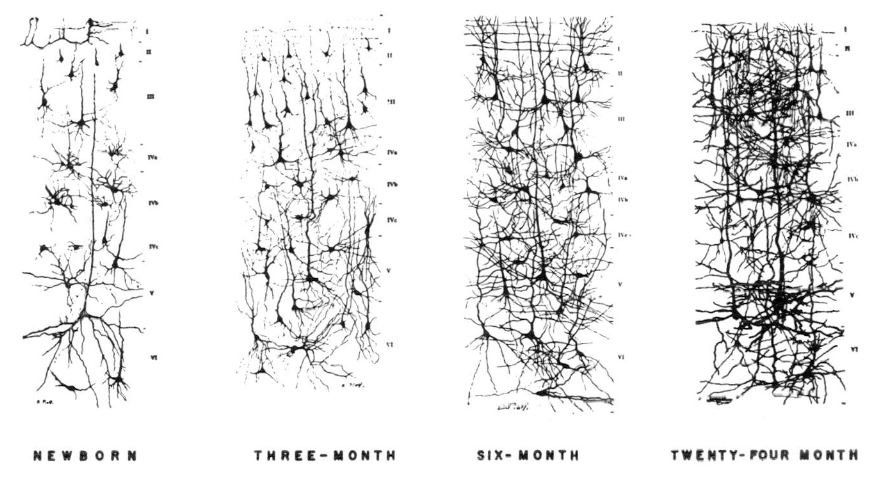

Fig. 6-9. Area striata, OC in human infant cortex. Drawing from Golgi-Cox (after Conel, 25).

However, the cognitive deficits found by Riesen may have as their bases a failure of development of the crucial cell-cell connections to provide the important "S-S" learning of maturation. This hypothesis can be directly tested histologically and electrophysiologically (and is being done in our laboratories).

The effects of sensory deprivation on the developing organism have been obtained from animal studies. The effects on the mature organism are illustrated by studies of man in whom behavioral changes are transitory but may be quite striking. If we consider the developing organism as a self-organizing system deprived of the sensory experience necessary to develop the equipment for continuing organization, then the mature organism might be described as a reasonably well-organized information-processing system, which, deprived of new information, utilizes memory stores to complete perceptions and organize action. When the mature organism is deprived of the controls of environmental feedback, internal and external events are not differentiated, and cognitive processes may lose the organization necessary to deal with the physical universe effectively. If the

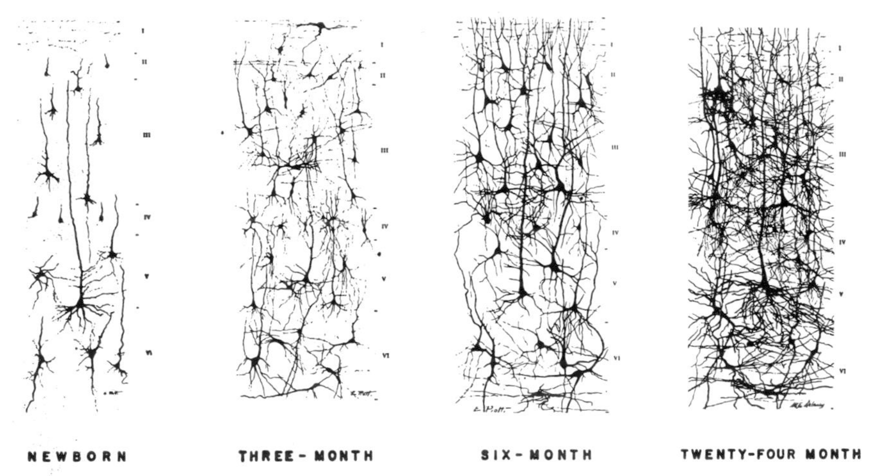

FIG. 6-10. Area peristriata, OA in human infant cortex. Drawing from Golgi-Cox (after Conel, 25).

animal raised in isolation doesn't know "which end is up," the isolated adult may be quite certain the wrong end is up. These changes are similar to those produced by other factors which disrupt information processing at some level of the neuraxis, such as sensory overload, amphetamine intoxication, and alcoholic delirium.

In summary, we would add our hypothesis to a long-standing conviction of many students of behavior that the brain as an organ of mind requires the input of information via sensory modalities for both its maturation and its normal function. The intrinsic developmental laws and autonomous activity make the central nervous system quite different than the passive response system postulated by naïve behaviorism, but for normal function the brain must operate as part of a dynamic loop of information transfer of which the real world is an integral part.

REFERENCES

1. Abelsdorff, G. Bemerkungen über das Auge der neugeborenen Katze, im Besonderen die retinale Sehzellenschicht. *Arch. f. Augenheilk. 53:* 257, 1903.
2. Abramson, Harold A., editor, *Problems of Consciousness.* Josiah Macy, Jr. Foundation, New York, 1950.
3. Adrian, E. D., and Mathews, B. H. S. The Berger rhythm: Potential changes from the occipital lobes in man. *Brain. 57:* 355, 1934.
4. Aristotle. *The Basic Works.* Edited by Richard McKeon. Random House, New York, 1941.
5. Azima, H., and Cramer, F. J. Effects of partial isolation in mentally disturbed individuals. *Dis. Nerv. Sys. 17:* 3, 1956.
6. Bach, L. Zur feinen Anatomie und Patologie der Ganglienzellen der Retina. Edinburgh. *Trans. VIII Inter. Ophthalm. Congress,* 1895.
7. Barrott, P. E. Use of the EEG in the study of imagery. *Brit. J. Psychol. 47:* 101, 1956.
8. Beach, F. A., and Jaynes, J. Effects of early experience upon the behavior of animals. *Psychol. Bull. 51:* 240–263, 1954.
9. Becker, H. Retrograde und transneurale Degeneration der Neurone. *Akad. Wiss. u. Lit. Abh. Math. nat. Rl. 10:* 651, 1952.
10. Béxton, W. H., Heron, W., and Scott, T. H. Effects of decreased variation in the sensory environment. *Canad. J. Psychol. 8:* 70, 1954.
11. Birsch-Hirschfeld, A. Beitrag zur Kenntniss der Netzhautganglienzellen unter physiologischen und pathologischen Verhaltnissen. *Arch. f. Ophthalm. 50:* 166, 1900.
12. Boell, E. J., and Shen, C. C. Development of cholenesterase in the central nervous system of Amblystoma punctatum. *J. Exper. Zool. 113:* 583, 1950.
13. Bombard, Alain. *The Voyage of the Heretique.* Simon & Schuster, New York, 1953.
14. Brattgård, S. O. The importance of adequate stimulation for the chemical composition of retinal ganglion cells during early postnatal development. *Acta radiol. Suppl. 96:* 1952.
15. Brattgård, S. O., and Hyden, H. Mass, lipids, pentose nucleoproteins and proteins determined in nerve cells by x-ray microradiography. *Acta radiol. Suppl. 94:* 1952.
16. Bremer, F. Cerveau "isole" et physiologie du sommeil. *Compt. rend. Soc. de Biol. 118:* 1235, 1935.
17. Brownell, M. E. Cataract delirium. *J. Michigan M. Soc. 16:* 282, 1917.

18. BURNEY, CHRISTOPHER. *Solitary Confinement.* Coward-McCann, Inc., New York, 1952.
19. BURNS, B. D. *The Mammalian Cerebral Cortex.* Edward Arnold, Ltd., London, 1958.
20. BYRD, RICHARD E. *Alone.* G. P. Putnam's Sons, New York, 1938.
21. CARLSSON, A. J. Changes in the Nissl's substance of the ganglion and the bipolar cells of the retina of the brant cormorant phalacrocorax pennicillatus during prolonged normal stimulation. *Am. J. Anat. 2:* 341, 1902.
22. CARMICHAEL, L. The development of behavior in vertebrates experimentally removed from the influence of external stimulation. *Physiol. Rev. 33:* 51–58, 1936.
23. CHOW, K. L. and NISSEN, H. W. Interocular transfer of learning in visually naïve and experienced infant chimpanzees. *J. Comp. Physiol. 48:* 229, 1956.
24. CLARK, W. E. LEGROS. Anatomy of cortical vision. *Tr. Ophth. Soc. U. Kingdom. 62:* 229, 1943.
25. CONEL, J. L. *The Postnatal Development of the Human Cerebral Cortex.* Harvard University Press, Cambridge, 1939, 1941, 1947, Vols. I, II, and III.
26. COOK, W. H., WALKER, J. G., and BARR, M. L. Transneuronal atrophy. *J. Comp. Neurol. 94:* 267, 1951.
27. DAVIS, J. M., MCCOURT, W. F., and SOLOMON, P. The effect of visual stimulation on hallucinations and other mental experiences during sensory deprivation. *Am. J. Psychiat. 116:* 889–892, 1960.
28. DRAKE, C., and STAVRAKY, G. An extension of the law of denervation to afferent neurones. *J. Neurophysiol. 17:* 229, 1948.
29. DUNN, E. H. A statistical study of the medullated nerve fibers innervating the legs of the leopard frog after unilateral section of the ventral roots. *J. Comp. Neurol. 19:* 236, 1909.
30. DURANTE, C. *Des Degenerescances secondaires du systeme nerveux.* Paris, 1895.
31. EINARSON, L. Cytological aspects of nucleic acid metabolism. Section 10 in *Metabolism of the Nervous System,* edited by D. Richter. Pergamon Press, New York, 1957.
32. ENGSTROM, A., and LINDSTROM, B. A method for the determination of the mass of extremely small biological objects. *Biochem. et Biophys. Acta. 4:* 351, 1950.
33. EVARTS, E. Effects of a series of indoles on synaptic transmission in the lateral geniculate nucleus of the cat. Chapter 8 in *Psycho-*

pharmacology, edited by H. Penns. Paul B. Hoeber, Inc., New York, 1958.

34. FREMONT-SMITH, F., in *Problems of Consciousness,* edited by H. A. Abramson. Josiah Macy, Jr. Foundation, New York, 1950, pp. 30–31.
35. GAGEL, O. Ganglienzellveranderungen im Ruckenmarksgrau nach Hinterwurzeldurchschneidung. *Z. Neur. 130:* 371, 1930.
36. GIBSON, WALTER. *The Boat.* Houghton Mifflin Co., Boston, 1953.
37. GOLDBERGER, L., and HOLT, R. R. Experimental interference with reality contact (perceptual isolation): Method and group results. *J. Nerv. & Ment. Dis. 127:* 99, 1958.
38. GOODMAN, L. Effect of total absence of function on the optic system of rabbits. *Am. J. Physiol. 100:* 46, 1932.
39. GUDDEN, v. Experimentaluntersuchungen uber das peripherische und zentrale Nervensystem. *Arch. f. Psychiat. 2:* 693, 1869.
40. HADDARA, M. A. H. Studies in the postnatal development of the visual cortex of the mouse. Ph.D. Thesis, University of London, 1955.
41. HAMBERGER, C. A., and HYDEN, H. Cytochemical changes in the cochlear ganglion caused by acoustic stimulation and trauma. *Acta oto-laryng. Suppl. 61:* 1945.
42. HAMBERGER, C. A., and HYDEN, H. Production of nucleoproteins in the vestibular ganglion. *Acta oto-laryng. Suppl. 75:* 1949.
43. HAMBERGER, C. A., and HYDEN, H. Transneuronal chemical changes in Deiters' nucleus. *Acta oto-laryng. Suppl. 75:* 1949.
44. HEBB, D. O. *The Organization of Behavior.* John Wiley, New York, 1949.
45. HELLSTROM, B., and ZETTERSTROM, B. The effect of light on the manifestation of the electroretinogram and on histochemically demonstrable SH-groups in the retina. *Exp. Cell Research. 10:* 248, 1956.
46. HERON, W. The pathology of boredom. *Scient. Am. 196:* 52, 1957.
47. HERON, W. Cognitive and physiological effects of perceptual isolation. In *Sensory Deprivation.* Edited by P. H. Solomon, *et al.* Harvard University Press, Cambridge, 1961.
48. HOAGLAND, H. In *Problems of Consciousness,* edited by H. A. Abramson. Josiah Macy, Jr. Foundation, New York, 1950, p. 29.
49. HOCHE, A. *Handbuch der pathologischen Anatomie,* herausgeg. von E. Flatau, L. Jacobsohn u. L. Limor. Berlin Bd. I, Teil, XVI. "Die sekundaren Degenerationsprozesse im Gehirn," Karger, 1904.
50. JACOB, H. C. Die transneuralen bzw. transsynaptischer Degenera-

tionen. *Handbuch der speziellen pathologischen anatomie und histologie.* Berlin, Springer, Verlag, 1957, p. 305.
51. Kalin, T. Some metric considerations in pattern recognition. *CRRB, AFCRL Research Report.* #327, Office of Aerospace Research, Bedford, Mass., July, 1961.
52. Kam, A. C. Beitrage zur Kenntis der durch die Grobhirnrinde bedingten sekundaren Veranderungen im Hirnstamme. *Arch. f. Psychiat. 27:* 645, 1895.
53. Kleitman, N., in *Problems of Consciousness,* edited by H. A. Abramson. Josiah Macy, Jr. Foundation, New York, 1950, p. 20.
54. Kubzansky, P. E. The effects of reduced environmental stimulation on human behavior: A review. *ARDC Study SR 1770,* Tech. Report #16, 1959.
55. Kubzansky, P. E. Methodical and conceptual problems in the study of sensory deprivation. *Am. Psychologist. 13:* 334, 1958.
56. Lifton, R. J. "Thorough reform" of western civilians in Chinese communist prisons. *Psychiatry. 19:* 173, 1956.
57. Lilly, J. Mental effects of reduction of ordinary levels of physical stimuli on intact, healthy persons. *Psychiat. Res. Report. 5:* 1, 1956.
58. Lindsley, D. Common factors in sensory deprivation, sensory distortion, and sensory overload. In *Sensory Deprivation.* Edited by P. H. Solomon, *et al.* Harvard University Press, Cambridge, 1961.
59. Linn, L., Kah, F. L., Coles, R., Cohen, J., Marshall, D., and Weinstein, E. A. Patterns of behavior disturbance following cataract extraction. *Am. J. Psychiat. 110:* 281, 1953.
60. Lissman, H. W. The neurological basis of the locomotory rhythm in the spinal dogfish (Scyllium canicula, Acanthias vulgaris). II. The effect of de-afferentation. *J. Exper. Biol. 23:* 162, 1950.
61. Loomis, A. L., Harvey, E. N., and Hobart, G. Cerebral states during sleep, as studied by human brain potentials. *J. Exper. Psychol. 21:* 127, 1937.
62. Marrazi, A. S. The action of psychotogens and a neurophysiological theory of hallucinations. *Am. J. Psychiat. 116:* 911, 1960.
63. Melzack, R. The genesis of emotional behavior: An experimental study of the dog. *J. Comp. Physiol. Psychol. 47:* 166-168, 1954.
64. Melzack, R., and Thompson, W. R. Effects of early experience on social behavior. *Canad. J. Psychol. 10:* 82–90, 1956.
65. Mendelson, J. H., *et al.* Catechol amine excretion and behavior during sensory deprivation. *AMA Arch. Gen. Psychiat. 2:* 147-155, 1960.

66. Merrien, Jean. *Les Navigateurs Solitaires.* Editones Denoel, Paris, 1954.
67. Meyer, J. S., Greifenstein, F., and Devault, M. A new drug causing symptoms of sensory deprivation: Neurological, electro-encephalography and pharmacological effects of Sernyl. *J. Nerv. & Ment. Dis. 129:* 54, 1959.
68. Minkowski, M. Uber den Verlauf, die Endigung und die zentrale Repräsentation von gekreuzten und ungekreuzten Schnervenfasern bei einigen Saugetieren und beim Menschen. *Schweiz. Arch. f. Neurol. 6:* 201, *7:* 268, 1920.
69. Morello, Michael. A study of the adjustive behavior of prison inmates to incarceration. *Dissertation Abstr. 19:* 2149, 1959.
70. Moruzzi, G., and Magoun, H. W. Brainstem reticular formation and activation of the EEG. *EEG Clin. Neurophysiol. 1:* 455, 1949.
71. Nissen, H., Chow, K. L., and Semmes, J. Effects of restricted opportunity for tactual, kinesthetic and manipulative experience on the behavior of a chimpanzee. *Am. J. Psychol. 64:* 485–507, 1953.
72. Parker, W. R. Post-cataract extraction delirium: Report of 11 cases. *J.A.M.A. 61:* 1174, 1933.
73. Posternak, J., Fleming, T. C., and Evarts, E. Effect of interruption of the visual pathway on the response to geniculate stimulation. *Science. 129:* 39, 1959.
74. Preu, P. W., and Guida, F. P. Psychosis complicating recovery from extraction of cataract. *Arch. Neurol. & Psychiat. 38:* 818, 1937.
75. Riesen, A. H. The development of visual perception in man and chimpanzee. *Science. 106:* 107, 1947.
76. Riesen, A. H., Kurke, M. I., and Mellinger, J. C. Interocular transfer of habits learned monocularly in visually naïve and visually experienced cats. *J. Comp. Physiol. Psychol. 46:* 166, 1953.
77. Riesen, A. H., and Mellinger, J. C. Interocular transfer of habits in cats after alternating monocular visual experience. *J. Comp. Physiol. Psychol. 49:* 516–520, 1956.
78. Ritter, Christiane. *A Woman in the Polar Night.* E. P. Dutton & Co., Inc., New York, 1954.
79. Rosenblatt, F., and Schneirla, T. Personal communication.
80. Schimke, R. T. Effects of prolonged light deprivation for the development of retinal enzymes in the rabbit. *J. Biol. Chem. 234:* 700, 1959.
81. Schneirla, T. Interrelationships of the "innate" and the "acquired"

in instinctive behavior. *L'instinct dans le comportement des animaux et de l'homme*, Masson et Cie, Paris.

82. SIEGEL, A. I. Deprivation of visual form definition in the ring dove. I. Discriminatory learning. *J. Comp. Physiol. Psychol. 46:* 115–119, 1953.
83. SIEGEL, A. I. Deprivation of visual form definition in the ring dove. II. Perceptual motor transfer. *J. Comp. Physiol. Psychol. 46:* 349–352, 1953.
84. SLOCUM, CAPTAIN JOSHUA. *Sailing Alone Around the World.* Rupert Hart-Davis, London, 1948.
85. SOLOMON, P., LEIDERMAN, P. H., MENDELSON, J., and WEXLER, D. Sensory deprivation: A review. *Am. J. Psychiat. 114:* 357, 1957.
86. STRÖEBE, H. Experimentelle Untersuchungen über die degenerativen und regenerativen Vorgange bei der Heilung von Verletzungen des Ruckenmarks, nebst Bemerkungen zur Histologie der sekundaren Degeneration. *Beitr. z. path. Anat. 15:* 1894.
87. TAMAKI, K. The effects of unilateral section of the perineal nerve of the albino rat on the number of medullated fibers in the intact nerve of the opposite side. *Anat. Rec. 56:* 219, 1933.
88. THOMPSON, W. R., and HERON, W. The effects of restricting early experience on the problem-solving capacity of dogs. *Canad. J. Psychol. 8:* 17–31.
89. TORVIK, A. Transneuronal changes in the inferior olive and pontine nuclei in kittens. *J. Neuropath. & Exper. Neurol. 15:* 119, 1956.
90. VERNON, J., and HOFFMAN, J. Effects of sensory deprivation on learning rate in human beings. *Science. 123:* 1074, 1956.
91. WALTER, W. GREY. Intrinsic rhythms of the brain. In *Handbook of Physiology*. Edited by W. Fied, *et al.* Williams and Wilkins, Baltimore, 1959, Vol. 1, p. 279.
92. WARRINGTON, W. B. Further observations on the structural alterations in the cells of the spinal cord following various lesions. *J. Physiol. 25:* 462, 1899.
93. WASE, A. W., and CHRISTENSEN, J. Stumulus deprivation and phospholipid metabolism in cerebral tissue. *Arch. Gen. Psychiat. 2:* 171, 1960.
94. WEISENKRANTZ, L. Sensory deprivation and the cat's optic nervous system. *Nature. 181:* 1047, 1958.
95. WEXLER, D., MENDELSON, J. H., LEIDERMAN, P. H., and SOLOMON, P. Sensory deprivation: A technique for studying psychiatric aspects of stress. *Arch. Neurol. & Psychiat. 79:* 225, 1958.

II. SOME SPECIFIC EFFECTS OF DEAFFERENTATION ON CENTRAL AND EFFERENT NEURONS

AUSTIN H. RIESEN

The preceding section by Dr. Mendelson has presented a comprehensive review of experimentation in the active research field dealing with effects of restriction of stimulation. As a participant in some of these studies I am happy to have this opportunity to discuss a portion of the work as it relates particularly to the early development of sensory systems and neuronal structural changes. There are signs of real progress in this area. Answers to major problems promise to be forthcoming. There is much evidence accumulating that certain afferent neural processes must be activated at optimum periods in early development and at high frequencies if subsequent afferent and central functions are to proceed within normally adaptive limits. What are the growth and metabolic factors that account for this dependence upon early function?

In collaboration with Chow, Newell, Rasch, Swift, and others, I have reported some effects of prolonged visual deprivation on the retinal cells of mammals (7, 30, 31). Some of this work has been discussed in the section just preceding. The processes involved are no less fundamental than those of the incorporation of protein into the neural substrate. There is support for the conclusions of workers in several different laboratories that the fundamental nature of these processes are the same in the understimulation of the visual system as in that of sensory nuclei of the vestibular, auditory, and sensory-motor systems (4, 13, 17, 18, 23). Ribonucleic acid depletion is found to occur in acute as well as in chronic schedules of under- and overstimulation. The results of many studies combine to lead to the implication that there are optimum levels of activity for the maximum growth of neurons. The hypothalamic nucleus (supraoptic) that is sensitive to NaCl levels was stimulated by 1.5 per cent NaCl added to drinking water (12). After two months the cells of this nucleus were found to contain 80 per cent more cytoplasmic RNA and 40 per cent more nucleolar RNA than did the same cells of control rats. A comparable range of mean increases in total volumes of nucleolus, nucleus, and cytoplasm was obtained.

In addition to the long-term changes, some very rapid effects are being demonstrated. These will be discussed further below. The fact of rapid ribonucleic acid turnover in neural metabolism is a challenge to the protein histochemist and the student of behavior, working both independently and collaboratively. At the present stage of knowledge many questions must be asked about the complex molecular structures of neurons and junctures or sites of juxtaposition of neurons. Some of these must play an important part in the modification of neural activity, as well as in neural growth and metabolism. Are there common factors in transneuronal degeneration, neural atrophy of disuse, and the alteration in RNA levels with restriction of afferent input? The long-term gross result is similar for techniques which have been employed in experimentation on these three problems (8, 9, 17, 18, 21, 31). Caution is needed in suggesting that they are fundamentally similar lest we fail to study carefully the early phases of change under each condition.

Ribonucleic acid (RNA) takes a variety of molecular forms as do also its "relatives," DNA and protein. Some workers have suggested that special radicals or chains within molecules may be directly correlated with specific functions. Thus, SH-groups in the retina are reported to be influenced by stimulation and correlated in early development with the appearance of ERG components (20). Cholinesterase activity is correlated with degree of environmental complexity (28). Other investigators have been content to demonstrate the immediate effects of stimulation on nucleic acid and lipid metabolism (13, 14), or to demonstrate protein turnover at usual levels of neural activity (27).

To account for the bimodal relation between level of stimulation and uptake of labeled amino acids by nerve cells a dual metabolic process is postulated. The distinction is made by Shapot (34) in terms of a metabolism of function as opposed to a "structural" metabolism, the former taking precedence when excessive afferent demands are imposed on the neural elements. The question of glia cell participation is raised most often in connection with the source of enzymes under heavy functional demands (23, pp. 287 ff.).

Various approaches to experimental deafferentation, restriction of stimulation, and heightened neural activation can be compared in both chronic and acute animal preparations, which have included mammalian species from rodents to primates.

TRANSNEURONAL DEGENERATION

The rate and extent of transneuronal degeneration depends upon the degree to which afferent structures have been eliminated and upon the stage of growth at the time of the deafferentation. Where there is convergent innervation from several afferent sources removal of a portion of the source results in slower and less extensive atrophy to the central neural structures. This condition holds for many of the experiments performed in the studies of the spinal cord and for the visual system of some mammals (9). Maximum rates of degeneration in mature nervous systems are reported after the removal of an eye of monkeys. Specific cells of the lateral geniculate body are dependent exclusively for stimulation on optic nerve fibers from one eye in these animals (15).

The extension of degenerative changes to fibers of the visual cortex and to the stratum opticum of the superior colliculus is achieved with fetal mammals. A. Hess (21) demonstrated marked loss in these structures only four days post-enucleation for the fetal guinea pig. The effect is here more quickly apparent in fibers which are rapidly proliferating than in a count of surviving cell bodies. This is in marked contrast to the slow loss of cytoplasm, gradual reduction in Nissl material, and eventual vacuolation of cytoplasm which requires months to develop in cells of the cat or rabbit geniculate body at maturity, following the disappearance of synaptic endings of the degenerated optic nerve (9). We may perhaps interpret these variations in rate of change as expressions of variations in rates of nucleoprotein metabolism.

EFFECTS OF RESTRICTED STIMULATION

Cell Viability

The prolonged absence of sensory activity may produce chronic metabolic depletions which in the extreme result in the death of nerve cells. This effect, like the more rapid forms of transneuronal degeneration, is seen unequivocally only in experimental primates, and has thus far been demonstrated only for the visual system. Chimpanzees (7, 31) initially develop pallor of the disk which is reversible up to about seven months, and then becomes irreversible with an attendant disappearance of cells from the ganglion cell layer of the retina. The lateral geniculate body also degenerates under these conditions, although the onset of this in relation to the changes in the retina has not been accurately determined chronologically.

Further evidence for a chronic effect of understimulation is found in Brattgård's study of rabbits kept in darkness from birth to ten weeks and then given normal light for three weeks. Levels of RNA in the ganglion cells recovered variably during the three weeks, as determined by comparisons with the group of animals studied immediately after the ten weeks of darkness. Some cells showed very little recovery, whereas others developed RNA densities approaching the normal values of stimulated animals. The recovery in ganglion cells of dark-reared rats (30) was incomplete even after nine weeks of normal stimulation, given after the initial 90 days of dark-rearing.

Alterations in Fiber Size

The history of evidence for a dependence upon functional connections (and function, as such?) for growth in length and diameter of neural processes goes back to the work of Weiss, Hamburger, and others upon developing motor nerves. The proper end organ for innervation was required if the motor fibers of spinal nerves were to grow into the soma, and once innervation was achieved, functional motor end-plates were a requirement for the maintenance of the fiber size.

Hypertrophy of fibers was demonstrated in mammalian thoracic nerves which proliferated to more than normal numbers of end-plates within a given muscle after its normal complement of fibers was reduced in number by surgical intervention (11). This has tentatively been interpreted as reflecting an increase in endoplasm following supernormal metabolic demands.

For the visual system deprived of stimulation the work of Weiskrantz (35) and of Rasch, *et al.* (30) demonstrates the reduced average thickness of the inner plexiform layer of the retina, and the study by Chow *et al.* (7) the atrophy of the optic nerve fibers. Further work is needed before the exact relationship between such changes and the changes in concentration of RNA in the cell soma, both nucleolar and cytoplasmic, can be stated. It would be tempting to assume a close connection between both manifestations of the altered functional demands.

RAPID CHANGES AFTER STIMULATION

Varying the levels of stimulation effects prompt changes in chemical, electrophysiological, and behavioral properties of the nervous system. Information is available for changes at the cellular level which agrees with and complements the findings from more macroscopic measures. Visual, auditory, vestibular, and spinal sensory systems have been studied, giving generality to the support for a principle of structural plasticity underlying functional plasticity.

Biochemical and Cytochemical Evidence

In his comprehensive review of current knowledge about the morphology and biochemistry of the neuron, Hydén (23) has summarized and evaluated the evidence for metabolic turnover and for protein synthesis associated with function. He regards the studies of Geiger (13, 14) as the most direct evidence for a nucleic acid and lipid metabolism brought about by brief periods of stimulation (via the brachial plexus acting on cells of the cat's sensory-motor cortex). The RNA composition of the cortex was altered by 30 sec. of stimulation at 25 volleys/second. The question of what specific mechanism is responsible for intraneural synthesis of protein remains unanswered. Koenig (27) used radioactive methionine (S-labeled) to demonstrate rapid turnover within nerve cells of ribonucleoproteins.

With ultraviolet microspectrography and x-ray radiography Hydén's group in Sweden has been showing through a long series of studies since 1941 that increased production of RNA accompanies activity at moderate levels of stimulation. Using Einarson's gallocyanin-chromalum staining method at pH 1.64 to bind nucleic acid ions, Bech (2) reported an increased chromaphilia in the retinal ganglion cells of rabbits after one hour in daylight. Transmission through small areas of cytoplasm was reduced from mean values of 52 per cent after 24 hours in darkness to 44 per cent following light stimulation. With 400 to 800 observations this difference is highly significant. Bech (2, 3) questions the more extreme differences reported by Brattgård (4), also studying ganglion cells of rabbits but with a different technique, on the grounds that he did not hold his observations to one class of cell and did not measure enough cells. Bech's observations were all made on the large ganglion cells, 15–36 μ in diameter.

Excessive stimulation produces a depletion of RNA and proteins. A. J. Carlson (5) demonstrated a fading of Nissl's substance in bipolar and ganglion cells of birds whose eyes were "fatigued" in strong light for 24 hours. Activity in motor root cells maintained to exhaustion has been found to reduce total cell mass and the RNA fraction (16, 22). Vestibular ganglion cells and cells of Deiters' nucleus respond to intense stimulation with a loss of RNA, as opposed to an increased concentration of RNA and an increase in total dry weight following moderate rotatory stimulation (17, 18, 24). Jonasson, Kyhlstedt, and Nylén (25) obtained cell degeneration in the vestibular ganglion in guinea pigs after three weeks of rotational stimulation for four to eight hours daily using acceleration and deceleration rates of 15°/second. Cells were shrunken, pyknotic, and had misshapen nuclei. Normal cells, as seen with hematoxylin and eosin staining, were interspersed among degenerated cells.

With a radioactive tracer method Shapot (34) in collaboration with Schniack measured protein turnover in rats stimulated to exhaustion and then permitted to sleep. S^{35}-methionine incorporation was low at the end of stimulation, greatly increased during 30 minutes of sleep, reaching control values with sleep periods of more than two hours.

Electrophysiological Changes

That these structural alterations do have significance for function is indicated by some prompt changes in electrical response when stimulation is withheld and then given in specifiable amounts or durations. Notable for its demonstration that simple reflexes may be used for studies of plasticity is the paper by Eccles and McIntyre (10). They severed the dorsal roots of the seventh lumbar and first sacral nerves just distal to the dorsal ganglion. After thus interrupting sensory impulses along the root these experimenters found in 21 to 40 days a reduced synaptic efficacy which could be largely restored by brief bursts of repetitive stimulation. Stimulation by tetanic electrical volleys produced enhancement of the reflex activity both for immediately succeeding stimulation and for stimuli given three hours later. This is in contrast to the usual post-tetanic potentiation which is measured in minutes.

With newborn kittens Zetterström (36) was successful in first delaying the appearance of the β-wave of the ERG by keeping the animals in darkness. Until the age of four weeks, when dark-reared kittens began to show the β-wave even without light stimulation, only 30 flashes of light given over 20 minutes were required to induce the β-wave. Such stimulation also was sufficient to greatly increase the sulfhydryl content of the outer nuclear layer of the retina, and to some extent the other nuclear layers showed the same effect, as determined by Bennet's stain (20). In longer-term studies with kittens, up to 1 year in darkness, only 2 days in light were required to reverse an effect of poor recovery of β-wave amplitude from stimulation by flashes of high intensity (1).

CONCLUSIONS AND IMPLICATIONS

Studies reviewed here leave no doubt that functional demands play a significant part in the development and the maintenance of neural elements. The metabolism of nerve cells and glial cells is, as Hamburger (19) aptly stated, a "steady state" or equilibrium, but it is steady only within broad limits and only so long as stimulation remains "adequate," and is characterized by continuous shifts in relative amounts of metabolic constituents. These shifts reflect in a remarkably sensitive manner the level of activity that is being induced at any given time. During early growth there is the additional metabolic demand of increments to the protein mass of the cell, and undoubtedly to the increments in length and proliferations of dendrites and axons. During this phase in the life history of the neurons they are maximally dependent upon an intact and active afferent system, but such dependence is also a permanent relationship.

Just as transneuronal degeneration has been used for anatomical mapping of the visual system (8, 15, 21, 29), the RNA and protein depletion of under- and overstimulation promises to be a technique for extending the functional neuroanatomy of sensory integrating systems. Still to be accomplished within the visual system is a study of the uniocular projections of the occipital cortex in animals possessing well-developed binocular vision. The disputed question of sites of binocular interaction may soon be settled by measurements of RNA concentration in cortical visual cells. Behavioral evidence is clear on the point that different neural elements are mediating monocular input within a given hemisphere, at least until there has been a considerable history of patterned stimulation transmitted from each eye (6,

32, 33). It is to be hoped that similar deprivation studies can be devised for investigations of other senses. At this point research will be providing answers to problems of learning and perception. Theorists are recognizing implications of studies on the protein and RNA metabolism of the central neural elements for an appreciation of the structural basis of learning and memory (23, 26).

REFERENCES

1. Baxter, B. L., and Riesen, A. H. ERG of the visually deprived cat. *Science. 134:* 1626–1627, 1961.
2. Bech, K. Classification and functional changes in the basophilia of the retinal ganglion cells. *Anatomiske Skrifter. 2:* 59–73, 1955.
3. Bech, K. The basophilic substances in the retinal ganglion cells and the physiological activity changes in these cells. *Acta ophth. Suppl. 46:* 9–105, 1957.
4. Brattgård, S. O. The importance of adequate stimulation for the chemical composition of retinal ganglion cells during early postnatal development. *Acta radiol. Suppl. 96:* 1–80, 1952.
5. Carlson, A. J. Changes in the Nissl's substance of the ganglion and the bipolar cells of the retina of the Brandt Cormorant *Phalacrocorax penicillatus* during prolonged normal stimulation. *Am. J. Anatomy. 2:* 341–347, 1902–3.
6. Chow, K. L., and Nissen, H. W. Interocular transfer of learning in visually naïve and experienced infant chimpanzees. *J. Comp. Physiol. Psychol. 48:* 229–237, 1955.
7. Chow, K. L., Riesen, A. H., and Newell, F. W. Degeneration of retinal ganglion cells in infant chimpanzees reared in darkness. *J. Comp. Neurol. 107:* 27–42, 1957.
8. Clark, W. E. LeGros. The anatomy of cortical vision. *Tr. Ophth. Soc. U. Kingdom. 62:* 229–245, 1942.
9. Cook, W. H., Walker, J. H., and Barr, M. L. A cytological study of transneuronal atrophy in the cat and rabbit. *J. Comp. Neurol. 94:* 267–292, 1951.
10. Eccles, J. C., and McIntyre, A. K. The effects of disuse and activity on mammalian spinal reflexes. *J. Physiol. 121:* 492–516, 1953.
11. Edds, Mac V., Jr. Experiments on partially deneurotized nerves. *J. Exper. Zool. 112:* 29–47, 1949.

12. EDSTRÖM, J. E., and EICHNER, D. Quantitative Ribonuklein-säureuntersuchungen an den Ganglienzellen des Nucleus Supraopticus der Albino-Ratte unter experimentellen Bedingungen (Kochsalzbelastung). *Z. Zellforsch. u. mikroskop. Anat. 48:* 187–200, 1958.
13. GEIGER, A. Chemical changes accompanying activity in the brain. In *Metabolism of the Nervous System,* edited by D. Richter, pp. 245–256. Pergamon, New York–London, 1957.
14. GEIGER, A., YAMASAKI, S., and LYONS, R. Changes in nitrogenous components of brain produced by stimulation of short duration. *Am. J. Physiol. 184:* 239–243, 1956.
15. GLEES, P., and CLARK, W. E. LEGROS. The termination of optic fibers in the lateral geniculate body of the monkey. *J. Anat. 75:* 295–308, 1941.
16. GOMIRATO, G. Quantitative evaluation of the metabolic variations in the spinal motor root cells, studied by biophysical method and following adequate stimulation. *J. Neuropath. & Exper. Neurol. 13:* 359–368, 1954.
17. HAMBERGER, C. A., and HYDÉN, H. Production of nucleoproteins in the vestibular ganglion. *Acta oto-laryng.* Suppl. *75:* 53–81, 1949.
18. HAMBERGER, C. A., and HYDÉN, H. Transneuronal chemical changes in Deiters' nucleus. *Acta oto-laryng.* Suppl. *75:* 82–113, 1949.
19. HAMBURGER, V. The life history of a nerve cell. *Am. Scientist. 45:* 263–277, 1957.
20. HELLSTRÖM, B., and ZETTERSTRÖM, B. The effect of light on the manifestation of the electroretinogram and on histochemically demonstrable SH-groups in the retina. *Exper. Cell Research. 10:* 248–251, 1956.
21. HESS, A. Optic centers and pathways after eye removal in fetal guinea pigs. *J. Comp. Neurol. 109:* 91–115, 1958.
22. HYDÉN, H. Protein metabolism in the nerve cell during growth and function. *Acta physiol. Scandinav.* Suppl. 17, *6:* 3–136, 1943.
23. HYDÉN, H. The neuron. In *The Cell,* edited by J. Brachet and A. E. Mirsky, Vol. IV, pp. 215–323. Academic Press, New York, 1960.
24. HYDÉN, H., and PIGON, A. A cytophysiological study of the functional relationship between oligodendroglial cells and nerve cells of Deiters' nucleus. *J. Neurochem. 6:* 57–72, 1960.
25. JONASSON, I., KYHLSTEDT, S., and NYLÉN, C. O. Tierversuche mit beschleunigter Rotation. *Acta oto-laryngol. 28:* 327–339, 1940.

26. KATZ, J. J., and HALSTEAD, W. C. Protein organization and mental function. In *Brain and Behavior:* A Symposium, edited by W. C. Halstead. *Comp. Psychol. Monogr. 20:* No. 1 (Whole No. 103), pp. 1–38, 1950.
27. KOENIG, H. An autoradiographic study of nucleic acid and protein turnover in the mammalian neuroaxis. *J. Biophys. & Biochem. Cytology. 4:* 785–792, 1958.
28. KRECH, D., ROSENZWEIG, M. R., and BENNETT, E. L. Effects of environmental complexity and training on brain chemistry. *J. Comp. Physiol. Psychol. 53:* 509–519, 1960.
29. LINDNER, I., and UMRATH, K. Veränderungen der sehsphäre I und II in Ihrem Monokularen und Binokularen Teil nach Extirpation eines Auges beim Kaninchen. *Deutsche Zeitschriff fur Nervenheilkunde. 172:* 495–525, 1955.
30. RASCH, ELLEN, SWIFT, H., RIESEN, A. H., and CHOW, K. L. Altered structure and composition of retinal cells in dark-reared mammals. *Exper. Cell Research. 25:* 348–363, 1961.
31. RIESEN, A. H. Effects of stimulus deprivation on the development and atrophy of the visual sensory system. *Am. J. Orthopsychiat. 30:* 23–36, 1960.
32. RIESEN, A. H., KURKE, M. I., and MELLINGER, J. C. Interocular transfer of habits learned monocularly in visually naive and visually experienced cats. *J. Comp. Physiol. Psychol. 46:* 166–172, 1953.
33. RIESEN, A. H., and MELLINGER, J. C. Interocular transfer of habits in cats after alternating monocular visual experience. *J. Comp. Physiol. Psychol. 49:* 516–520, 1956.
34. SHAPOT, V. S. Brain metabolism in relation to the functional state of the central nervous system. In *Metabolism of the Nervous System,* edited by D. Richter. Pergamon Press, New York–London, 1957, pp. 257 ff.
35. WEISKRANTZ, L. Sensory deprivation and the cat's optic nervous system. *Nature. 181:* 1047–1050, 1958.
36. ZETTERSTRÖM, BIRGITTA. The effect of light on the appearance and development of the electroretinogram in new-born kittens. *Acta physiol. Scandinav. 35:* 272–279, 1955–56.

CHAPTER 7

Oscillatory Activity in the Nervous System

I. SPONTANEOUS OSCILLATORY SYSTEMS AND ALTERATIONS IN STABILITY

W. GREY WALTER

BASIC FEATURES OF SPONTANEOUS OSCILLATION

THE word "spontaneous" in the title above introduces the most bewildering of the many unsolved problems in central neurobiology. "Spontaneous" activity is a difficult concept to define since the phrase implies that the behavior of a system may depend on its own free will rather than on its previous state; such a notion, though romantically attractive, is not very susceptible to scientific study. Paradoxically, oscillations are basically in the class of phenomena which are strictly state-determined; the position and velocity of a pendulum are precisely fixed by their previous values. Some of the implications of these difficulties have been discussed elsewhere (11, 12, 13). Briefly, two inferences may be made when a state-determined system exhibits spontaneous oscillations: first, there must be some sort of reflexive, retroactive, or feedback pathway whereby two sets of variables can mutually influence one another; second, in the history of the system there must have occurred some event or events that initiated the oscillation.

These two legitimate inferences have a number of important

corollaries. An oscillatory system implies at least two variables (e.g., in the case of simple harmonic motion such as of a pendulum, position and velocity). Since these variables must interact to sustain oscillation, such a system is complex in the special sense that the parts influence one another. Such a system cannot be investigated by isolation of the components. The components whose interaction permits sustained oscillation do not determine the frequency or period of oscillation; this is fixed by the constants of the system (in the pendulum by its length and the constant of gravitation). Since a spontaneous oscillation must have been initiated by some event, it may be considered as preserving the information that the event occurred. In a very simple case the information may be equivocal. If we find a pendulum swinging we cannot tell how or by whom it was set in motion, although we can by prolonged observation of the amplitude of oscillation estimate its damping coefficient, and by extrapolation when the oscillation must have started.

There is a fairly clear distinction between simple oscillations of the pendulum or sine-wave type and those generally called relaxation oscillations. The latter require mutual interaction between variables; these may be linear processes coupled by a nonlinear operator. In this class are the filling and flushing of a cistern with an autosiphon and a "time-base" circuit as used for a cathode-ray oscilloscope. A concept of great significance for neurobiology implicit in such systems is the *threshold.* The water level or potential difference rises steadily to a certain value, at which another process is suddenly initiated in such a sense as to reverse the original change—the cistern flushes or the time-base flies back. Another important feature of relaxation oscillations is that the notion of phase-relations is much more difficult to apply than in the case of a sinusoidal oscillation. In a sine oscillation, such as that of a pendulum, one of the interacting variables, say position, is constantly and precisely 90° out of phase with the other, say velocity. That is, the velocity is of value zero when the displacement is greatest and maximum when the displacement is zero. In a relaxation oscillator the time relations are less straightforward; the rate of flow into the tank (or capacitor) may be constant while the level (or voltage) rises, and is reversed to another value as the discharge takes place.

Mathematically the level or voltage is the integral of the flow or current (the latter variables being, of course, the first derivatives of the former). The same is true of the variables in the sinusoidal case, but the time-relations of maxima and minima and zero values which are simple and regular in the sinusoidal case are less easily defined in the discontinuous linear one, particularly in the limiting case when the change-over or flyback are practically instantaneous. In these theoretical conditions the reversal of sign of the current flow rises instantly to an infinite limiting value, a paradox that cannot be treated by conventional differential calculus. Oliver Heaviside devised an operational calculus for the similar transient problems in cable conduction theory, but this is of limited practical value in neurobiological applications.

The distinction between sinusoidal and simple harmonic oscillation on the one hand and discontinuous relaxation oscillation on the other is not as academic as it may seem, since elementary excitable structures—axons and muscle fibers, for example—exhibit discharges which are mainly of the latter type—"spikes" and asymmetrical potential waves, while aggregates of interconnected excitable elements—central nervous tissue particularly—display rhythmic oscillations of astonishingly pure sinusoidal waveform. It is easy to explain why a nerve fiber should generate a relaxation oscillation, since the mechanism of nervous propagation may be considered as depending literally on the discharge and recharge of a polarized structure, quite closely analagous to a cistern and siphon. It is not so easy, however, to account rigorously for the regularity, purity, amplitude, and low frequency of central nervous system oscillations, but it is important to define this problem in considering the relation of these phenomena to abnormal states.

"Spontaneous" Oscillation in Isolated Peripheral Nerve

The typical response of a nerve axon to stimulation is, of course, the single all-or-none spike, propagated without decrement with a wake of absolute and relative refractoriness. The basis for this type of behavior is a state of passivity, but excitable structures can easily be induced to generate spontaneous activity, and this may in a sense be a more "normal" state for most tissues than the passive one cultivated in the elementary classroom. The familiar isolated frog's nerve can be made to discharge spontaneously by injury and particularly by deprivation of calcium. Such spontaneous nervous activity is associated with a reduction of the threshold to constant currents of long duration (the "rheobase"), and with a rise in the time constant of "accomodation" which is increased by removal of calcium until a point when it becomes infinite and "spontaneous" activity appears. Cowan and Walter (5) found that the quaternary ammonium salt, tetraethylammonium iodide, produced changes in nerve fibers similar to those caused by calcium deficiency and further showed that the spontaneous activity was associated with large rhythmic action potentials which tended to be synchronized in whole nerve trunks. The tendency to rhythmic synchronization was particularly marked immediately after anodal polarization, a condition in which normal nerve is relatively inexcitable. Repetitive oscillatory responses to anodal "superpolarization" occurred even before spontaneous activity appeared, and lasted for several seconds.

Observations of this sort show that there is a smooth transition from passive excitable conditions to spontaneously active ones, even in isolated nerve fibers, and there is no a priori need to postulate an extracellular circuit to account for oscillatory activity in a relaxation system. The degree to which such a system tends toward spontaneous activity can be measured in terms of excitation threshold and accomodation time-constant, for which there are quite strict analogues in mechanical, hydraulic, or electric terms.

FACTORS AFFECTING STABILITY

The stability of an excitable system includes two notions; first, the extent to which it remains passive or inactive without stimulation, and second, the constancy of the parameters of activity when stimulated or spontaneously active. A pendulum is extremely stable in both senses—it is motionless unless "stimulated," and maintains a very constant frequency and amplitude of oscillation when set in motion.

As already pointed out, the stable oscillation of a "stimulated" pendulum preserves the information that the stimulus occurred; in physiological terms it is an "after-discharge" which can or could be exploited as a simple memory device. In fact, a simple damped electric oscillation is used in an electronic analogue of conditional learning as a third-degree memory trace of significant association (12). Just as in a clock, the energy of the oscillations can be used in an escapement to regulate and direct the information-flow within the system, and in this way the memory trace can be made to modify behavior. The extreme stability of such a system provides a tag or label for the process, as the frequency or wavelength of a radio station can be used to identify its transmission.

In contrast, a simple relaxation oscillator may possess passive stability until initiated, but does not generate a series of damped oscillations when stimulated and therefore does not possess the information-storage capacity of a sinusoidal system. The chain swings long after the cistern has flushed. When "spontaneously" active, however, a relaxation oscillator can be extremely stable, particularly in amplitude, since the variations may be limited absolutely to the full range of available energy in an all-or-none fashion. As mentioned above, the relaxation oscillator depends upon momentary interaction between two processes at the limits of operation; between these limits the two processes are independent. That is, the time-constants of charge and discharge may be quite different and independently variable. The most elementary representation of a relaxation oscillator with these characters is, of course, the action potential of an axon which is all-or-none, and may show independent variations in the time-constants of the rising and falling phases. A system of this sort lends itself particularly well to transmission of information by modulation of pulse repetition rate or pulse interval, and this is in fact the mode of action in the peripheral nervous system as well as in many artificial data-processing devices.

In the simplest cases, therefore, harmonic oscillators would seem best adapted to the preservation of information and relaxation ones to its transmission. Unfortunately, in more complex systems, where several elements of either type may interact, the distinction is less clear. When several harmonic generators are intercoupled the over-all waveform of their compound oscillation may lose any semblance of sinusoidal regularity, although the pattern may be repetitive at the frequency of the slowest component (10). Similarly, an assembly of relaxation oscillators may generate an output approximating very closely to a pure sine wave. Both these effects are represented in neurobiological systems. The large rhythmic wave-and-spike transients typical of a cortical after-discharge when recorded with large electrodes are often the result of instrumental synthesis from several sinoid components. The repetitive discharges of a hyperexcitable nerve trunk, though certainly compounded of many brief action potentials, often have a smooth, slow rhythmic character quite unlike the elementary components.

These effects have caused considerable difficulty in the interpretation of central nervous electrical activity which displays mainly a wide variety of intrinsic rhythms, some of great stability and purity of waveform. These were presumed at first to be the envelopes or resultants of the more familiar axon or neuron spikes, but closer study has shown that this explanation is insufficient. Intrinsic brain rhythms are phenomena peculiar to neuronic aggregates, and must be considered in relation to the function of such structures in the central nervous system.

NEUROBIOLOGICAL RHYTHMS

The high stability of peripheral nerve fibers and their correlated tendency to respond to artificial stimulation with a single binary pulse should not distract attention from the fact that in normal conditions nerve fibers are carrying rhythmic trains of impulses at a wide range of frequencies, from about 5 to 500 p/sec. The single impulse or synchronous volley used by experimenters is an entirely artificial situation, never encountered in normal conditions. Repetitive firing of sensory nerves is, of course, ensured by the action of sense organs, and the prolonged trains of impulses in motor nerves by repetitive firing of the spinal motoneurons. The sense organs and motoneurons, though of different origin and structure, have several properties in common; for example, a spinal neuron can act as a mechano-receptor when prodded gently with a microelectrode, producing trains of impulses which decline rapidly in frequency during sustained irritation, exactly as in the adaptation of a sense organ. It is unlikely that mechanical deformation of neurons plays any part in the normal transactions within the central nervous system (though it has been suggested that neuroglial cells may be able to nudge adjacent neurons that have become inattentive). In abnormal conditions, however, mechanical disturbance in the form of trauma, edema, and tumor growth does have a marked effect on intrinsic brain rhythms, and the proven sensitivity of neurons to this modality may play a part in the initiation of pathological oscillatory discharges associated with organic brain disease.

Physical Constants in Cortical-mass Reaction

In the central nervous system, repetitive, often rhythmic, activity is the rule, even in nerve fibers which seem to resemble the typically passive structures in peripheral nerve. Artificial stimulation of central systems confirms this: a single stimulus is ineffective and meaningless. Even slowly repeated stimuli are relatively powerless to evoke a response, and it is possible to estimate the efficacy of repetitive stimulation by plotting families of excitability curves taking account of the four essential parameters: pulse amplitude (PA), pulse width (PW), pulse repetition frequency (PRF), and pulse-train duration (PTD).

Using the conventional coordinates in which pulse amplitude is the ordinate and pulse width the abscissa, a family of amplitude-width curves can be plotted with PRF as a parameter (Fig. 7-1). In the case of normal human visual cortex, stimulated by constant voltage pulses from a low-impedance (500Ω) source with chronic implanted electrodes 150 μ in diameter and 4 mm. long

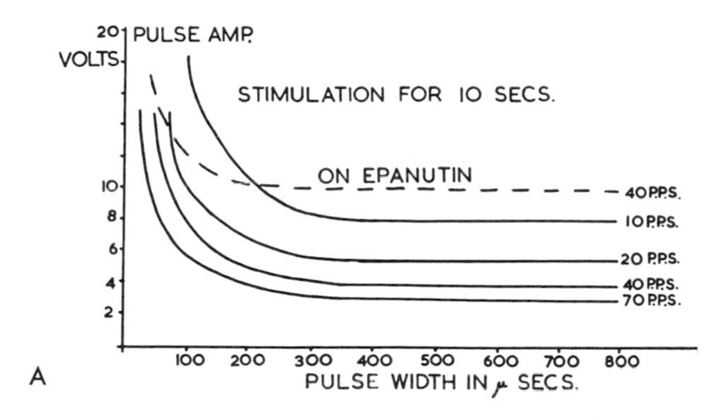

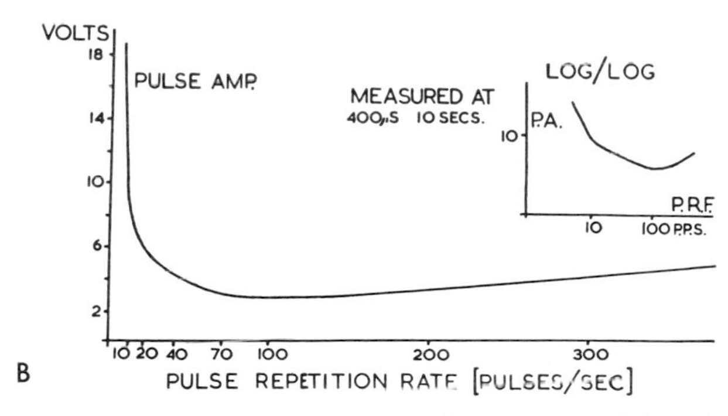

FIG. 7-1. *A*, Amplitude-duration curves showing excitability characteristics of normal human visual cortex for production of oscillatory after-discharges illustrated in later figures. *Solid lines* show variation of rheobase and chronaxie with pulse repetition frequency as a parameter. *Broken line* shows effect of diphenylhydantoin sodium (Epanutin) on excitability. *B*, Variation of rheobase with pulse repetition frequency. (*Inset*) On a double logarithmic scale the linear segment between 10 and 100 p/sec. with a negative gradient of 1:3 indicates the range of constant energy requirement.

(2 sq. mm. area) separated by 8 mm., such curves exhibit the following effects. The voltage threshold (for 800 u sec. pulses) at 70 p/s (equivalent to the rheobase) is 3 V., at 40 p/s it is 4 V., at 20 p/s 5.5 V., and at 10 p/s 8 V. The essential character of this relation is that the product of the PRF and the square of the PA (voltage) is *constant* within the stated limits. This square-law relation suggests a constant energy requirement. Now the criteria

for response used in these experiments were three; local subjective sensation (phosphenes), localized after-discharge, and sustained local rise in oxygen availability (O_2a, indicating vasodilatation caused by increased CO_2 production). The concordance of these subjective, physiological, and metabolic criteria suggests that the conditions set up in the cortical tissue by the stimuli were within the normal range—that is, they were not pathological disturbances and were relevant to the physiology of cortical responsiveness and rhythmicity.

The concordance of responsiveness and the constancy of stimulus-energy requirements are maintained between PRF limits

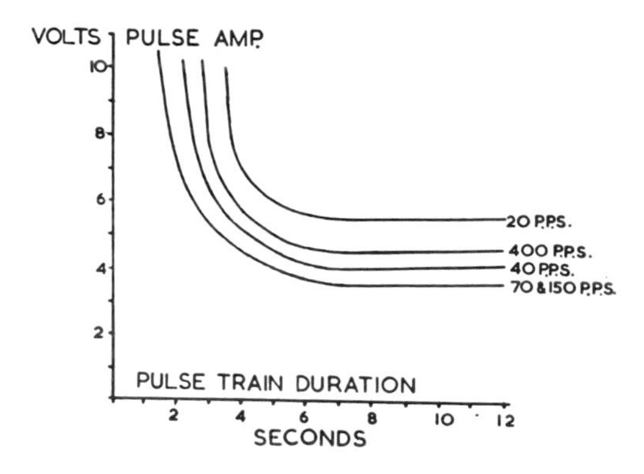

Fig. 7-2. Variation of rheobase with pulse train duration; pulse repetition frequency as parameter. In optimal conditions (70–150 p/s) the threshold for after-discharges is extremely high for pulse trains shorter than 2 sec.

of about 10 to 100 p/s. Below this range the effectiveness of an electric stimulus drops very sharply—the threshold rises from 8 to 16 V. between 10 and 8 p/s. The subjective response, also, changes at stimulus frequencies below 10 p/s; instead of clear local phosphenes there is a sensation of dark shapes, poorly defined in position and character. At frequencies above about 100 p/s the threshold rises slowly to about 5 V. at 400 p/s; the sensation remains localized, however.

The relation between pulse train duration and threshold has also been studied (Fig. 7-2). Pulse trains of about 10-sec. duration are, so to say, rheobasic, that is, longer stimulation is no more effective as judged by subjective or objective criteria. Shorter PTD's than 2 sec. are not followed by after-discharges unless the PA is doubled. The "chronaxie" of PTD is about 2 sec.

Below this duration even very large stimuli are not followed by after-discharges.

Oscillatory Cortical After-discharges to Electrical Stimulation

Whatever the parameters of the stimulus and the modality of the subjective sensation, the after-discharge maintains certain constant characters. With stimuli such as those specified above, a supraliminal stimulus (accompanied by subjective sensation) is followed by a stereotyped after-discharge which lasts from one to about 20 groups according to the stimulus strength (Fig. 7-3). The threshold for the after-discharge is higher than that for the subjective sensation, but the after-discharge itself is associated with a sensation, described as lights and shadows. This ends abruptly with cessation of the after-discharge. The waveform of the after-discharge is quite characteristic, closely resembling the "wave-and-spike" pattern associated with petit mal epilepsy in clinical electroencephalography. The frequency of the wave-and-spike after-discharge varies very little, from 2.5 to 3.5 c/s, again resembling the pathognomonic wave-and-spike patterns of the EEG. The two phenomena, though so much alike in appearance, differ in one essential respect; the after-discharge is strictly localized to a cortical region within a few millimeters of the stimulating electrode, whereas the petit mal wave-and-spike, of course, may involve almost the whole brain.

This contrast illustrates particularly clearly one of the fundamental facts about cerebral rhythms; their significance is not uniquely related to their frequency or waveform. The distribution and geometry of the oscillatory activity, that is its space-relation, are as important as its other properties. This fact has an obvious technical implication; ambiguities of interpretation can be avoided only by multiple simultaneous recording. The need for multichannel equipment has long been recognized in clinical scalp EEG where clinical interpretations must be based on analysis of compound cerebral electrograms, but direct study of cerebral electrophysiology, particularly in animals, is still often limited to one or few regions. In considering the stability of

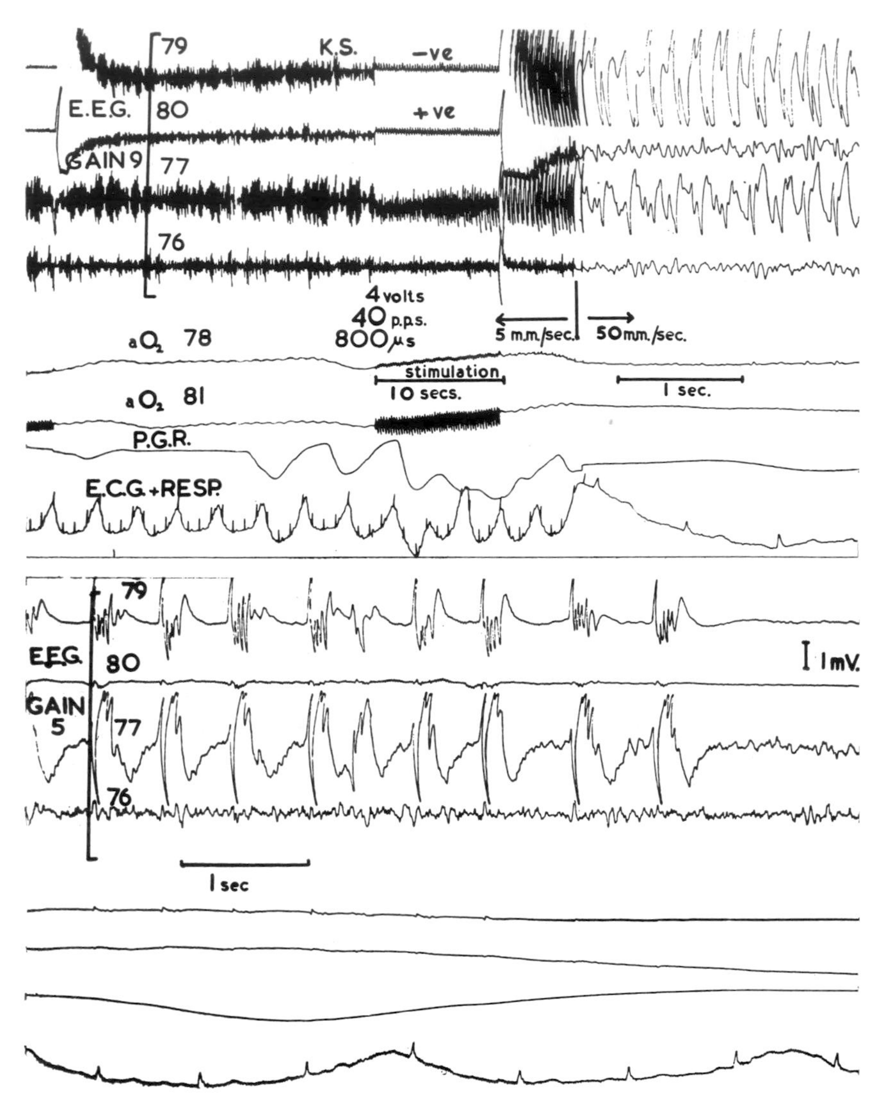

FIG. 7-3. Prolonged localized oscillatory after-discharge evoked in normal visual cortex by intracerebral electric stimulation at electrode **79.** The 2-mV. wave-spike rhythm spreads only one electrode forward (**77**) and does not disturb intrinsic activity elsewhere. It ceases abruptly without decrement. All electrocortical records are referred to average of 50 or more other electrodes.

cerebral oscillations, therefore, spatial factors must be taken into account as well as the more obvious ones of time and frequency.

The limited range, stereotyped pattern, and localized functional effects of cortical after-discharges to mild stimulation, all indicate that this phenomenon is the sign of limited retroaction in a local circuit, probably involving some hundreds or thousands of internuncial relays. Although localized, such a mechanism when activated evidently involves a major metabolic adaptation since the level of O_2a rises beyond the limit attainable by voluntary inhalation of CO_2 (Fig. 7-4). The blood vessels in the activated region dilate to an extreme degree and remain so for about one minute after an oscillatory discharge, outlasting the stimulus by only a few seconds. It seems likely that this represents a maximal (and therefore all-or-none) response of a local neuronic aggregate. The maximal response repertoire of such a system is strictly limited, practically to the one pattern, since the discharge can only be maintained if all the elements contribute fully, and this condition is achieved only by synchronous activation of the whole domain. Each domain however has its own invariant electric signature (Fig. 7-5). It is possible to estimate the size of such a self-excitatory domain by observing the extent to which an after-discharge involves adjacent regions. Electrodes 8 mm. away from an active region show almost no correlated activity (though they may display augmentation of certain intrinsic rhythms). An electrode less than 1 mm. away from a stimulated region exhibits a replica of the discharge. It seems likely that the minimum volume of sensory cortex capable of sustaining synchronous electric oscillation after stimulation is between 30 and 100 cu. mm. Sholl (8) reports that the packing density of neurons in human visual cortex is about 70,000 per cubic millimeter; so even assuming the lower limit of size, over 2 million neurons could be involved in the oscillatory mechanism of the local after-discharges described above. In an assembly with a million or so excitable elements, each furnished with elaborate axonic and dendritic appendages, the connectivity of the system must be extremely high, whatever limitations are imposed on individual neuronic interactions.

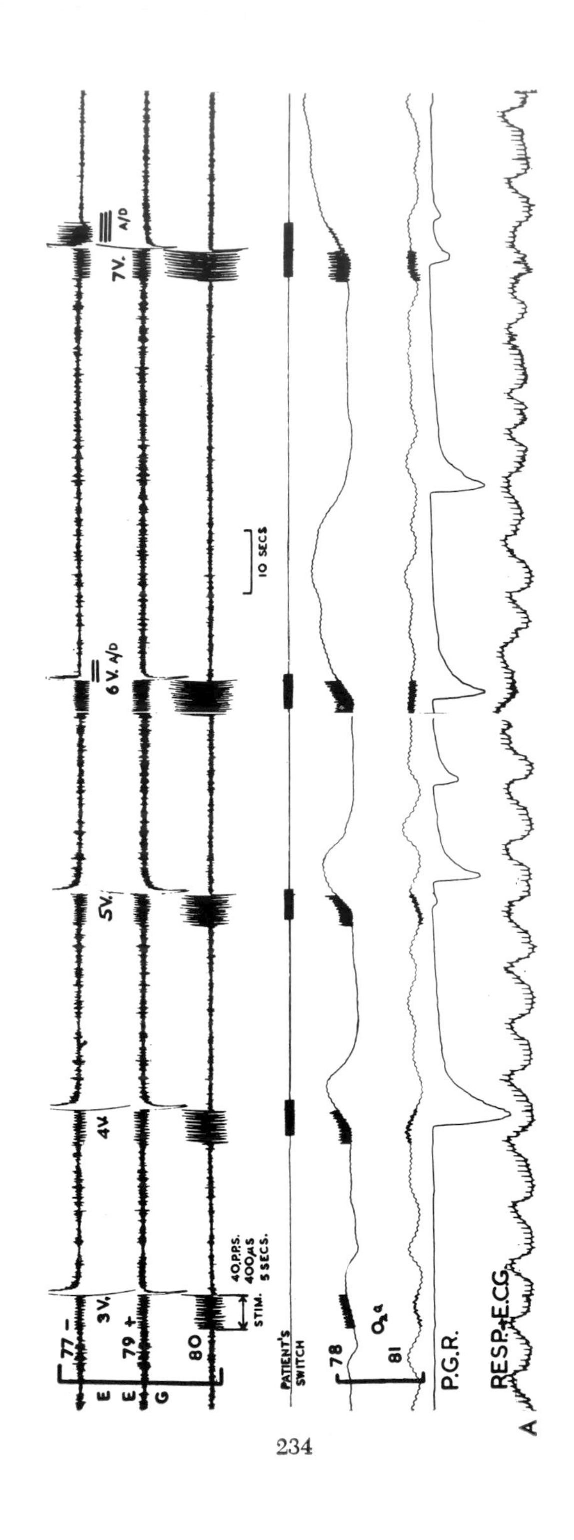

E
E
G
77 -
79 +
80
3V.
4V.
5V.
6V. A/D
7V. A/D
40 P.P.S.
400 µS
5 SECS.
STIM.
10 SECS
PATIENT'S SWITCH
78
O2 4
81
P.G.R.
RESP.+E.C.G.
A

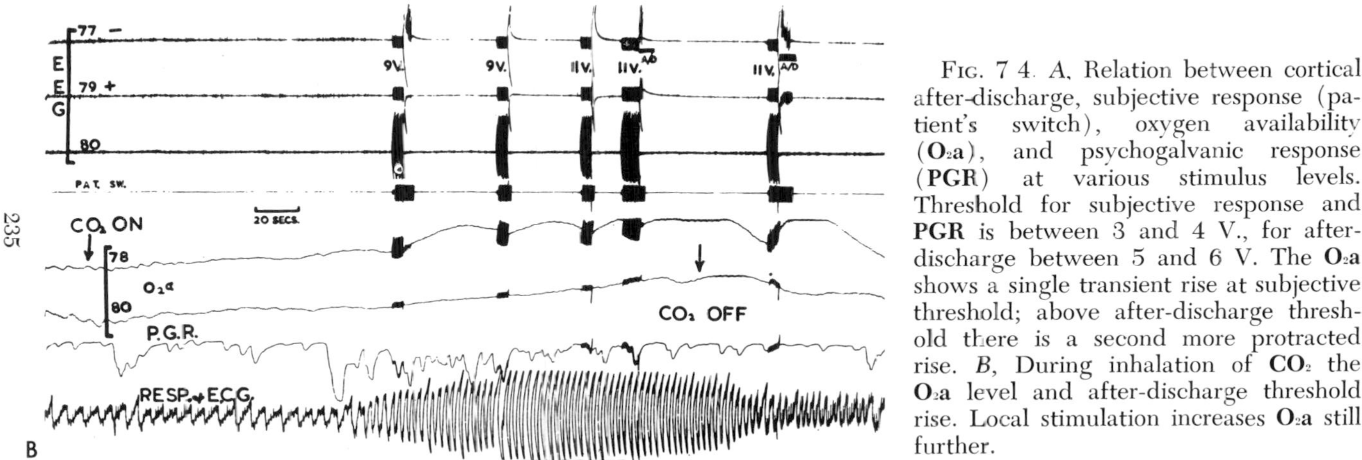

FIG. 7 4. *A*, Relation between cortical after-discharge, subjective response (patient's switch), oxygen availability (**O_2a**), and psychogalvanic response (**PGR**) at various stimulus levels. Threshold for subjective response and **PGR** is between 3 and 4 V., for after-discharge between 5 and 6 V. The **O_2a** shows a single transient rise at subjective threshold; above after-discharge threshold there is a second more protracted rise. *B*, During inhalation of **CO_2** the **O_2a** level and after-discharge threshold rise. Local stimulation increases **O_2a** still further.

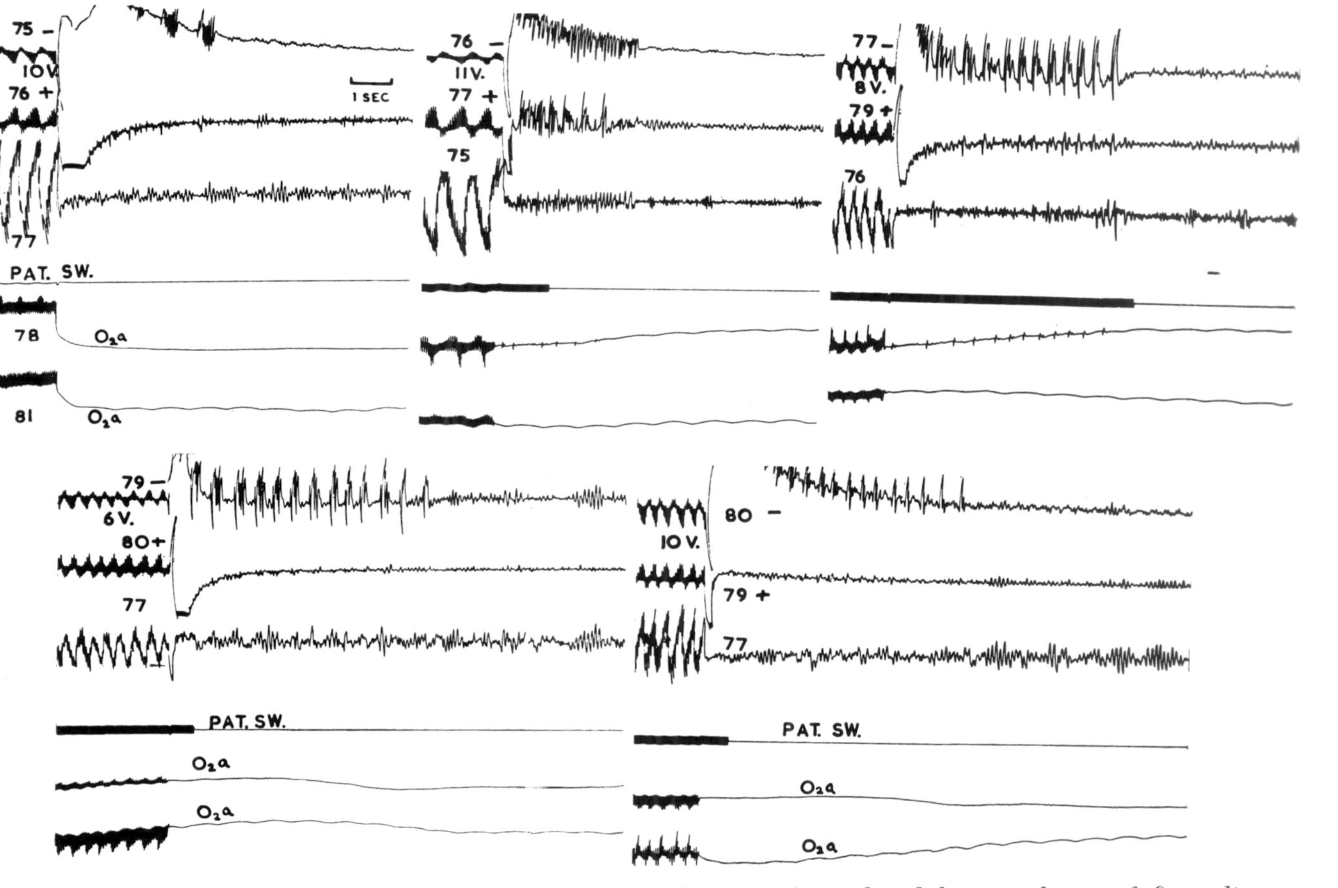

FIG. 7-5. Types of after-discharge and subjective response (**PAT.SW.**) produced by stimulation of five adjacent occipital intracerebral electrodes. The longest subjective response, outlasting the after-discharge, was from electrode **77** at 8 V. The longest after-discharge was from electrode **79** at 6 V. Oxygen availability (**O_2a**) changed only close to stimulated electrodes.

Limitation of After-discharges

That large regular persistent after-discharges can be sustained in such a system is not surprising; what is more peculiar is that the inherent stability is high enough to prevent incessant discharges. From the cell density and number alone, one might have expected all neuronic aggregates to be capable only of continuous epileptic discharges. A clue to how the likelihood of such catastrophic developments is reduced to the observed level of about 1 per cent of the human population is contained in the figures quoted above relating to the variation of threshold with PRF and PTD. At stimulus rates below about 10 per second the threshold rises rapidly—so rapidly that, in effect, impulses arriving at less than this rate are extremely unlikely to set up persistent oscillations. At higher frequencies also the threshold rises, though less steeply. The frequency range of efficient excitation is only from about 15 to 150 p/sec., about 3 octaves, and this means that, provided impulses do not arrive too often over a large region at these rates, excessive discharge is unlikely. Any mechanism, therefore, that tends to limit the frequency of excitation will have a stabilizing influence. So also will any process tending to limit the *duration* of a stimulating situation. Even stimuli of twice the threshold amplitude at the optimal frequency must be delivered for more than 2 sec. to produce an after-discharge. The main limiting factor here seems to be true duration rather than number of stimuli; for a PTD of 2 sec. the after-discharge threshold is twice as high as for 10 sec. and is the same for PRF's of 70 and 150 p/sec., although the number of stimuli is obviously more than twice as great for the latter.

The subjective response is not affected in the same way as the after-discharge by reduction of PTD. Short trains of stimuli produce brilliant phosphenes, and only two stimuli can be effective at twice the threshold intensity needed for prolonged trains.

These observations indicate how effectively central neuronic aggregates are protected against overresponse to stimulation by "noise," that is, by random uncoordinated signals, even though these may be of sufficient intensity to activate individual subsystems.

Cerebral Metabolism and Oscillatory After-discharges

As would be expected, the excitability of central nervous system structures and their tendency to spontaneous activity or rhythmic after-discharges are greatly affected by changes in metabolic state and by neurotropic drugs. The excitation-response characters of neuronic aggregates depend on propagation and retroaction through many polysynaptic internuncial relays. Even if all the elements in such a system were identical, which they are not (Sholl describes seven distinct types of neuron), the effect of any general agency would be amplified by a factor in which the number of relays is the index.

Simple metabolic changes involving oxygen and CO_2 tension have marked effects on the responsiveness of human sensory cortex, though these are often confused by indirect effects on other brain regions. For example, voluntary hyperpnea reduces the pCO_2, thereby constricting the cortical blood vessels. This vasoconstriction results in appreciable cortical hypoxia, but at the same time certain diffuse activating systems are relatively inhibited (just as the pneumotaxic centers are). The net effect is that the threshold for electrical excitation is reduced. On the other hand, when CO_2 is inhaled the cerebral blood vessels dilate and the electrical threshold is raised. In most regions of the neocortex at least, the caliber of the blood vessels is automatically adjusted through the pCO_2 so as to maintain constancy of O_2a, both systemically and locally. This homeostatic mechanism is rather sluggish, with a latency of about 2 sec. and recovery time of about 10 sec. Local transient deficits of O_2a may occur, therefore, and these may be crucial if there is a general hypoxia, either hypoxic as at high altitudes and in respiratory disease and inefficient anesthesia or ischemic as in cardiovascular or blood disorders. The sluggish response of the cerebral vasomotor system ensures at least that under normal conditions it is too heavily damped to participate in destructive oscillations, and the relation between cerebral activity and vasomotor function is an essentially

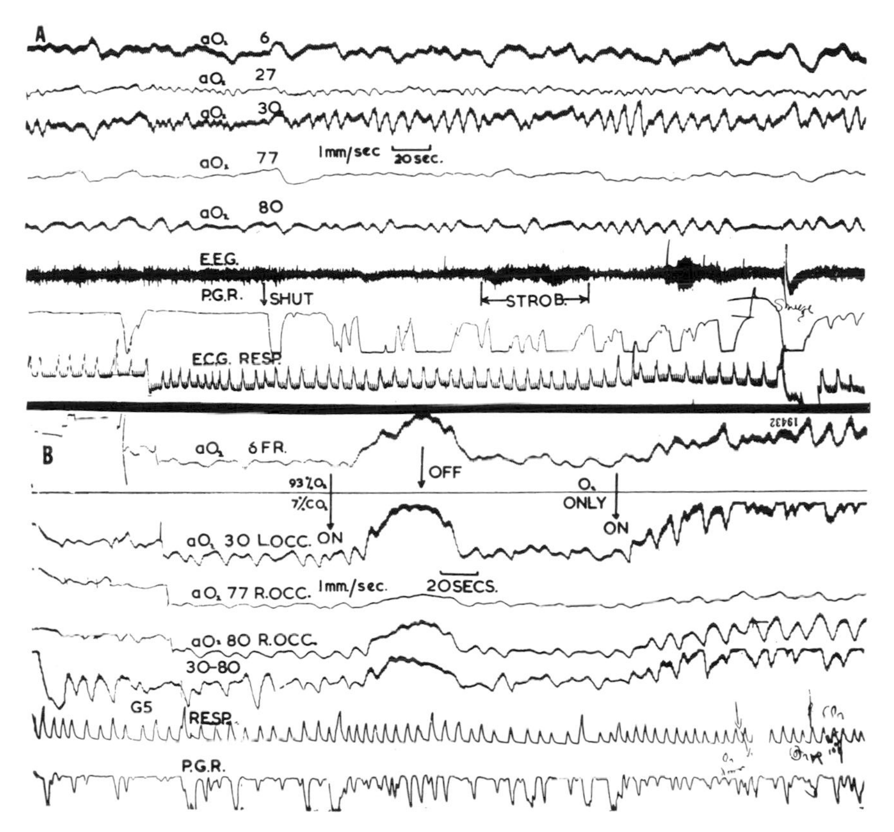

FIG. 7-6. *A*, Spontaneous oscillations of O_2a in five intracerebral regions. The amplitude and rhythmicity show marked regional variation. In occipital electrode **30**, the spontaneous rhythm is augmented by closing eyes, suppressed by photic stimulation. *B*, Rhythmic fluctuations in O_2**a** are diminished by inhalation of CO_2, promoted by O_2, though both raise O_2**a** level.

stable one. That a slight tendency to oscillate does exist is seen in records of O_2a taken with intracerebral noble metal electrodes; these usually show rhythms at about 6 per minute which are attenuated during functional activity, but these oscillations never grow to excessive size (Fig. 7-6).

The complex stability of the neurovascular interactions is, however, inadequate to deal with extreme conditions, in particular those contrived by voluntary effort as in overbreathing, or by unlikely coincidence, as in rhythmic sensory stimulation. Hyperpnea for a few minutes in normal young people evokes large slow (2–3 c/s) delta rhythms in the frontal regions, and potentiates the evolution of bilateral synchronous wave-and-spike discharges in about 20 per cent of epileptics who exhibit this pattern. Once initiated, such a discharge may continue for up to a minute and is accompanied by gross lapse of awareness—a petit mal seizure. In other patients hyperpnea may precipitate a major convulsive seizure, which of course is also self-sustaining and usually eventually self-limiting (6). Similarly, rhythmic massive visual stimulation by flicker can evoke wave-and-spike discharges in some 25 or 30 per cent of young epileptics, and similar but less persistent phenomena in about 5 per cent of normal people. This effect is most common when the rhythmic stimuli are delivered just at the moment when the subject closes his eyes.

Considering the known facts of cortical excitability and vasomotor control it is not surprising that the stability of the system is inadequate to resist the stresses of alkalosis and rhythmic stimuli. The way in which stability is restored is another matter. In the extreme case of a major convulsion it has been suggested that the marked hypoxia, due to maximal combined activity of cerebral structures and musculature with respiratory arrest, may be sufficient to terminate the oscillatory regime (6). The clinically familiar state of Todd's paralysis and other evidence of cerebral exhaustion following major seizures would support this view, but the explanation is inadequate for the abrupt cessation of physiological after-discharges or the wave-spike rhythms of petit mal which leave no impairment. Even after a wave-spike episode lasting a minute a patient may regain full functional efficiency within seconds, and a cortical region that has just been sustaining a prolonged after-discharge shows a sustained *rise* in O_2a associated with local vasodilatation, and is fully excitable as soon as this measure approaches the normal level. There is, therefore, no evidence that local hypoxia plays any part in the limitation of oscillatory states other than those associated with convulsive activity, and in fact a more likely explanation is that the level of pCO_2 (which is regulated systemically within limits by the respiratory centers and intracortically by vasomotor responsiveness) is the controlling agency.

Coherent After-effects of Sensory Stimulation

Further evidence of neurometabolic interaction is gained by study of the effects of sensory, as opposed to electrical, stimulation of the human cortex. It has already been suggested that local electrical stimuli with implanted electrodes may activate about one million cortical neurons. Maximal stimulation of the eyes will presumably activate about a similar number of nerve fibers in the optic nerves. Sholl (8) has suggested that impulses in a single primary visual fiber will be dispersed among about 5000 neurons around its terminal branches. This means, of course, that there must be considerable overlap in the projection of visual fibers since the number of neurons in human visual cortex is nothing like 5,000,000,000. A single maximal flash of light would, therefore, provide maximal excitation for about 100 msec. for a vast aggregation of neurons by a large number of interlaced pathways. As expected, the electrical response to such a stimulus is large, stereotyped, complex, protracted, and distinctive of each locality in the visual cortex (Fig. 7-7). The primary visual response is not greatly affected by attention, habituation, mental state, or metabolic variations. In certain cortical regions, however, this response is followed by a series of waves forming a characteristic rhythm which is phase-locked to the stimulus, and this component is far more variable than the primary response. It is most prominent when the subject attends to the sensory stimulus, particularly when this is delivered at random intervals and is made a signal for action as in a conditioning experiment. The phase-locked "ringing" rhythm (which by definition is very stable in frequency as well as in phase) is also augmented very markedly by inhalation of CO_2 and attenuated by voluntary hyperpnea. These responses are the reverse of those produced by changes in respiratory CO_2 on the intrinsic rhythms.

This phenomenon has been observed in scalp records by Barlow (1) and Brazier (2) in their studies of evoked responses by

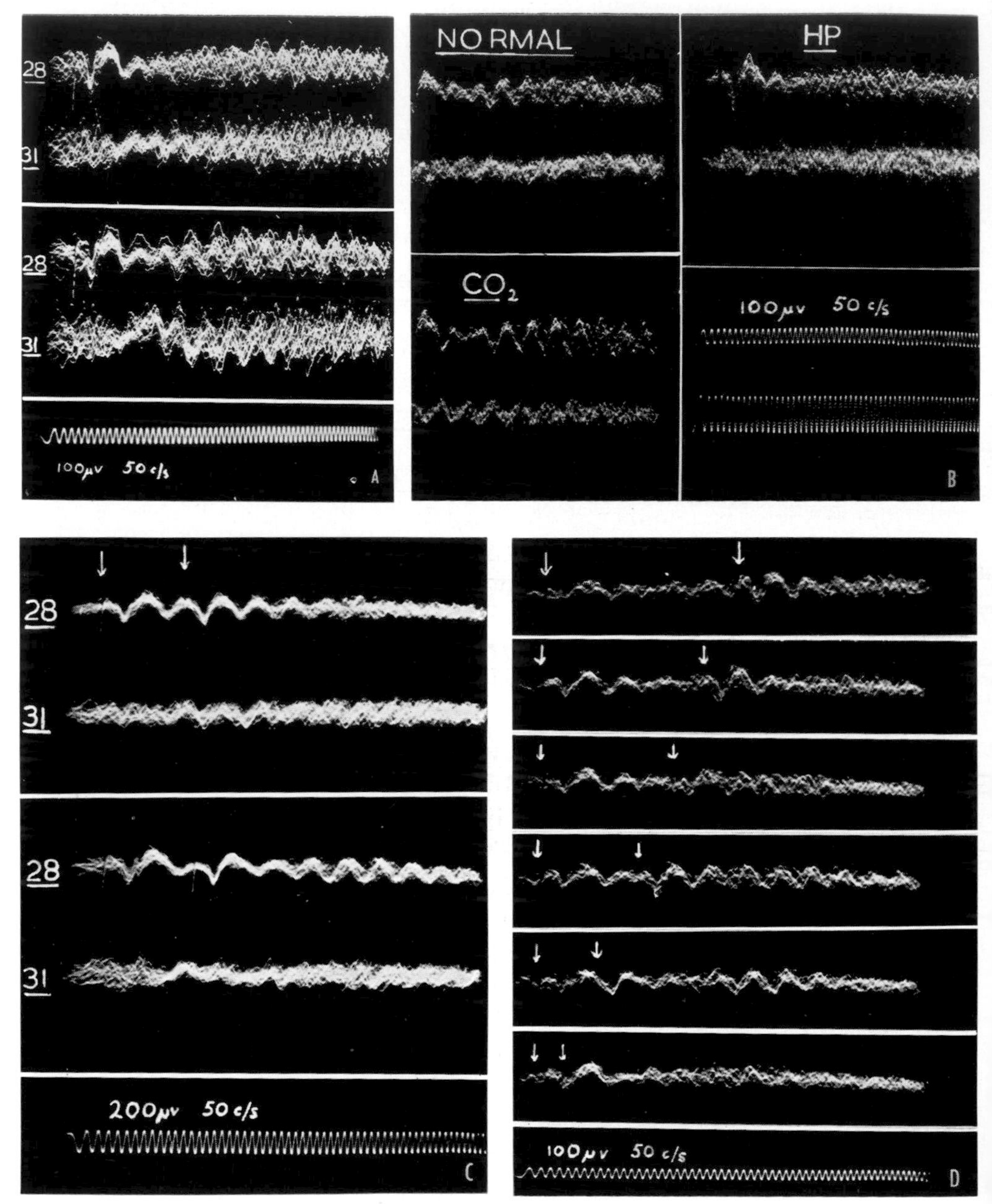

FIG. 7-7. For descriptive legend see opposite page.

auto- and crosscorrelation techniques. It should not be classified as an after-discharge in the same category as those evoked by electrical stimulation, since it obviously involves an entirely different mechanism. It is potentiated rather than suppressed by hypercapnia, and is closely related to the subjective significance of the stimulus rather than to its intensity. Furthermore, the time-relation of the ringing rhythm to the primary response is characteristic; there is usually a latency of about 300 msec. before it appears, and its phase of maximum clarity is rarely less than half a second after the primary response. The total duration of the ringing "after-thought" can be several seconds, with complete coherence of phase in any particular region. The frequency of ringing is usually within the alpha band of the person concerned, but is not necessarily that of the dominant component of the alpha rhythm, and in some people is at a quite different rate —in one case at 25 c/s. Barlow and Brazier described this effect as "pacing" of EEG rhythms, but the discrepancy in frequency between intrinsic and ringing rhythms can be so great that this seems an inadequate term. The physiological and psychological association of the phenomenon suggests that it is a true reverberatory effect, preserving information about the stimulus as a

---

FIG. 7-7. Coherent rhythmic after-effects of visual stimulation. *A*, Twenty responses to single flashes at random intervals of about 1 sec. Implanted electrodes in visual cortex 2 cm. apart. Upper pair subject inattentive; lower pair subject responding with key movement to each flash indicated by dotted signal. The coherent "ringing" between electrodes **28** and **31** is enhanced during responsive attention. The primary response is localized to electrode **28**, but the after-effect is phase-reversed between **28** and **31** (both of which are referred to the average of 67 other electrodes), indicating electrical reciprocation between these regions. After-rhythm frequency: 12.5 c/s. Note transient flattening just before start of after-rhythm. *B*, Effect of voluntary hyperpnea and inhalation of CO_2. Paired flashes at random intervals. (*Top channel*) intracerebral visual cortex; (*lower*) occipital scalp where after-rhythm is just visible in CO_2 record. *C*, Effect of regularity of stimulus. Paired flashes at 220 msec. (*Top traces*) stimuli at regular intervals of 1 sec.; (*lower*) stimuli at random intervals. Note transient "noise-suppression" at electrode **31**. *D*, Effect of stimulus separation: paired flashes at random intervals. (*Top trace*) 500 msec. between flashes; (*bottom trace*) 40 msec. The optimal separation for after-rhythm is between 150 and 250 msec.

significant event, by activation of diffuse projection mechanisms through delay circuits which can sustain an oscillation with adequate stability to avoid runaway or dispersion.

Intrinsic Spontaneous Oscillations—Alpha Rhythms

The coherent after-responses to sensory stimulation seem to form a sort of transition state between true after-discharges and intrinsic "spontaneous" oscillations. The intrinsic component most obviously related to sensory after-effects is the familiar alpha rhythm, but the definite article here is perhaps misleading. Many people exhibit no coherent alpha rhythms at all, either in scalp or depth recordings, and the complexity of alpha activity seems to increase steadily with refinements in technique. However, scalp records from some people often show extremely pure and steady rhythms; the frequency may be constant to 1 per cent over periods up to 10 sec. or more, and this frequency stability provides a delicate measure of sensory activation and mental alertness (13).

Subjects with particularly steady "monorhythmic" alpha activity usually show a slight acceleration during mental activity; the frequency may rise by about 0.5 c/s, but this effect is not constant from one region to another. Adjacent electrodes on the scalp often exhibit rhythms at frequencies differing by 0.25 to 0.5 c/s and the two hemispheres are frequently discrepant, particularly during mental effort. The more carefully the fine structure of the alpha rhythm is studied the less do these phenomena seem to implicate a central pacemaker.

People with more complex alpha rhythms show quite different effects from those whose steady component rises smoothly in frequency with activation. There are many abrupt shifts in frequency, and the trend during mental effort is sometimes downward. The regional discrepancies are even more marked, and with quite closely spaced electrodes three or more frequency domains can be discerned in toposcopic presentations, sometimes holding sway for periods of about 1 minute. The reign of any particular local component is interrupted by brief sudden shifts upward or downward, but usually one frequency is statistically more probable in any particular region over a long period. This pattern of interlaced turbulent vortices is extremely confusing to interpret, particularly with conventional bipolar derivations, and for exact studies the best arrangement seems to be to use a rather large number of electrodes with an average reference circuit embracing them all. Cooper (3) has shown that bipolar records can seriously exaggerate the phase and time differences in records of activity from sources which are not radial, symmetrical, and stationary, and there is actually ample evidence that the alpha rhythms, whether simple or complex in any particular conditions, do not appear simultaneously in all cortical regions, and emanate from neuronic generators of very variable geometry.

The sweep of alpha rhythms over the head can be plotted most easily in people with relatively pure frequencies. Cooper and Mundy-Castle (4) have found that in the majority of normal subjects the direction of sweep is predominantly anteroposterior, whereas in a group of mentally disturbed patients it tended to be in the reverse direction. Although the population studied was small (36 people), the likelihood of the association between sweep direction and mentality being accidental was less than 1 in 1000. Furthermore, successive studies of a few normal subjects have shown that the normal anteroposterior sweep may reverse in direction during periods of prolonged mental stress. The rate of sweep is usually about 2.5 meters/sec., at least when it is noticeable, but obviously very high rates of sweep would tend to go unseen, even with very refined techniques.

Although the discrepancies in frequency and phase of alpha rhythms in adjacent regions and homologous zones of the two hemispheres are too great to support the suggestion of a common pacemaker, it seems likely that subcortical relations are involved at least occasionally, both in the maintenance of stability and in the more obvious effects of sensory activation.

Assuming that, for purposes of discussion, it is meaningful to consider an alpha component as an entity in that it has metrical attributes in terms of amplitude, frequency, topology, and so forth, alpha components exhibit a remarkable degree of long-term stability. When studied by analysis of frequencies, the spectra of alpha rhythms of any particular person show little change over periods of up to 20 years, but the size of sample necessary to establish a characteristic pattern for any given person varies considerably. At one extreme 110-sec. epochs of analysis may be indistinguishable. At the other, a score of analyses must be integrated and averaged over periods of several minutes to obtain invariance between samples. Individual measures of alpha-spectrum variance are very consistent, and seem related to psychological measures of range of interests and imagination; these factors have suggested that the degree of variation in these terms may be an index of cerebral "versatility," correlated not with the ability to perform intelligence tests, but with the intrinsic repertory of dynamic cerebral states.

As would be expected from the evidence of high inherent stability, the frequencies of alpha rhythms cannot be altered very much by external agencies. Most reports of such effects are attributable to confusion of alpha rhythms with quite different phenomena. For example, the familiar effect of voluntary hyperpnea is to evoke low-frequency delta rhythms particularly in the frontal lobes. In such conditions the alpha-rhythm frequency usually remains unchanged and rarely falls more than 0.5 c/s. Some drugs can produce similar shifts. For example, administration of alcohol in tolerable social doses produces in most people a frequency drop of about 0.5 c/s associated with symptoms of mild inebriation (4). With larger doses the frequency may be depressed by 1 c/s, but in this state the subject is grossly intoxicated and usually lapses into stupor. On the other side much the same is true; activating drugs can be tolerated about to the point at which the frequency of a given alpha component has risen by 0.5 c/s (13). Above this level there are usually serious signs of agitation and distress. There are exceptions to this rule, but in general the alpha rhythms maintain their functional relations only over the range ±0.5 c/s.

This degree of stability is numerically higher than that of most other biological rhythms that are subject to environmental control. It was originally reported that alpha frequency was a function of body temperature, but this has not been confirmed. At extremes of fever and hypothermia other effects supervene, but, in the physiological range, alpha frequency seems to be stabilized against diurnal variations of $\pm 1^\circ$ C.

The relations of intrinsic alpha rhythms to sensory and motor function have been discussed in detail elsewhere (9, 13). These are elusive and certainly interfered with by other effects which are difficult to control experimentally or allow for statistically. Cooper and Mundy-Castle (3) found that when the alpha frequency of one subject was reduced by about 10 per cent during the action of alcohol his *shortest* reaction times were increased by the same factor as compared with normal performance. They suggest that the *shortest possible* reaction times for any given person may be related to an intrinsic alpha frequency or period, whereas longer reaction times are due to variations in other factors such as general vigilance or motivation.

This notion recalls the concept previously mentioned, that intrinsic rhythms, or minimal retroactive periods, may be of essential value in limiting the speed or repetition rate of action or reaction in certain parts of the nervous system. Even very large repetitive artificial stimuli cannot evoke extraordinary effects in visual cortex if they last less than 2 sec. or so, and even then must provide synchronous excitation of quite a large neuronic domain. The intrinsic alpha rhythms permeate all such domains to some extent, and if they involve only a proportion of the local neuron population, they will tend to limit the dissemination of synchronized overactivity, rather as regular inoculation of a proportion of a community against an infectious disease will prevent the development of epidemics without reducing the susceptibility of unprotected individuals.

If this concept of intrinsic rhythms as limiting or "gating" agencies is combined with the information about the time-relation of the alpha sweep, there emerges the more intricate conjectural hypothesis that these phenomena may mediate a sort of scanning process whereby the inward and outward flow of signals from any particular set of domains is regulated in a relatively orderly sequence.

The concept of cortical scansion has been thoroughly ventilated by several experimenters and theoreticians and need not be explored in detail here, but it is important to realize that the idea is an ineluctable inference from the observed effects of rhythmic fluctuations in excitability with respect to time, combined with variations in these with respect to space. Comparisons with familiar artificial scanning mechanisms—television and radar, for example—though illustrative, need not be taken too seriously, since there is ample evidence that within the brain the intrinsic and evoked rhythms, whatever their functions, are extremely complex in their interactions with signals, with one another, and with brain topology. Electronic scanners are usually arranged to operate more or less independently of the signals they display, and follow a rigid sequence so as to present in effect a Cartesian or polar diagram. There are already in use more sophisticated systems in which the velocity and even the geometry of the scanning raster is modified according to the signals emitted or received. A system designed to seek and follow a target, for example, may scan steadily in a helical pattern until a target is identified; the scansion is then interrupted, and the system is transformed into a goal-seeking device so as to hold and compute base—target topology and trajectories. Systems of this type may be more closely analogous to the intrinsic brain rhythms, since their oscillations "block" on signals, and when several are carefully synchronized they display a similar constancy of frequency at rest with desynchronization in active conditions, when each element is dealing with a different situation.

Intrinsic Oscillations—Delta Rhythms

In the early days of EEG, some confusion was caused by the assumption that all brain rhythms were identical in provenance, mechanism, and function. As soon as the clinical associations of the slower rhythms were realized, this elementary difficulty was resolved, but there is still no simple satisfactory explanation of these phenomena, which seem so similar in diverse conditions. The slow rhythms, first designated as "delta" with reference to cerebral dystrophy produced by expanding lesions, are not essentially pathognomonic; they are present in normal children, at all ages during deep sleep, and in most young people during voluntary hyperpnea. The conclusion is that there must be cerebral mechanisms capable of sustaining very slow rhythmic oscillations over very extensive regions. Study of delta rhythms with chronic implanted electrodes has confirmed this supposition and has shown that there are at least two classes of delta rhythm. One class includes the focal delta adjacent to or congruent with organic disturbance produced by mechanical or chemical lesions. Delta rhythms of this type are characteristically irregular, monophasic (that is, negative waves referred to an average reference), and polyrhythmic, suggesting superimposition of several local processes with relatively little and occasional interaction. These delta rhythms are almost certainly pathognomonic in a mature brain, but similar effects occur in normal immature brain regions, and may therefore be associated with low-functional cell density. The tendency to generate local delta rhythms is not constant in all brain regions; a given local disturbance has been found to produce dramatic and persistent delta rhythms in the frontal lobes, sporadic and transient effects in the temporal cortex, and no delta rhythms at all in parieto-occipital gray matter. Focal delta rhythm of this type is relatively unaffected by metabolic change or by mental vigilance.

The other large class of delta rhythm is synchronous in many regions, often in both hemispheres; it is monorhythmic and often as stable in frequency as the normal alpha rhythms. In striking contrast to the local polyrhythmic delta, the widespread synchronous rhythms are dramatically dependent on systemic metabolic factors; hyperpnea evokes or emphasizes them and inhalation of CO_2 suppresses even quite prominent synchronous delta rhythms. This effect has been exploited in clinical applications to expose resistant focal delta rhythms which are masked by the more widespread but responsive components (Fig. 7-8). As is well known, inhalation of CO_2 has two main effects on the nervous system—dilatation of cortical blood vessels and activation of the diffuse projection systems (which anatomically include the respiratory centers). The suppression of synchronous delta by CO_2 appears to depend on both these factors since delta rhythms

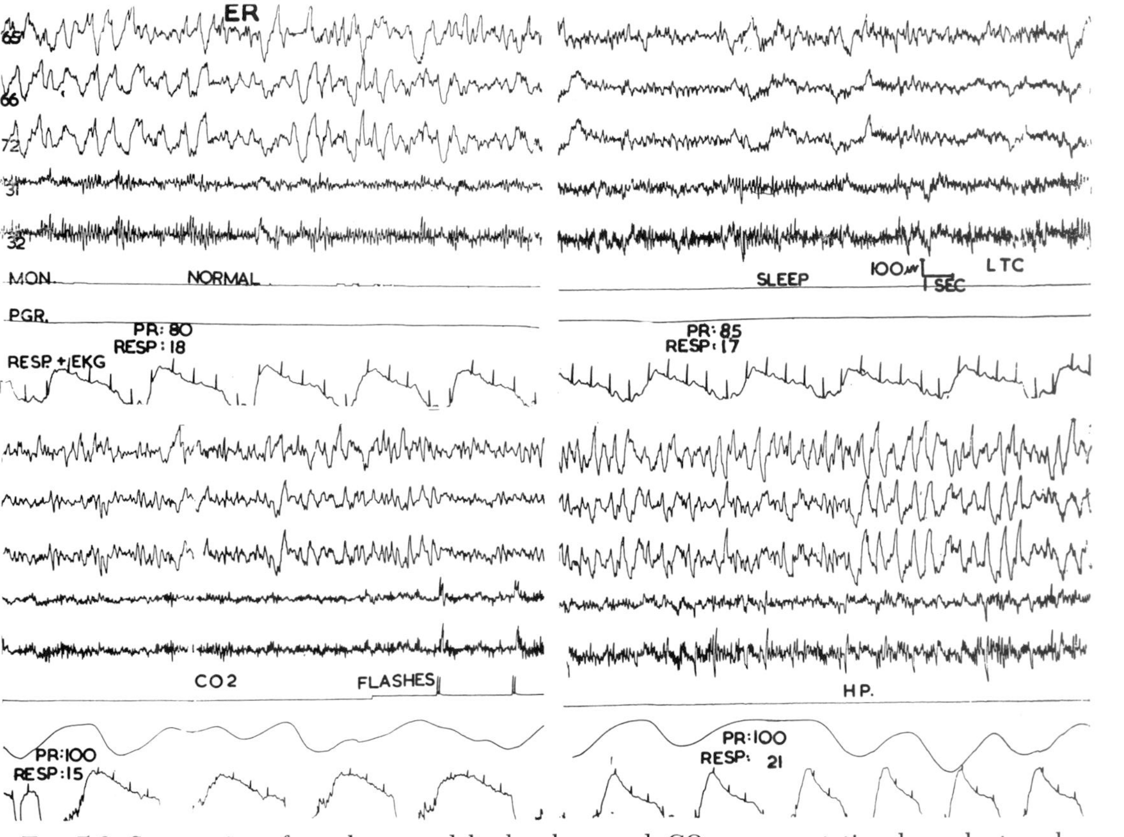

FIG. 7-8. Suppression of synchronous delta by sleep and CO_2; augmentation by voluntary hyperpnea. Intracerebral recording from implanted silver-silver chloride electrodes in right upper lateral frontal cortex (**65, 66, 72**) and right occipital visual area (**31, 32**). Delta rhythms are produced by silver intoxication only in frontal cortex. Light sleep suppresses frontal delta but slightly augments occipital slower rhythms. CO_2 diminishes frontal delta and occipital alpha but potentiates after-rhythms. Hyperpnea augments all intrinsic rhythms.

may also be attenuated in certain conditions by psychological alerting and also by provision of a high oxygen tension in the inspired air. A significant observation is that the delta rhythms of deep sleep are not affected by inhalation of CO_2, but are instantly suppressed by arousing stimuli. This shows that mere

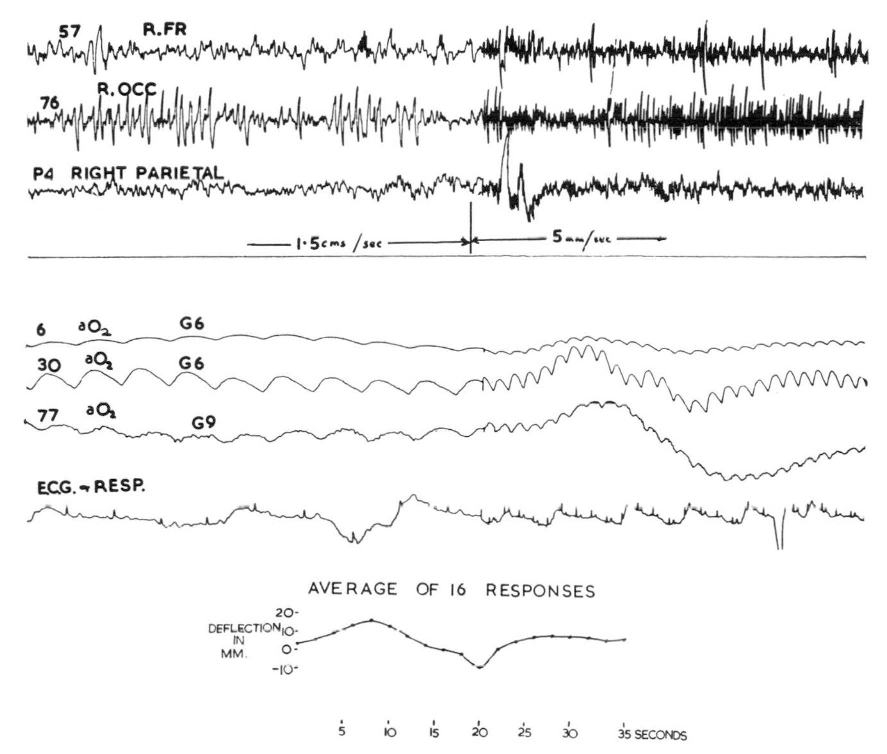

FIG. 7-9. Changes in intracerebral rhythms and oxygen tension during awakening. Arousal-activation is followed by stereotyped triphasic fluctuation in O_2a, synchronous in all regions but relatively most prominent in occipital cortex.

dilatation of cerebral blood vessels is inadequate to suppress centrally mediated delta rhythms. In accord with this conclusion, measurements of intracerebral oxygen tension show no marked change during sleep, but arousal is followed by a stereotyped triphasic fluctuation in oxygen availability as the sleeper awakens (Fig. 7-9). This metabolic sign of awakening is *preceded* by the activation-desynchronization pattern typical of EEG arousal, suggesting that both have a common cause—initiation of the alerting mechanisms of the diffuse projection systems, which seem to become less sensitive to CO_2 during sleep while retaining their sensitivity to significant combinations of sensory signals.

The association of delta rhythms with suspended or diminished function suggested many years ago that they might have a positive protective function (14), and this has been called the "phylactic hypothesis." Crucial evidence in favor of this has been obtained from chronic intracerebral recordings in cases of temporal lobe epilepsy. For example, in one patient a strictly localized delta process was discovered in the depths of the temporal lobe, and the changes in this were followed over a period of several weeks (Fig. 7-10). While anticonvulsants were exhibited the delta rhythm was regular, stable, and persistent, even during the most active sensory or mental stimulation. In this condition there were no focal spikes or paroxysmal discharges. The delta rhythm sometimes appeared, delayed by about 100 msec. in the frontal lobe, and the patient was free from clinical signs and symptoms. When the anticonvulsant medication was withdrawn, however, spikes began to appear on the positive half-cycle of the delta rhythm, which became less regular and more responsive to stimulation—even opening or closing the eyes was accompanied by brief delta suppression. As the medication wore off over a period of several days the delta rhythm became steadily less rhythmic until each wave came to resemble a "sharp wave," and the paroxysmal patterns became more frequent and widespread, culminating finally in a clinical seizure. The involvement of central as well as local mechanisms in this process is indicated by the changes seen in this patient during sleep, when also the delta rhythms were suppressed and replaced by paroxysms of "polyspikes." This effect suggests why "sleep activation" can be of value in the EEG investigation of temporal lobe epilepsies—the limiting or protective function of the local but centrally coordinated delta rhythms is suspended so that paroxysmal disturbances are permitted to influence cortical regions inaccessible during waking life.

The apparent similarity between withdrawal of anticonvulsant medication and sleep has been investigated by measuring the changes in cortical excitability to electric stimuli with implanted electrodes in normal cortex. This procedure was necessary as a preliminary to treatment in a number of patients. The only compound so far investigated to have a marked effect on cortical thresholds in clinical doses was a preparation of diphenylhydantoin sodium, which raised the subjective and after-discharge rheobase by a factor of *two- to threefold.* The after-discharges were shorter, more ragged, and less stereotyped. This dramatic effect on electric excitability threshold developed over a period of several days and persisted also for nearly a week after withdrawal of the hydantoinate. A similar time-scale of absorption and elimination has been found by chemical analyses (Schiller and Buchtal—7). In contrast barbiturate and other anticonvulsants raised the threshold only slightly and had no effect on the after-discharges. There was no change in excitability during sleep using after-discharges as criteria of response; the subjective response was so slight that the patient often slept through a series of stimulation trials. Referring to the previous discussion on the mechanism of local oscillatory after-discharges, the decrease in cortical excitability with anticonvulsants would inevitably diminish to a significant degree the number of elements within any particular domain which would be responsive to bio-electric stimulation (which, of course, has a strict maximum of available energy in terms of electric or humoral activating potential). It is perhaps significant that the dose of anticonvulsant needed to raise the electric threshold significantly was the same as that usually prescribed for the control of spontaneous major seizures; the dose which doubled the rheobase was twice the usual maintenance dose.

The inference from these and related observations is that hydantoinate anticonvulsants act directly by raising the threshold for cortical excitation, whereas those of other types influence the nonspecific projection systems so as to diminish cortical excitability indirectly through physiological mechanisms. This latter effect is not reflected in pronounced rises in local thresholds

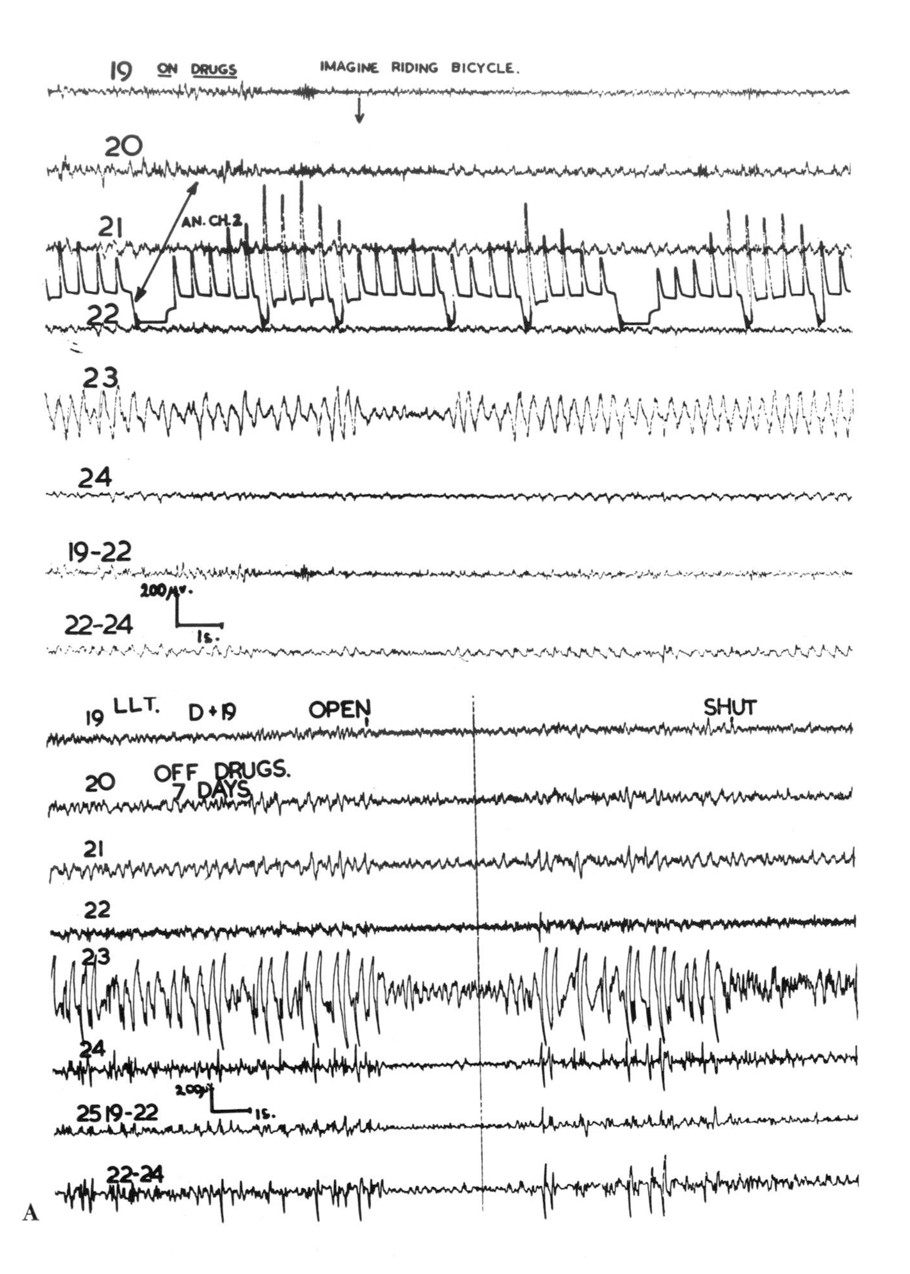
19 ON DRUGS
IMAGINE RIDING BICYCLE.
20
21
AN. CH. 2
22
23
24
19-22
200μV.
22-24
1s.
19 LLT.
D+19
OPEN
SHUT
20
OFF DRUGS.
7 DAYS
21
22
23
24
200μ
25 19-22
1s.
22-24

A

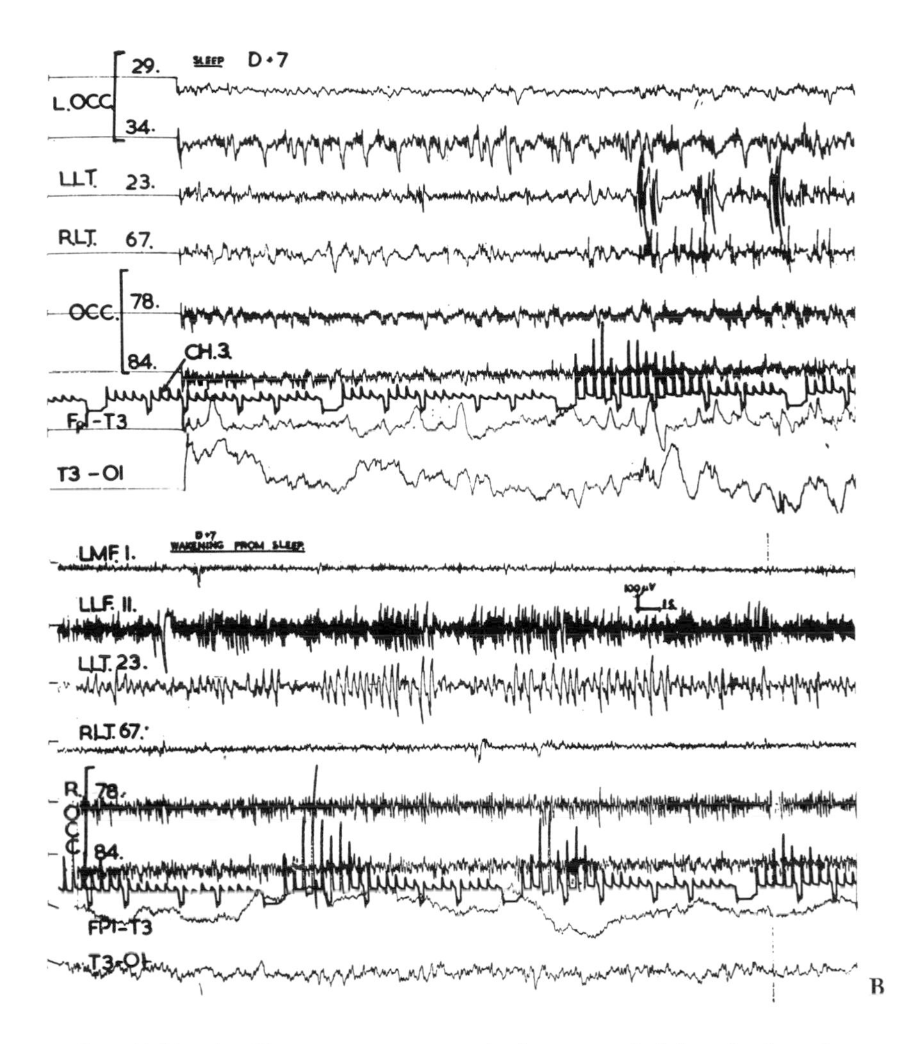

FIG. 7-10. *A*, Changes in intracerebral temporal delta rhythm during withdrawal of medication. All chronic electrodes implanted in left temporal lobe; 8 mm. between contacts, referred to average of 67 other electrodes. Under medication delta localized to single electrode, suppressed briefly by intense visual effort. Without drugs, spikes appear on positive half-cycle, rhythm becomes irregular and more responsive to changes in mental state, and "sharp-wave" components appear in adjacent regions. *B*, Replacement of focal intratemporal delta by polyspikes during sleep. Frequency analysis of sleep and waking records are similar, suggesting presence of same components but in different phase relations in the two states.

to electric stimulation since the strength of this can easily be increased to the necessary degree, and once initiated by artificial means the paroxysmal after-discharge persists even when the threshold is slightly elevated by reduction of nonspecific activation. The difference in action of the various anticonvulsants justifies the practice of prescribing these in various combinations; a dose of, say, hydantoinate sufficient to raise local cortical thresholds to a satisfactory degree in a given case may have undesirable side effects, but the quite independent action of another compound on the nonspecific projection systems can exert the adjuvant action needed to reduce to a tolerable level the probability of spontaneous seizures.

In discussing the transition from passive irritability to spontaneous activity in peripheral nerve, the relation between rheobase depression and instability was mentioned. The measurements of intracerebral excitability in normal human cortex suggest that similar, though far more complex, relations exist at the highest level, and these may be closely related to clinical manifestations of cerebral instability. Of such outward sign the epileptic seizure is the most spectacular but by no means the only condition. The induction of gross, widespread paroxysmal discharges in some normal subjects by rhythmic stimuli and the electric evocation in normal cortex of wave-spike after-discharges demonstrate that in the higher nervous system stability is a relative not an absolute concept. The relativity in this case is statistical or probabilistic rather than logical or unitary since it concerns vast populations and their interactions. The development of a clinical epileptic discharge from a localized paroxysm involves magnification by a factor of at least 1000 in terms of neuron population size. The problem of how this magnification factor is attained—and how in the clinic it may be diminished—remains a theoretical enigma, although the empirical solution by medication and surgical intervention is adequate in most cases. Evidence has been presented that in the most favorable circumstances these tactics may exploit pre-existing strategic safeguards, implicit in cerebral organization and displayed in the spontaneous oscillatory rhythms with their paradoxical relation to physiological function and philological nicety.

REFERENCES

1. Barlow, J. S. Rhythmic responses to flash and alpha activity. *EEG Clin. Neurophysiol. 12:* 317–326, 1960.
2. Brazier, M. A. B. Long persisting electrical traces in the brain of man. Moscow Colloquium on EEG of Higher Nervous Activity, October, 1958. *EEG Clin. Neurophysiol. Suppl. No. 13,* 1960.
3. Cooper, R. An ambiguity of bipolar recording. *EEG Clin. Neurophysiol. 11:* 819–820, 1959.
4. Cooper, R., and Mundy-Castle, A. C. Spatial and temporal characteristics of the alpha rhythm: a toposcopic analysis. *EEG Clin. Neurophysiol. 12:* 153–165, 1960.
5. Cowan, S. L., and Walter, W. Grey. Tetra ethyl ammonium iodide ions on nerve. *J. Physiol. 91:* 101–125, 1937.
6. Meyer, John S., and Portnoy, H. D. Post-epileptic paralysis. *Brain. 82:* 162–185, 1959.
7. Schiller, P. J., and Buchtal, F. Diphenylhydantoin and phenobarbital in serum in patients with epilepsy. *Danish M. Bull. 5:* 161–163, 1958.
8. Sholl, D. A. *The Organization of the Cerebral Cortex.* Methuen, London; Wiley, New York, 1956.
9. Short, P. L., and Walter, W. Grey. Physiological variables and stereognosis. *EEG Clin. Neurophysiol. 6:* 29–44, 1954.
10. Walter, W. Grey. Epilepsy. In *Electro-encephalography* edited by D. Hill and G. Parr. Macdonald, London, 1950.
11. Walter, W. Grey. The functions of electrical rhythms in the brain. *J. Ment. Sc. 96:* 1–31, 1950.
12. Walter, W. Grey. *The Living Brain.* Duckworth, London; Norton, New York, 1953.
13. Walter, W. Grey. Intrinsic rhythms of the brain. In *Handbook of Physiology, American Physiological Society.* Williams & Wilkins, Baltimore, 1959.
14. Walter, W. Grey. The technique and application of electroencephalography. *J. Neurol. Psychiat. 1:* 359–384, 1938.

II. NORMAL AND ABNORMAL OSCILLATORY PHENOMENA IN THE ELECTRICAL ACTIVITY OF THE BRAIN*

MARY A. B. BRAZIER

There are at least two types of oscillatory phenomena that may be disturbed in disease of the brain—one is the activity (present in the electroencephalogram of most subjects when relaxed) that, if examined by autocorrelation, is revealed as being, on the average, periodic and phase-locked with itself for an appreciable length of time; the other is the rhythmic oscillation that follows a sensory stimulus. This would appear to differ from the after-discharge which is easy to see in anesthetized animals (as Bartley and Bishop described so long ago). It is difficult to find these oscillatory phenomena in the unanesthetized animal and is also difficult to detect them in the unanalyzed tracing of man because of the competing EEG activity.

In many types of brain lesion the oscillatory phenomenon highlighted by autocorrelation will be absent in the affected region. Sometimes, however, there are more subtle situations where the electrical sign is the disturbance only of the oscillation set up by a sensory stimulus.

Although it is reasonable to suppose that the basic element in each case is the apical dendrite, there is growing evidence for regarding the periodic oscillations of the resting EEG and the periodic sensory-induced oscillation as independent phenomena

* From the Neurophysiological Laboratory of the Massachusetts General Hospital (aided by grants from the National Institute of Neurological Diseases and Blindness (B 369 Physiology), the U.S. Navy (Office of Naval Research NR 101-445), and the U.S. Air Force (Office of Scientific Research, AF-49-(639)-98); the Research Laboratory of Electronics of the Massachusetts Institute of Technology (supported in part by the U.S. Army (Signal Corps), U.S. Air Force (Office of Scientific Research, Air Research and Development Command), and the U.S. Navy [ONR]; and the Department of Neurology at the Harvard Medical School.

and therefore as providing the clinical electroencephalographer with two separate characteristics of the brain's electrical activity that may give him diagnostic leads.

In all this work my colleague, Dr. John Barlow, and I have used an automatic averaging technique which emphasizes only those potential swings that are phase-locked to the stimulus and averages out the background activity that is only randomly related to the incidence of the stimulus.

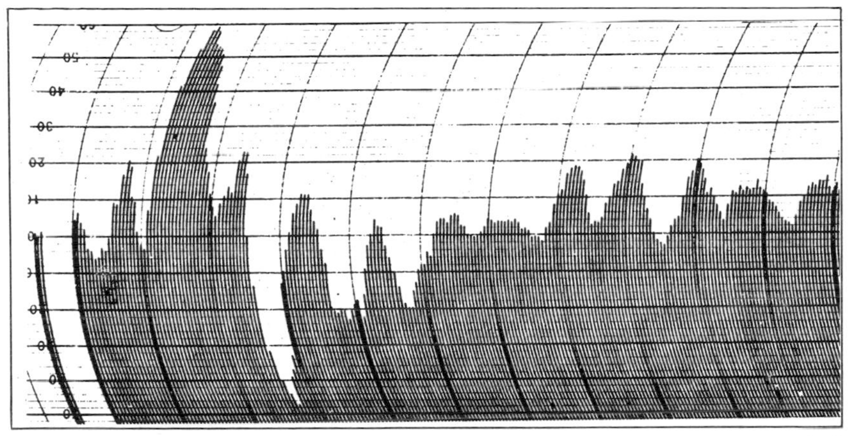

FIG. 7-11. Response to aperiodically delivered flash in man, recorded from scalp electrodes. The groups of pen deflections that stand apart at the beginning of the record are for calibration only. The pen deflections are at intervals of 5 msec., and their envelope gives the average waveform of the response. (Brazier, M. A. B. *The Electrical Activity of the Nervous System*, 2nd ed. London, Pitman; New York, Macmillan; 1960.)

First, a few generalizations: there is growing evidence that the focus of maximum activity of the sensory-induced oscillation is not necessarily the same as the focus of maximum alpha. We suspect that some oscillatory discharge is set up by all types of sensory stimulation and that its characteristics differ with the region of cortex from which it is derived. It is most readily evoked in the visual system where oscillatory behavior is so prominent in the cortex. In scalp recordings from man our electrodes are never over primary receiving cortex but are nearer to it for the visual than for the auditory system.

When the sensory-induced phenomenon is evoked in cortex

which has a strong natural rhythm (as in the case of visual cortex) its oscillations are very striking and long-lasting, but their frequency is not necessarily the same as that of the inherent alpha, and in fact there is evidence from our autocorrelation studies that both oscillatory phenomena can be going on at the same time. This suggests that different populations of neurons can occupy themselves with these two activities simultaneously.

Figure 7-11 shows a typical oscillation evoked by flash in normal man. The flash was delivered aperiodically at slow rates, with no interval between flashes of less than 1 sec. This average was computed by the Evoked Response Detector constructed at Massachusetts Institute of Technology by Barlow and Brown, and the envelope of the pen deflections gives the waveform.

It was mentioned earlier that there is evidence for some neuronal activity persisting as an alpha rhythm not paced by the flash, and this is illustrated in Figure 7-12.

The autocorrelation at the top reflects the periodic oscillation of the resting alpha rhythm in this subject. At the bottom is the average of about 70 responses evoked by flash delivered aperiodically so that the phase was reset by every flash and the flashes occurred randomly. The autocorrelation in the center strip was processed from the same strip of EEG as the evoked responses while the flash was being delivered. This shows that some independent oscillatory phenomena persisted in its own phase relations in spite of some neurons having submitted to their rhythm being reset in phase by every flash.

Figure 7-13 gives another example from another normal subject. The photically induced oscillations are found to have a different frequency from the alpha oscillations. The slight difference in frequency of the two autocorrelograms can probably be accounted for by the somewhat increased alertness of the subject while being flashed.

Figure 7-14 demonstrates the disruption that can be found in disease states that affect this system. The patient had had a cerebrovascular accident in the right hemisphere. The autocorrelogram did not detect any abnormality in the resting EEG, but the use of a flash (this time periodic at 1/sec.) revealed a normal primary response but an absent evoked oscillation.

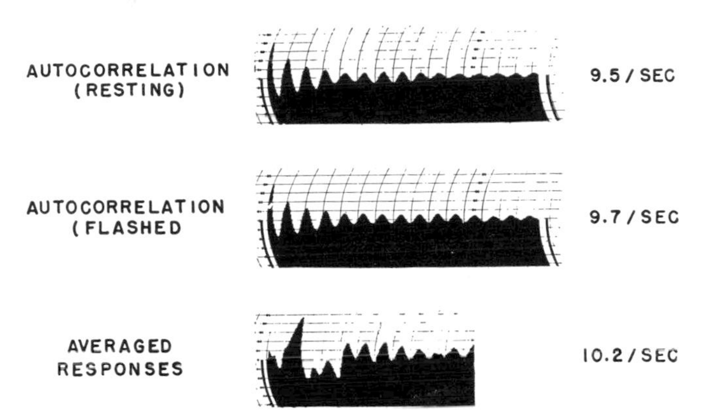

Fig. 7-12. Effect of slow random flash on frequency. *Top,* Autocorrelogram of the EEG of a normal subject at rest. *Center,* Autocorrelogram while being flashed aperiodically. *Bottom,* Averaged evoked response processed from the same strip of recording as that shown in the center correlogram. (Brazier, M. A. B. Long-persisting electrical traces in the brain of man and their possible relationship to higher nervous activity. *Proc. Colloq. on EEG and Higher Nervous Activity, Moscow, USSR. EEG Clin. Neurophysiol. Suppl. 13,* 1960.)

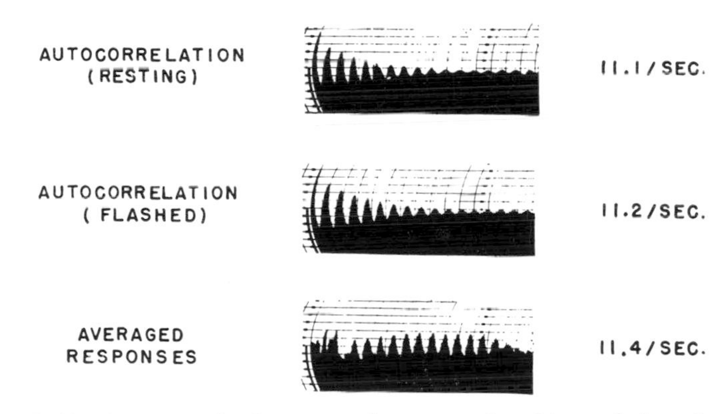

Fig. 7-13. An example from another normal subject of the phenomena described in Figure 7-12. (Brazier, M. A. B. Long-persisting electrical traces in the brain of man and their possible relationship to higher nervous activity. *Proc. Colloq. on EEG and Higher Nervous Activity, Moscow, USSR. EEG Clin. Neurophysiol. Suppl. 13,* 1960.)

Turning now to other sense modalities, one finds that regions of the cortex that do not themselves have prominent inherent rhythms (as, for example, the sensory-motor cortex in man) tend to give shorter lasting trains of oscillations, remote in frequency from those usually encountered in the normal EEG or in the photically evoked responses. Possibly they constitute a completely different phenomenon—we have not yet enough data to decide this point.

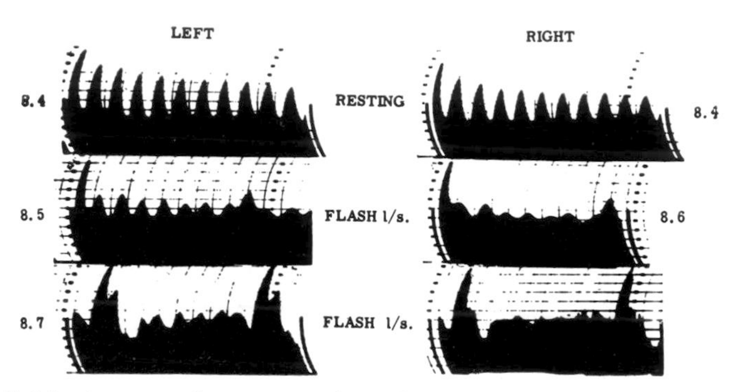

FIG. 7-14. Autocorrelograms and evoked responses in a patient with a right-sided cerebrovascular accident. *Top two records,* Autocorrelograms while at rest. *Center two records,* Autocorrelograms while being flashed. *Bottom two records,* Responses evoked by periodic flash at 1/sec. Records on the left are from the left hemisphere, those on the right from the right hemisphere.

In Figure 7-15, for example, in the upper trace is the average response at the skull over the hand area to a light tap on the index finger of a normal subject. A different computer has been used for this averaging process, the display being in the form of a single line. This is the ARC-1 computer at Massachusetts Institute of Technology. In the lower trace is the late response in the hand area (on the skull) to tapping of the contralateral foot. This is presumably not the specific response (which would be in the inaccessible leg area) but the late nonspecific response that our averaging techniques find very widely distributed over the cortex. There is, therefore, no primary response, but a suggestion of a slow oscillation that dies out after about three waves.

Finally, I would mention the response to auditory stimuli, and, in the context of this symposium on abnormal nervous activity, will illustrate by a clinical case. The auditory cortex is, of course, remote in man from any of our recording electrodes on the scalp, and indeed it seems to be in relation to the vertex response that we are most likely to find an oscillatory effect, though not a long-persisting one.

We are indebted to Dr. Louis Bakay for the opportunity to examine this patient, who was a 43-year-old woman whose presenting complaint was of attacks which were in some ways psychomotor in type, but which were characterized by her hearing "jazz music." These auditory episodes were extremely distressing to her.

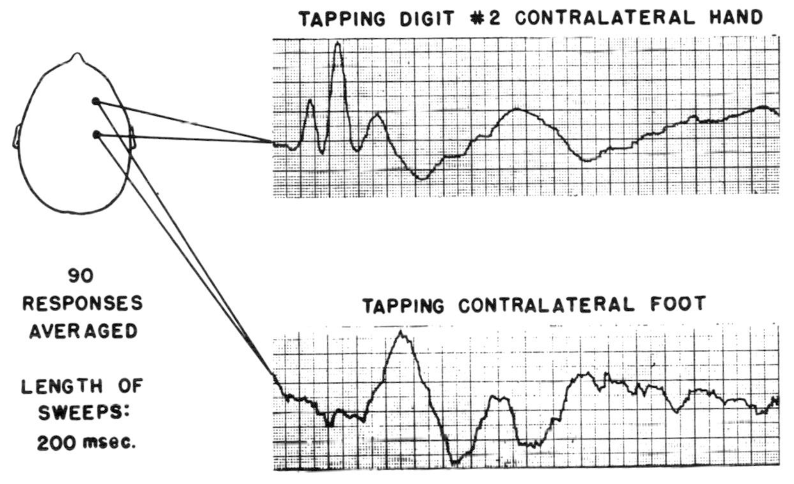

FIG. 7-15. Responses recorded by scalp electrodes over the hand area of the skull in man, evoked by light tapping of the finger and of the foot. Responses averaged by the Average Response Computer. Latencies should not be calculated from these graphs which do not include the hammer-circuit time lapse. (Storm van Leeuwen, W., and Brazier, M. A. B. Unpublished records.)

The recordings in Figure 7-16 were taken during a repetitive auditory stimulus and were then processed through the Average Response Computer in the laboratory of Communications Biophysics at Massachusetts Institute of Technology. As these are scalp recordings no electrodes were on the primary auditory receiving area, and hence no early primary responses are visible. The only striking abnormality that emerged was a difference between the two hemispheres when electrodes were linked to the vertex. There was a short train of oscillations on the right and none on the left. At surgery the patient was found to have an encapsulated cyst in the left temporal lobe.

In this case, the electrical abnormality was detected only by the disturbance of evoked vertex oscillation and not by autocorrelation. Crosscorrelation studies of the two hemispheres showed excellent symmetry between frontal cortex (which showed a beta rhythm bilaterally), the temporal regions as available to scalp electrodes, and the occipital alpha (Fig. 7-17). The

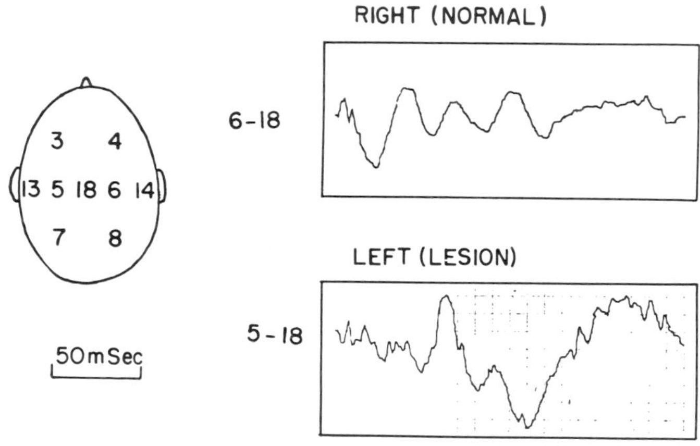

FIG. 7-16. Average response to click in a patient with a left temporal lobe cyst. Symptoms described in the text. (Brazier, M. A. B. An exploration of the electroencephalogram in terms of its statistical characteristics. In *Neural Mechanisms, Information, Theory and Behavior*. Battle Creek, Michigan, 1960).

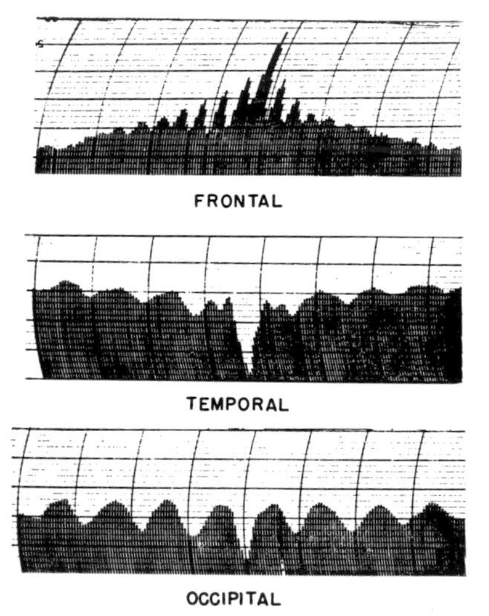

FIG. 7-17. Crosscorrelograms of homologous areas in a patient before disturbance of the cortex by surgery for removal of a cyst deep in the left temporal lobe. (Whether the direction of the center peak [at zero delay] is upward or downward is instrumentally determined and depends only on the polarity setting used.)

cyst was successfully removed by surgery, the operative manipulations causing some inevitable disturbance of cortex in the mid-temporal and anterior temporal regions. As a consequence of this disturbance, the crosscorrelations between hemispheres in the anterior part of the head now showed a lack of symmetry as shown in Figure 7-18.

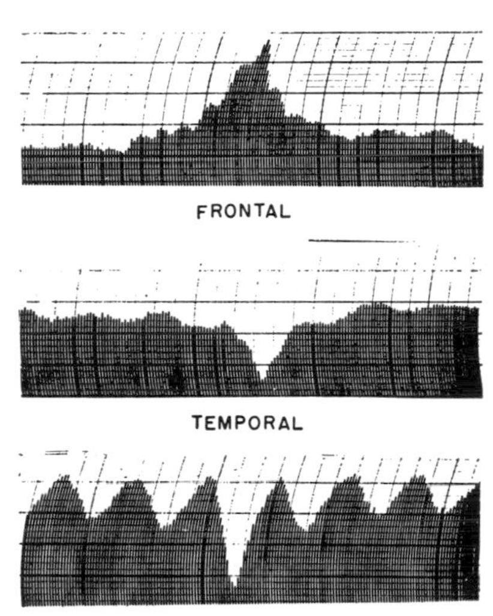

FIG. 7-18. Crosscorrelograms from the same patient three months after the cortex in the anterior left hemisphere had been disturbed for surgical removal of the cyst.

In the search for what these oscillatory responses may mean, one wonders whether they represent some further processing of the message after its initial arrival at the receiving cortex—a sign of its transfer into association areas or its transfer into storage. Such a case as has just been described suggests that here the neuronal mechanism responsible for such further processing was disordered—disordered to the extent of losing its oscillatory response to a stimulus and of producing abnormal sensations of sound in the absence of input from the peripheral auditory mechanisms.

REFERENCE

For some discussion of the various computer techniques used for the data presented in this brief note see:

BRAZIER, M. A. B. Some uses of computers in experimental neurology. *Exper. Neurol. 2:* 123–143, 1960.

CHAPTER 8

Nervous Activity in Abnormal Fluid Media

ICHIJI TASAKI

IN recent years, many neurophysiologists in this country appear to believe that the problem of nerve excitation has been completely solved and, consequently, that there is nothing we can do on this problem but elaborate the so-called sodium theory (8). For those neurophysiologists, it may seem entirely superfluous to attempt to re-examine the electrochemical basis of the existing excitation theory or to formulate an alternative theory. Nevertheless, I am convinced that one can formulate an alternative theory of nerve excitation which seems to me to be fairly reasonable (26).

This alternative theory is based partly on the study of nervous activity in abnormal fluid media, partly on the analysis of the stability of the nerve membrane, and partly on the results of our own experiments on the movement of radioisotopes across the squid axon membrane. At this time we are concerned mainly with nervous activity in abnormal fluid media.

In the following discussion, I deliberately avoid the usage of the term "equilibrium potentials." I wish to treat the nerve membrane at rest as a layer of permselective material, without substituting it with an equivalent circuit representing parallel connection of many separate batteries.

Several years ago, Scatchard and Helfferich (19) pointed out that, when an artificial membrane contains both monovalent and divalent ions, the membrane potential varies tremendously depending on whether or not the fluid on both sides of the membrane is stirred. They could reverse the membrane potential simply by stirring the fluid on one side of the membrane. Obviously, it is impossible to stir the solutions on either side of a biological membrane. It is very unlikely that the system is in equilibrium. As shall be seen later, the presence of both divalent and monovalent ions is essential in maintenance of excitability of nerve cells.

In addition to the concept of equilibrium potentials, I also avoid the conventional concept of "pumps." This is based on my belief that, when we arrive at certain levels of understanding of the processes involved, we need not employ such anthropomorphic expressions. Some time ago, Prigogine (18) mentioned the possibility that the cross-coefficients in thermodynamics of irreversible processes may account for the characteristic distribution of substances across the living cell membrane. Through the surface membrane of a living cell, there is always a constant flow of metabolites; this continuous flow of matter can, in principle, separate two similar cations, such as potassium and sodium ions across the membrane (26). Using H^+ and NH_4^+ (sometimes in combination with Ca^{++}) as metabolites and a cation exchanger as a model of the nerve membrane, we could actually separate Na^+ and K^+ by a factor of about 3:1 or more from a 1:1 mixture of these cations.

The thermodynamic consideration presented in the forthcoming article (26) is very general. It appears to me that almost any physicochemically conceivable pump mechanism can formally be considered as a kind of "interference" between the flow of one substance with the distribution of another. The necessity of metabolism for maintenance of the normal distribution of sodium and potassium is well known (17).

In this conection, I should point out the difficulty of using thermodynamics of irreversible processes for quantitative studies on membrane phenomena. In a recent paper, Karl Sollner at the National Institutes of Health (13) enumerates the difficulties involved in attempting to calculate the ion fluxes and the membrane potential in a simple system in which there are only two cations and water across an ideally permselective membrane. He concludes:

> An approach along these lines to the problem of the ratios of the electromigration across permselective membranes of coexisting species of critical ions is an undertaking of a major magnitude. This prompts us, for the time being, to stop further work in this direction.

With these introductory remarks in mind, let us start discussion of various phenomena which are known to occur in nerve fibers and cells immersed in abnormal fluid media.

EXCITATION IN SODIUM-DEFICIENT MEDIA

Almost all the excitable tissues examined so far are known to be capable of developing action potentials in sodium-deficient fluid media. A long time ago, Osterhout (16) showed that the excitable plant cell, *Nitella,* develops large action potentials in the complete absence of sodium in the medium. Fatt and Katz (5) demonstrated that the crustacean muscle fiber can develop larger action potentials when sodium in the medium was replaced with choline, tetrabutylammonium, or other quaternary ammonium ions. Lorente de Nó and his associates (11, 12) demonstrated the dispensability of sodium ions in the frog myelinated nerve fiber.

I do not wish to go into the details of these previous investigations (cf. review, 23). Instead, I want to discuss an interesting observation, made by Koketsu and his co-workers (9, 10), and confirmed by myself, on the nerve cells in the frog dorsal root ganglion.

It is possible to pierce individual nerve cells in the excised dorsal root ganglion with a hyperfine glass pipette electrode and to excite the cells by pulses of electric current sent into the cell through the electrode. The action potential elicited could be recorded by the use of the same microelectrode. When sodium chloride in the surrounding Ringer's solution was replaced with an osmotically equivalent amount of sucrose, the nerve cells immersed in this sodium-deficient solution gradually lose their

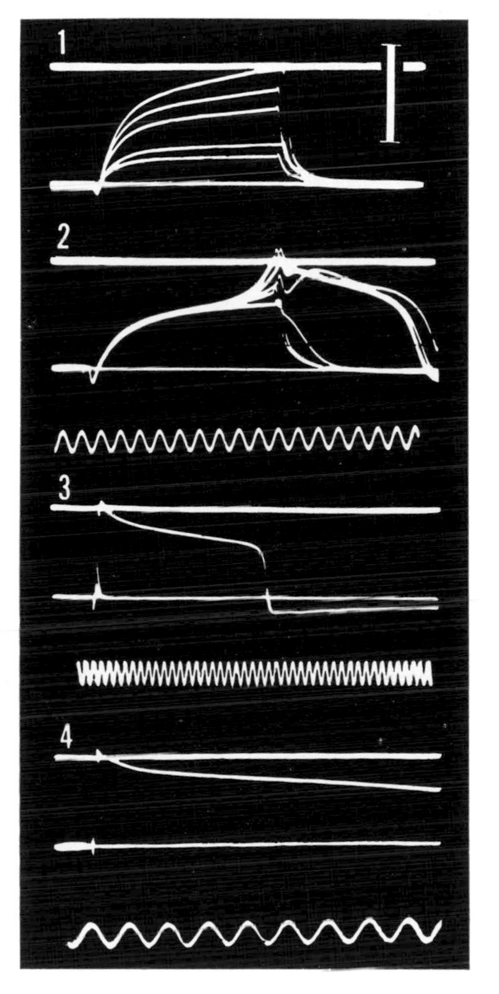

FIG. 8-1. Effect of injection of tetraethylammonium (TEA) into a cell body in the frog dorsal root ganglion immersed in sodium-free sucrose solution. Record *1*, obtained immediately after impalement, shows no response to strong depolarizing pulses; Record *2* shows responses to repeated application of outward currents through the microelectrode filled with TEA. Records *3* and *4* were taken after further injection of TEA into the same cell. Calibration, 50 mV.; 1000 cps (Records *1*–*3*) and 100 cps (Record *4*). (Koketsu *et al.*, 9.)

ability to develop distinct all-or-none action potentials. At this stage, Koketsu and his co-workers injected either tetraethylammonium (TEA) chloride (or hydrazine) into the cell electrophoretically through the microelectrode. They found that the ability of the nerve cell to develop large action potentials was restored by this procedure (Fig. 8-1).

It is obvious that the TEA or hydrazine injected into the cell cannot be assuming the role of sodium ions in the sodium theory. These chemicals were injected intracellularly; therefore, their concentration in the surrounding medium should be close to zero. Should the nerve cell membrane become permeable specifically to these ions, the potential variation would make the cell interior more negative relative to the potential of the medium. Since the action potential observed following the injection represents, as the normal action potential does, a transient rise in the intracellular potential, it is evident that there was no specific increase in the permeability to these injected ions.

Another observation on the nerve cell in the toad dorsal root ganglion (24) may further illustrate the situation we are facing in the discussion of excitation phenomena in abnormal fluid media.

When about a quarter of the sodium chloride in normal frog Ringer's solution was replaced with the osmotically equivalent amount of barium chloride, the nerve cell immersed in the medium was found to develop action potentials slightly larger in amplitude than the cells in normal Ringer's solution (up to 150 mV.). Replacement of a greater portion of sodium chloride with barium chloride brought about no further change in the amplitude of the action potential. Even when sodium chloride in Ringer's solution was completely replaced with barium chloride, the action potential remained large and showed an overshoot of more than 50 mV.

When a ganglion cell in such a sodium-deficient medium was stimulated repetitively, the action potential started to prolong (Fig. 8-2, Records *4–5*). The prolongation of the action potential on repetitive stimulation was first described in the frog nerve fiber (22) and is at present known to occur in many excitable tissues. In the ganglion cell immersed in barium-rich Ringer's solution, the extent of prolongation of the action potential was so marked that the process of repolarization was often indefinitely

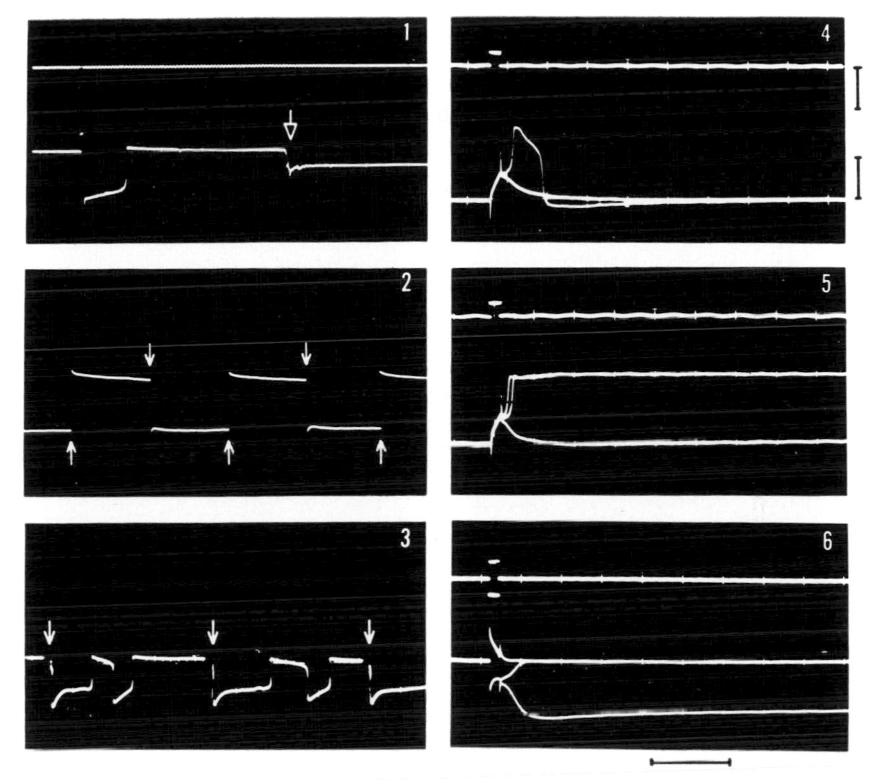

FIG. 8-2. Electric responses recorded from individual nerve cells in frog dorsal root ganglia immersed in barium (sodium-free) Ringer's solution. The lower trace shows the intracellular potential (positive-upward) recorded with a microelectrode; the calibration 50 mV., applies to all records. The *large arrow* in Record *1* indicates the moment at which the microelectrode was withdrawn from the cell. The upwardly directed *small arrows* indicate delivery of cathodal (outward) current pulses and those facing downward anodal pulses. Records *4–6* were taken from one cell; a short period of repetitive stimulation intervened between Records *4* and *5* and a period of about 5 min. between Records *5* and *6*. On each record, three sweeps (at 2-sec. intervals) were superposed. The *horizontal bar* at the bottom represents 400 msec. for Record *1*, 2 sec. for Record *2*, 1 sec. for Record *3*, and 40 msec. for Records *4–6*. Temperature 22° C. (Tasaki, 24.)

delayed (Fig. 8-2, Records *5–6*). When the recording microelectrode was suddenly withdrawn from the cell during this "indefinitely long plateau" of the action potential, a sudden fall was observed in the recorded potential (Fig. 8-2, Record *1*). If we designate this stationary potential level as the resting potential, the polarity of this resting potential is opposite to that of the ordinary nerve cell.

Under these circumstances, "action potentials of reversed polarity" were often observed (Fig. 8-2, Record *1*). When a brief *anodal* shock of the intensity above a certain critical value was delivered to the cell, the cell membrane underwent a transient hyperpolarization followed by a phase of first gradual, and finally abrupt depolarization. The entire time course of such a *hyperpolarizing action potential* looked like a mirror image of a normal, i.e., depolarizing action potential. In some cells, I could record repetitively fired hyperpolarizing responses to single anodal shocks (Fig. 8-2, Record *3*).

Now, I want to ask the following questions: Does this observation indicate that under these abnormal conditions the so-called sodium-carrier molecules are carrying barium ions? Or, is it under these circumstances more reasonable to postulate a specific barium-carrier mechanism? What is the role of such carrier mechanisms in the ganglion cell into which TEA or hydrazine was injected (Fig. 8-1)?

Some may say: "The configuration of the action potentials presented in the figure is quite abnormal showing a pronounced 'shoulder'; the mechanism of production of such an abnormal action potential may be totally unrelated to that of the normal action potential." I do not want to comment on this objection yet. I simply quote Spyropoulos' record (Fig. 8-3) demonstrating a progressive change in the configuration of the response of the toad nerve fiber (immersed in normal Ringer's solution) on repetitive stimulation. Following propagation of a large number of nerve impulses, a "normal" nerve fiber does produce prolonged action potentials with a prominent shoulder.

In addition, I refer to Koketsu's observation that injection of TEA in sodium-free medium results in an "abnormal" action

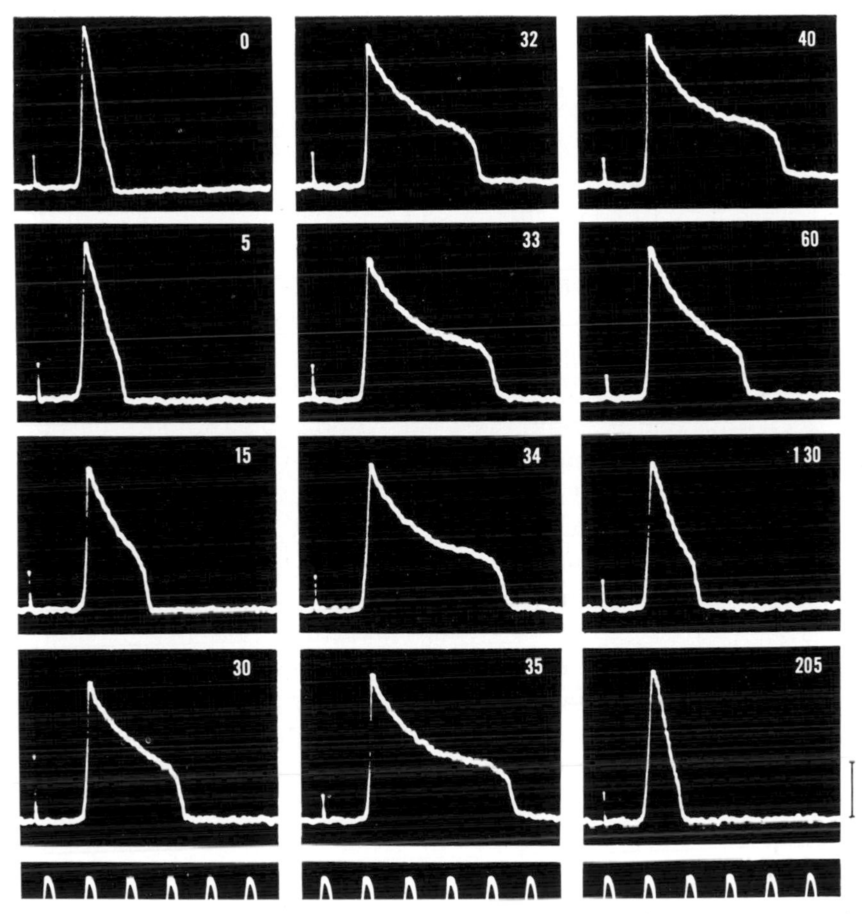

FIG. 8-3. Action current prolongation during and following 30-minutes' tetanic stimulation at 150 shocks per second. The time in minutes from the beginning of tetanization is indicated on the upper right-hand corner of each frame. Tetanization was interrupted for a few seconds when tracings were photographed. Test stimuli were delivered at 2 shocks per second. Toad motor nerve fiber. Vertical bar subtends 10^{-9} A; time 1000 cps. Temperature 22° C. (Spyropoulos, 22.)

potential, whereas injection of hydrazine yielded an action potential which shows only a slight departure from the normal.

Finally, I want to state that the configuration and other properties of these "abnormal" action potentials are very similar to those of the normal action potentials of the cardiac muscle.

EXCITABILITY IN POTASSIUM-RICH MEDIA

Since the time of Biedermann (1880) and Bernstein (1902),* it is well known that potassium salts have a special effect upon the surface membrane of the muscle and the nerve. It was believed, until quite recently, that excessive potassium ions in the medium reduced the potential difference across the surface membrane and rendered the nerve and muscle inexcitable.

In recent years, it was found that this was not the whole story about the action of excessive potassium on the nerve fiber. A nerve fiber (frog nerve fiber or squid giant axon) immersed in a potassium-rich medium does not respond to cathodal current pulses but does respond to *anodal current pulses* with an all-or-none action potential (20, 25) of the reversed polarity. When the resting membrane potential, reduced by excessive potassium, is restored by a maintained anodal current, the membrane becomes capable of developing an action potential of the normal polarity (15, 25). Quite recently, Hagiwara (personal communication) observed a similar phenomenon in fish ganglion cells immersed in potassium-rich media.

An example of the records obtained with a squid giant axon immersed in a potassium-rich medium is presented in Figure 8-4. The potassium content in the medium was increased from the normal value of the sea water in Woods Hole (9 mM.) to 100 mM. The axon was stimulated with an intracellular wire electrode, and the potential variation across the surface membrane was recorded with another wire electrode in the axon. To cathodal current pulses (flowing outward through the membrane), no response was observed (*upper row* in Fig. 8-4). But, in response to stimulating current flowing in the opposite direction, there was an "action potential of reversed polarity" accompanied by a simultaneous change in the membrane impedance. The amplitude of such hyperpolarizing responses is not affected by whether or not the sodium ions in the medium are replaced with choline.

* Cf. R. Höber: Physikalische Chemie der Zelle und der Gewebe, Verlang von W. Engelmann, 1926, Chap. 12.

One might immediately realize that there is one thing in common between the hyperpolarizing response in the nerve cell in the barium-rich medium (Fig. 8-2) and the response in potassium-rich medium (Fig. 8-4). In both cases, hyperpolarizing responses appear when the membrane is in the depolarized state. This comparison suggests that the nerve fiber in a potassium-rich medium may represent a state in which the membrane potential

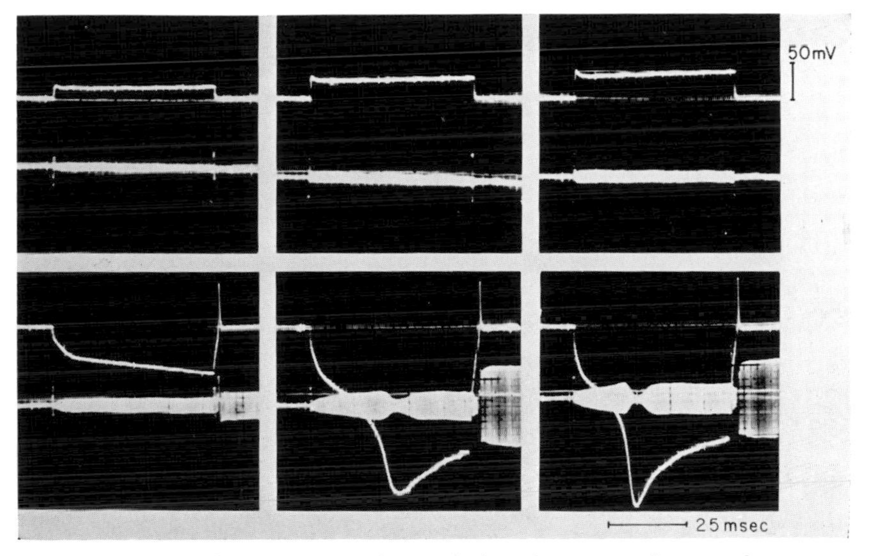

FIG. 8-4. Simultaneous recording of the change in the membrane impedance (*lower trace*) and the membrane potential (*upper trace*) obtained from a squid giant axon immersed in a mixture of one part of isosmotic potassium chloride solution and approximately four parts of normal sea water. (For the detail of the technique, cf. 25.)

is arrested at the level of the shoulder without undergoing a sudden repolarization.

Figure 8-5, taken from Spyropoulos' paper (22), shows that this is actually the case. In this experiment, a node of Ranvier of the toad nerve fiber was subjected to a sudden rise in the potassium-ion concentration during activity. Using a glass pipette of about 10 μ in diameter, a small volume (approximately 0.3 $mm.^3$) of a potassium-rich solution was ejected toward the exposed node while the node was developing a prolonged action potential. The ejection was done electromechanically by the use of barium titanate whose volume varied with the voltage applied. It is seen in Figure 8-5 that the step of repolarization was com-

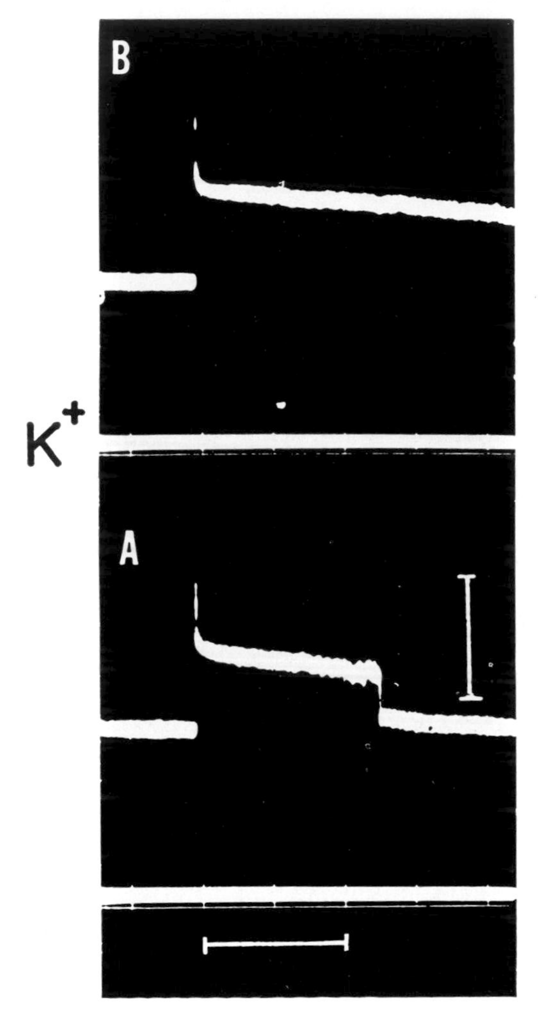

Fig. 8-5. Effect of a small amount of potassium-rich solution ejected toward a node of Ranvier during the plateau of the electric response. The voltage pulse applied to the capadyne was 5 msec. in duration. Calibrations 1 sec. and 3×10^{-9} A. Temperature 23° C. (Spyropoulos, 21.)

pletely prevented by a sudden rise in the potassium concentration in the medium.

The nerve membrane in potassium-rich media is, so to speak, in a "permanently active state" or, to use our own terminology, in the upper stable state. In response to anodal current pulses, the membrane is capable of undergoing a transition to the lower stable state (namely to the normal resting state) in an all-or-none manner. This transition is what we call "generation of a hyperpolarizing response."

PERMEABILITY OF NERVE MEMBRANE TO POTASSIUM AND SODIUM IONS

It is generally assumed that the nerve membrane is far more permeable to potassium ions than to sodium ions in the resting state. Two lines of evidence have been advanced in support of this view; one is based on potential measurements in potassium-rich media, and the other on the determination of the movements of radioactive tracers across the nerve membrane.

It is well known that the resting potential of the nerve fiber is insensitive to a variation of the potassium concentration in normal Ringer's solution or in normal sea water unless the concentration is raised above a certain level. In case of the toad nerve fiber, the external potassium concentration $[K]_o$ has to be raised from the normal level in Ringer's solution (2 mM.) up to 15–25 mM. in order to reach the range where there is a linear relationship between log $[K]_o$ and the membrane potential. A surprising fact is that $[K]_o$ has to be in this range too in order to demonstrate excitability to anodal currents and inexcitability to cathodal currents. In the squid axon also, the relation between log $[K]_o$ and the resting potential becomes linear only when $[K]_o$ is high enough to make the axon excitable to anodal currents.

Thus, it seems obvious to me that the results of potential measurements do not support the assumption of high potassium permeability of the resting nerve membrane. Instead, they indicate that the nerve membrane in the active state (in the stationary level of the upper stable state) is highly permeable to potassium ions.

Then, do the experiments with radioisotopes of sodium and potassium ions prove that the surface of the resting normal nerve fiber has a high permeability specifically to potassium ions?

Figure 8-6 shows the results of our recent measurements of the effluxes of the radioactive sodium and potassium ions injected into a squid giant axon (27). Following injection of a mixture of the tagged ions Na* and K*, the axon was transferred into a bath of normal sea water and the amount of Na* and K* appearing in the sea water was analyzed by the method of gamma-spectrometry. The effluxes of the radioisotopes were expressed in percentage of the amounts present in the axoplasm.

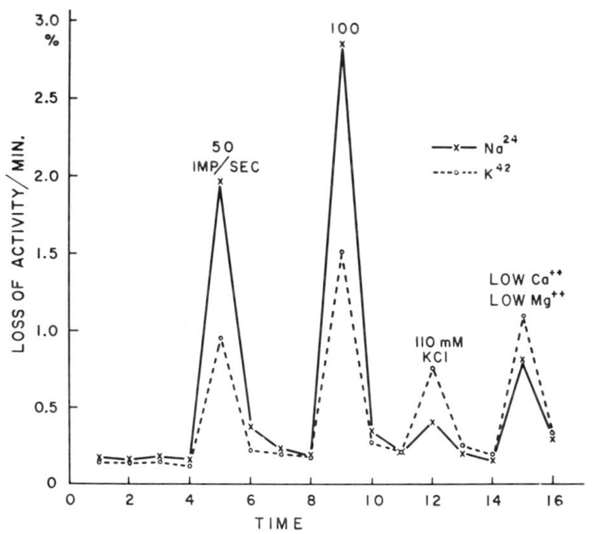

FIG. 8-6. Effects of repetitive stimulation, depolarization by sea water containing 110 mM. potassium chloride, and of sea water containing no divalent ions upon the efflux of radioactive sodium and potassium ions through squid axon membrane. The fiber diameter was approximately 500 μ. The unit of time, 5 min. (Tasaki *et al.*, 27.)

The amount of K* that leaves the axon in one minute is of the order of 0.2 per cent of the amount of K* present in the axon at that moment. The corresponding figure for Na* was 1.5–2.5 times as great as that for K*. When the axon was stimulated at a frequency of 50 or 100 impulses/second, there was a marked increase in the effluxes. When the normal sea water around the axon was replaced with a potassium-rich medium or with a calcium-free, magnesium-free medium, there was also a pronounced increase in the effluxes, the efflux of K* being higher than that of Na* in this case.

The enhanced efflux of K* in potassium-rich media can be taken as an indication of the high potassium permeability in this state; this is borne out also by the results of potential measurements. There is no absolute specificity to potassium ions under these conditions; the efflux of Na* is also enhanced by maintained depolarization.

The enhancement of the effluxes of Na* and K* during activity can be regarded as the reflection of the increased permeability to these ions. Again, the difference between K* and Na* is rather small. It is impossible for me to conclude from these data that the nerve membrane at rest is permeable specifically to potassium ions.

Some people assume that Na* is carried through the resting membrane by a special pump mechanism and the efflux of Na* observed does not reflect a high sodium permeability. If this be the case, does the alleged pump work more when the nerve is stimulated repetitively? In potassium-rich media or in media with low concentrations of divalent ions, is the efficiency of the sodium pump greater than at rest?

If we regard the process mentioned in the opening pages of this chapter as the mechanism of separation of sodium and potassium ions by the nerve membrane, the movement of Na* across the resting nerve membrane (Fig 8-6) is a reflection of a high sodium permeability in the resting state. Our measurement of the influxes of tagged sodium and potassium supports this view also.

In conclusion, neither potential measurements nor tracer experiments give direct support to the generally accepted view that the resting nerve membrane is highly permeable to potassium ions but not to sodium ions. Instead these experiments suggest that the selectivity of the nerve membrane between sodium and potassium is not very high.

FIXED NEGATIVE CHARGE IN NERVE MEMBRANE

It has been suggested that the nerve membrane may be permeable to chloride and that the resting potential may be maintained partly by this negatively charged ion. Quite recently, we tested this point by the use of radioactive chloride (Cl^{36}). We found (21) that the efflux per minute of the tagged chloride injected into the squid giant axon is about 0.03 per cent or less of the amount of the tagged chloride in the axoplasm; this is only about one-tenth or less of the value for tagged potassium. We found also that Br, sulfate and phosphate ions move very slowly through the resting membrane. Furthermore, repetitive stimulation did not increase the fluxes of these negatively charged tracers.

Based on these findings, we postulate that the nerve membrane has a fixed negative charge, as was suggested a long time ago by Michaelis (14) and by Teorell (28). During activity, the nerve membrane undergoes a marked increase in cation permeability with the anion permeability remaining low. Hence, the nerve membrane is considered to remain negatively charged during activity.

It appears reasonable to relate the fixed negative charge to the existence of lipid substances in the membrane. It is known, for example, that cephalin reversibly combines with calcium, sodium, and potassium but not with chloride (1, 2, 4).

The postulate of the existence of a fixed negative charge in the membrane opens up a new and wide domain of speculation as to the mechanism of nerve excitation.

It is expected that in a membrane with a fixed negative charge various divalent cations compete with monovalent cations for the negative sites. Using a cation-exchange membrane, Gregor and Wetstone (6) and Coleman (3) investigated the related problems. In the squid axons, there is evidence for competitive and preferential sorption of calcium and magnesium ions in the membrane. In Figure 8-6 it is seen that the effluxes of Na^* and K^* are strongly (and reversibly) affected by a variation in the concentration of the divalent ions in sea water. This can best be understood on the assumption that, in normal sea water as well as in calcium-rich media, a large portion of the negative sites are occupied by the divalent ions.

Although many divalent cations are sorbed preferentially by a membrane with a fixed negative charge, the mobilities of these ions are not necessarily low (6). The squid axon membrane shows a surprisingly high permeability to radioactive calcium ions injected into the axoplasm (27). The rate of loss of intracellular Ca^* is about 30 or more times as high as that of the intracellular K^* when measured immediately following injection.

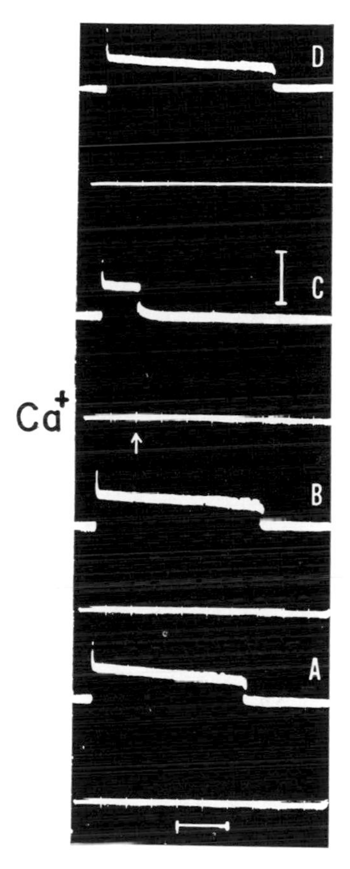

FIG. 8-7. Effect of a small amount of calcium-rich solution applied to a node of Ranvier during the plateau of the response. The duration of the voltage pulse applied to the capadyne was 5 msec. Calibrations 1 sec. and 3×10^{-9} A. Temperature 23° C. (Spyropoulos, 21.)

Analyses of the stability of the nerve membrane to electrical perturbations suggest that excitation phenomena in the nerve can be treated as a reflection of a competition between the cations in the extracellular medium and the potassium ions at the negative sites. More recent studies by Spyropoulos (21) on initiation and abolition of electrical responses by thermal and chemical pulses yielded a strong support to the hypothesis that the main chemical event occurring at the onset of the action potential is an exchange of the divalent ions in the membrane with monovalent ions. An example of these (Fig. 8-7) is the experiment demonstrating abolition with a brief pulse of rise in calcium concentration in the medium surrounding the node of Ranvier. The abrupt termination of a prolonged action potential is, according to this hypothesis, due to an exchange reaction in the reverse direction.

In the past, the importance of calcium ions in excitation has been stressed by a great number of investigators. The most notable among them appears to be Heilbrunn (7).

I regret that I am unable to go into the details of our ideas of the nature of the ionic currents during activity, of our elaborate analysis of the stability of the nerve membrane, and of our reinterpretation of the voltage-clamp experiments.

REFERENCES

1. Alexander, A. E., Teorell, T., and Aborg, E. G. *Tr. Faraday Soc. 35:* 1200, 1935.
2. Christensen, H. N., and Hastings, A. B. *J. Biol. Chem. 136:* 387, 1940.
3. Coleman, N. T. *Soil Sc. 74:* 115, 1952.
4. Drinker, N., and Zinsser, H. H. *J. Biol. Chem. 148:* 187, 1943.
5. Fatt, P., and Katz, B. *J. Physiol. 120:* 171, 1953.
6. Gregor, H., and Wetstone, D. M. *Discussion Faraday Soc. 21:* 162, 1956.
7. Heilbrunn, L. V. *The Dynamics of Living Protoplasm.* Academic Press, Inc., New York, 1956.
8. Hodgkin, A. L., and Huxley, A. F. *J. Physiol. 117:* 500, 1952.
9. Koketsu, K., Cerf, J. A., and Nishi, S. *J. Neurophysiol. 22:* 177, 1959.
10. Koketsu, K., and Nishi, S. *J. Physiol. 150:* 440, 1960.
11. Larramendi, L. M., Lorente de Nó, R., and Vidal, F. *Nature, London. 178:* 316, 1956.
12. Lorente de Nó, R., Vidal, F., and Larramendi, L. M. H. *Nature, London. 179:* 737, 1957.
13. McClintock, R., Neihof, R., and Sollner, K. *J. Electrochem. Soc. 107:* 315, 1960.

14. Michaelis, L. *Kolloid Z. 62:* 2, 1933.
15. Mueller, P. *J. Gen. Physiol. 42:* 163, 1958.
16. Osterhout, W. J. V. *Electrochemistry in Biology and Medicine,* pp. 213–224, edited by T. Shedlovsky. John Wiley & Sons, Inc., New York, 1955.
17. Osterhout, W. J. V., and Stanley, W. M. *J. Gen. Physiol. 15:* 667, 1932.
18. Prigogine, I. *Thermodynamics of Irreversible Processes.* Charles C Thomas, Publisher, Springfield, Ill. 113 pp., 1955.
19. Scatchard, G., and Helfferich, F. Membrane phenomena. *Discussion Faraday Soc. 21:* 70, 1956.
20. Segal, J. *Nature, London. 182:* 1370, 1958.
21. Spyropoulos, C. S. *Am. J. Physiol. 200:* 203, 1961.
22. Spyropoulos, C. S. *J. Gen. Physiol. 40:* 19, 1956.
23. Spyropoulos, C. S., and Tasaki, I. *Ann. Rev. Physiol. 22:* 407, 1960.
24. Tasaki, I. *Nature, London. 184:* 1574, 1959.
25. Tasaki, I. *J. Physiol. 148:* 306, 1959.
26. Tasaki, I. In preparation.
27. Tasaki, I., Teorell, T., and Spyropoulos, C. S. *Am. J. Physiol. 200:* 11, 1961.
28. Teorell, T. *Proc. Soc. Exper. Biol. & Med. 33:* 282, 1935.

DISCUSSION

Dr. Shedlovsky: It is no secret to you that I have seen Dr. Tasaki's paper before. I am not a neurophysiologist, and I shall not attempt to discuss the neurophysiological aspects of the experiments he mentioned. There are a few things I want to say, however, and one of them rather emphatically; namely, that as long as a cell is alive, considerations of classical thermodynamics are of limited interest, because they deal with equilibrium, and that is as good a definition as I know of death.

Dr. Tasaki referred to thermodynamics of irreversible processes. This is of prime importance in biology. It has to do with steady states. I am sure everyone here is familiar with the chemostat, an apparatus for maintaining a steady state with input and output fluxes. The thermocouple, a device consisting of two different kinds of metals, is another example. The theory of thermocouples was given by Thompson many years ago, not in terms of irreversible thermodynamics, but with concepts which amounted to the same thing. Here, there is interaction between heat flux and electrical flux. The flow of heat from one junction to the other sets up an electrical potential difference, and the theory is best developed in terms of thermodynamics of irreversible processes, which involves Onsager's principle of microscopic reversibility.

Dr. Tasaki spoke of ions and of metabolites. Can non-ionic metabolite fluxes influence the fluxes of ionic species? This is possible, although the effect on the resulting electrical potentials may not be very large.

Here is an experiment we have done, which may, incidentally, be important in connections other than neurophysiology. Imagine a tube filled with salt crystals, potassium chloride, for instance, from one end to the other. Let the solvent in one-half of the tube be aqueous, and in the other a mixture of water and methanol. Finally, imagine both ends of the tube in contact with calomel and mercury.

In this system all ion species are in equilibrium. The dissolved potassium chloride is in saturation equilibrium with the solid salt throughout the length of the tube. You can get no work from equilibrium, but a definite though small electrical potential is observed between one mercury pool and the other. It can arise only from something in this system which is not in equilibrium, and this, of course, is the water and the alcohol which interdiffuse.

What happens when such a cell operates? If we allow current to flow through this cell, mercurous chloride is reduced to mercury at one electrode, and the reverse occurs at the other. In addition, it can be shown that a certain amount of salt will pass from the solid phase to solution near one electrode, while the reverse will happen at the other, due to ionic transference. Since the chemical potentials of mercury, of calomel, and of salt are equal on both sides, because the system is isothermal, and solid salt phases and pure liquid mercury are present in excess, these transports can yield no work. However, if the relative interactions between the two solvents and the positive and negative ions, K^+ and Cl^- in this case, are different, an ionic space charge will be set up in the region of solvent interdiffusion. Electrical work can thus result from the diffusion of non-ionic substances in the presence of ions. Were we to consider a cell similar to the one I have just discussed, but not saturated with salt, this effect would tend to be masked by the familiar ionic diffusion potential of "concentration cells."

We find with our saturated cells potentials as high as 10 mV., at high concentrations of methyl alcohol and potassium chloride. They are lower with sodium chloride, and also when ethyl alcohol is used instead of methyl alcohol.

Another example of interacting fluxes, which has a bearing on active transport, is Osterhout's old experiment with water and trichloroacetic acid. He took a U-tube which had a layer of guaiacol in the bottom, water on one side, and a solution of trichloroacetic acid in water on the other side. The chemical potential of water is, of course, greater in pure water than it is in the solution, and one would therefore expect water to move from the side containing water to the one containing the solution. However, just the reverse takes place. This is because the flux of water from its chemical potential is exceeded by the water-carrying flux of acid moving in the other direction, a water pump, if you like. After a time, of course, the trend is reversed until, finally, equilibrium is established.

Now to return to Dr. Tasaki's paper. He has presented some interesting experimental results. Some of these results appear to be contradictory to predictions one would make on the basis of the Hodgkin theory. To what extent do they imply that the Hodgkin theory is wrong and that Tasaki's ideas are right, or that Tasaki's ideas are wrong and the other's right? I find it difficult to judge.

If I understand Dr. Tasaki's paper correctly, it is his view that in the experiments that he has described a shift occurs from one relatively stable state to another. Would you agree with that Dr. Tasaki?

DR. TASAKI: I do.

Dr. Shedlovsky: Dr. Tasaki mentioned Dr. Teorell from Sweden. He has devised an interesting model experiment which demonstrates sustained oscillations of electrical potential difference and also pressure difference across a membrane which may be sintered glass. With hydrochloric acid on one side and lithium chloride on the other, and appropriate lead-in electrodes from an adjustable D.C. voltage source, such oscillations are obtained at certain values of current. They are recorded by probe electrodes placed near the membrane, and by a differential pressure gage. The phenomenon is due to a competition between electro-endosmosis and ionic diffusion in the membrane which produce oscillations between two not-too-steady steady states. These correspond to two different ionic composition profiles in the membrane with different endosmotic characteristics due to different membrane resistances. Teorell's work has been published, and is doubtless known to many of you. It is an interesting model to consider, even though it says nothing about the nature of the battery which supplies the D.C. voltage source. It may, however, be of more than trivial interest for bioelectric phenomena, and from a point of view which is different from that usually considered today.

CHAPTER 9

Defective Metabolism of Lipids in Nervous Tissue

MANFRED L. KARNOVSKY, GUIDO MAJNO,
HUGO W. MOSER,* and CLIFFE D. JOEL

THE complex lipids, such as the phosphatides and the cerebrosides are, with cholesterol, the most interesting and important lipid classes of nervous tissue. In the past few years, there has been tremendous progress in determining the metabolism, particularly the biosynthesis of these compounds. The mode of conversion of acetate to fatty acids and the site(s) of synthesis in the cell have been the subject of vigorous investigation. Figure 9-1 presents an outline of our present understanding of the "patterns of assembly" of the phosphatides and sphingosides. We owe this information largely to the work of Kennedy (8), who has reviewed the field, and his collaborators. Some of the important pathways were worked out in nervous tissue itself (4), while others were discovered in other tissues (particularly liver) and their existence confirmed in nervous tissue through the work of

This work was supported by the Eugene Higgins Trust through Harvard University, a grant from the National Institute of Mental Disease and Blindness, United States Public Health Service, and a grant from the National Multiple Sclerosis Society.

* Work performed during the tenure of a National Multiple Sclerosis Society Postdoctoral Fellowship.

Rossiter and his collaborators (18). The pathways of biosynthesis of cholesterol from acetate via mevalonic acid, squalene (a C_{30} terpenoid hydrocarbon), and lanosterol have emerged in the past decade, through the effort of a number of investigators, especially Bloch and Popják, and their collaborators (16). Little has been done concerning the steps of cholesterol synthesis in

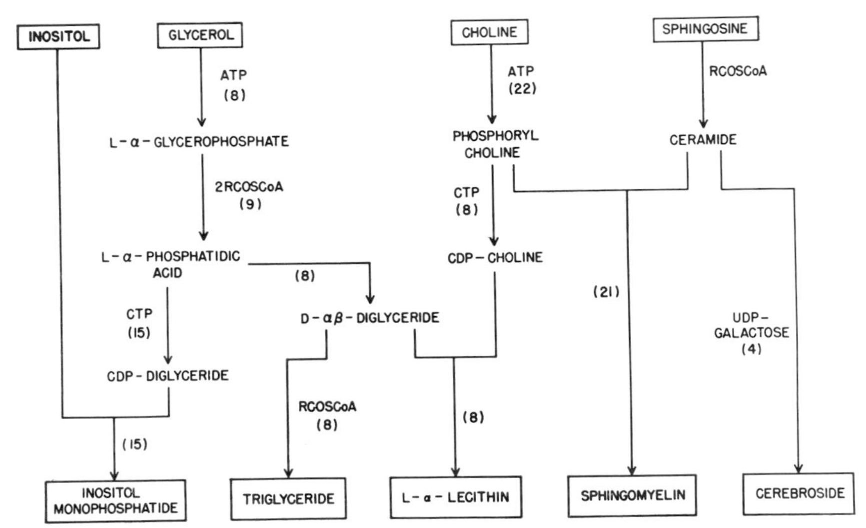

FIG. 9-1. Biosynthesis of complex lipids. A considerably oversimplified scheme is presented for orientation. The individual references are to be found in the list at the end of this chapter. **ATP** refers to adenosine triphosphate; **CTP** is cytidine triphosphate; **CDP-choline** is cytidinediphosphate-choline; and **CDP-diglyceride** is cytidinediphosphate-diglyceride. **UDP-galactose** is uridinediphosphate-galactose. **RCOSCoA** refers to long-chain fatty acylthioesters of coenzyme A. The scheme given for choline phosphatides is equally applicable to ethanolamine phosphatides.*

nervous tissue specifically, but there is no reason to believe these to be different from those of other tissues.

For this discussion of metabolic defects which might occur in nervous tissue with respect to the lipids, only a few situations have been selected. This chapter deals with aspects of defective lipid metabolism in nervous tissue studied experimentally in our laboratory. The selection comprises the following:

* New data indicate that cerebroside synthesis may proceed by attachment of the sugar moiety to sphingosine followed by acylation.

1. The classic lesion of lipid metabolism in nerves is Wallerian degeneration. Cutting of a nerve produces gross histological and chemical changes which have been studied in considerable detail over many years. The physical interruption of the fibers causes the axon and myelin to break up together. The advent of isotopic methods made detailed investigations of dynamic events going on as a result of transection accessible to study. Rossiter and his school have conducted a notable attack on this problem. Some of their findings will be reviewed later.

2. A type of lesion which involves the lipids of the nervous system is that caused by the administration of chemical agents

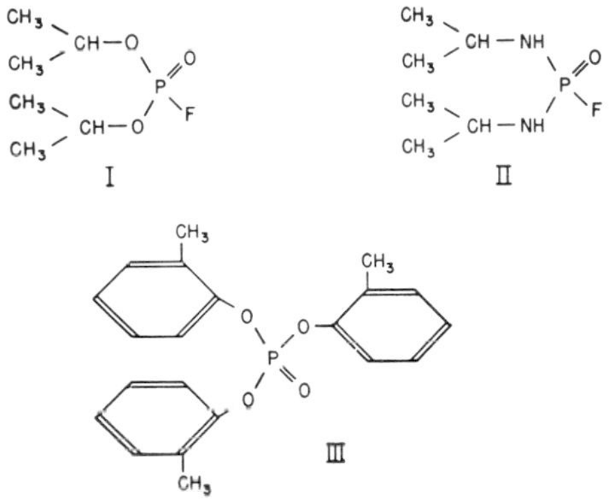

FIG. 9-2. Formulas of three organophosphorus compounds.
I,diisopropylphosphorofluoridate (DFP)
II,bis(monoisopropylamino)-fluorophosphine oxide (mipafox)
III, triorthocresyl phosphate (TOCP)

such as the organophosphorus compounds mipafox (bis(monoisopropylamino)-fluorophosphine oxide) and tri-orthocresyl phosphate (TOCP) (Fig. 9-2). The latter causes the well-known "ginger paralysis" (20) of which our daily press reported a tremendous incidence recently in North Africa following the use for cooking of olive oil which had been adulterated with surplus aviation oil containing TOCP. The chemical agents react, it is postulated, on the cell body, and the results bear a resemblance to Wallerian degeneration.

3. Finally we have also touched on some effects of a lesion-causing agent of biological origin, i.e., a diphtheria toxin-antitoxin preparation. Here the agent appears to be specific for the myelin.

The experiments reported conform to one general type: the animals were treated and, after a suitable period, were killed.

Fragments of nervous tissue were removed for incubation in vitro with labeled lipid building blocks. Respiratory data were usually obtained during the incubation. The tissue lipids were extracted at the end of the incubation, carefully freed of contaminating radioactive substrates, and counted. Details of all these procedures may be found elsewhere (10–13).

WALLERIAN DEGENERATION

The morphological events of Wallerian degeneration have been investigated very thoroughly over the whole time-course of

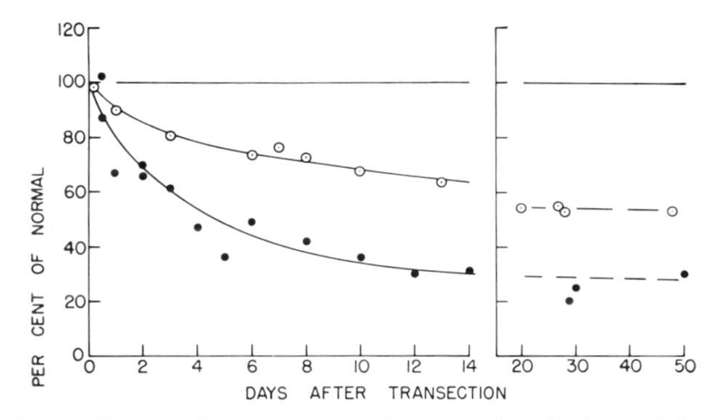

FIG. 9-3. Wallerian degeneration: dry weight (⊙) and lipid content (●) of rat sciatics at various stages after transection, calculated as percentages of fresh weight. The results are expressed as a percentage of values for normal tissue which were set at 100.

the condition. With respect to biochemical changes, however, little attention has been paid to early events, i.e., to the stages which occur during the first few days after cutting the nerve. This time includes the period during which the Schwann cells have not yet begun to proliferate. Further, no great amount of information is available on the biochemical events going on in the proximal segment of a cut nerve or in the regenerating nerve tissue formed across a gap between transected stumps. A number of such studies, using rats, have been made in our laboratories, and some results are reported in Figures 9-3 to 9-6. In Figures 9-3 and 9-4 are shown the changes in dry weight, lipid

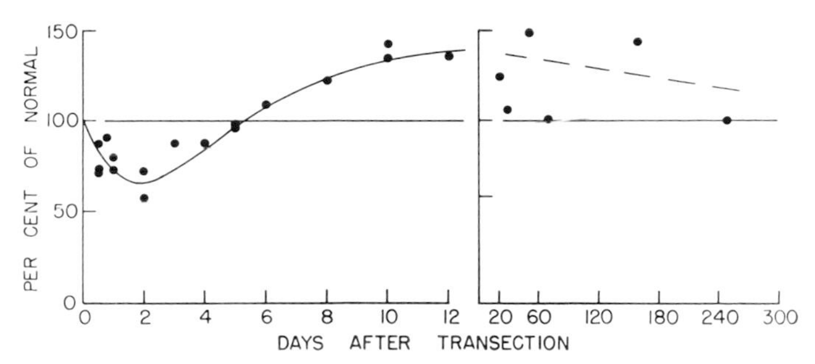

FIG. 9-4. Wallerian degeneration: respiration of rat sciatics at various stages after transection. Results are expressed as a percentage of the values obtained for normal sciatics of rats of the same age (32 μl. O_2 per 100 mg. fresh weight and hour).

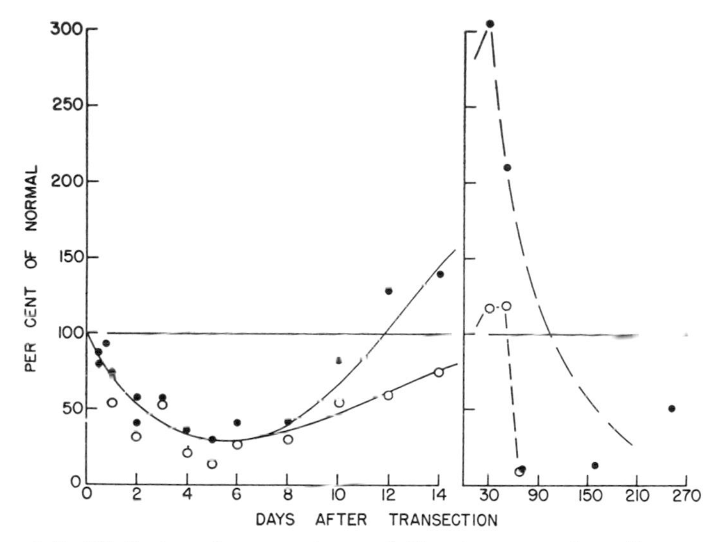

FIG. 9-5. Wallerian degeneration: relative incorporation of acetate-1-C^{14} into the lipid of rat sciatics at various stages after transection. Results are expressed as a percentage of the values obtained for normal sciatics: (●) relative specific activity (calculated from measurements of c.p.m./100 mg. lipid), and (○) relative total activity (calculated from measurements of c.p.m. incorporated into lipid by 100 mg. of fresh nerve)

content, and oxygen uptake of the distal segment of a transected nerve with time. In Figures 9-5 and 9-6 are shown the changes in the incorporation of acetate-1-C^{14} at various stages after transection, and the incorporation of phosphate-P^{32}. It is of particular interest to note that after cutting a rat sciatic nerve there is a marked drop in the incorporation of acetate-1-C^{14} into the lipids of the distal segment and at the same time a marked rise in incorporation of phosphate-P^{32}. The biphasic nature of the curve of incorporation of acetate-1-C^{14} has been explained in the following fashion: The degenerating nerve might be thought to

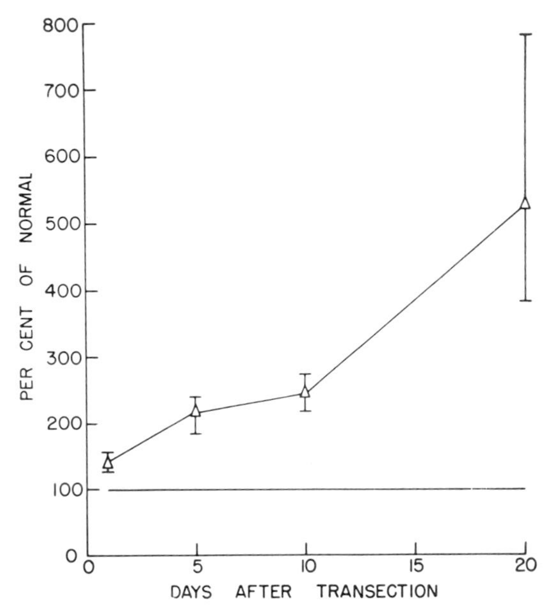

FIG. 9-6. Wallerian degeneration: relative incorporation of phosphate-P^{32} into the lipids of rat sciatic at four stages after transection. Results are expressed as a percentage of the specific activity (c.p.m./100 mg. lipid) of the values obtained for normal sciatics.

contain two categories of lipid; (*a*) lipids of the former myelin sheath now degenerating and (*b*) lipids of proliferating Schwann cells. In category (*a*) incorporation of acetate into lipids might drop to very low values, and in category (*b*) acetate incorporation could possibly be rather high. The curve shown represents the sum of the two effects. During the first five days incorporation of activity into lipids of category (*a*) decreases, and since these lipids constitute the bulk of the lipid the over-all specific activity diminishes. After five days, as the Schwann cells proliferate the activity incorporated into increasing amounts of lipid of category (*b*) causes the upward swing in specific activity. In several laboratories it has been found that the incorporation of phosphate-P^{32} into the lipids of the distal segment of severed nerves increases from the earliest times studied. There is evidence that the Schwann cells, soon after transection of the nerve, are already undergoing hypertrophy and that these regenerating Schwann cells synthesize some lipid moieties more rapidly than others. The data concerning phosphate-P^{32} and acetate-1-C^{14}

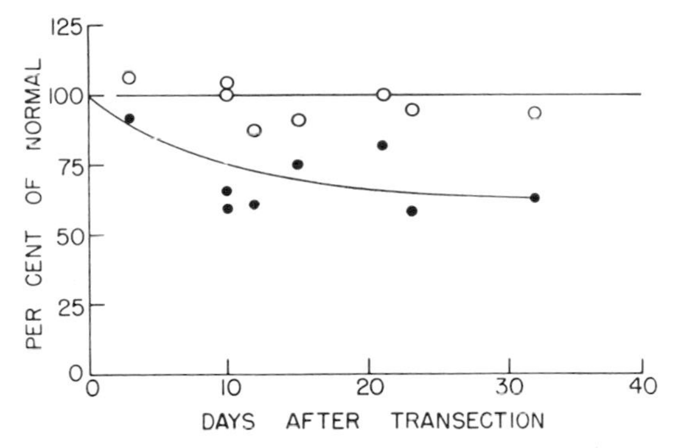

FIG. 9-7. Proximal stumps of transected rat sciatics: (○) oxygen uptake (as a percentage of normal values), and (●) incorporation of acetate into the lipids (expressed as a percentage of the specific activity values [c.p.m./100 mg. lipid] obtained for normal sciatics).

suggest perhaps that phosphatides are being made more actively than is cholesterol.

In a study of transected central tracts (7), the changes observed were comparable with those in peripheral nerve undergoing Wallerian degeneration, except that they were in general less dramatic and more protracted in time.

It is a matter of considerable interest that the *proximal* stump of severed rat sciatics also exhibits a depression of incorporation of acetate-1-C^{14} into lipid, as is shown in Figure 9-7. The incorporation of phosphate-P^{32} was again found to increase dramatically, being 185 per cent of normal at 15 days. Oxygen uptake and lipid content showed no significant change in this tissue, and there was not the extensive increase in water content which had been noted in the case of the distal part. Degenerating fibers were only an occasional histological finding in this tissue, and were insufficient to explain the changes in incorporation of activity. There was also no secondary rise in the incorporation of acetate-1-C^{14} into the lipids in distinction to the true Wallerian degeneration of the distal part.

The passage of events in regenerating nerves has been the subject of some investigation, mostly through the use of crushed

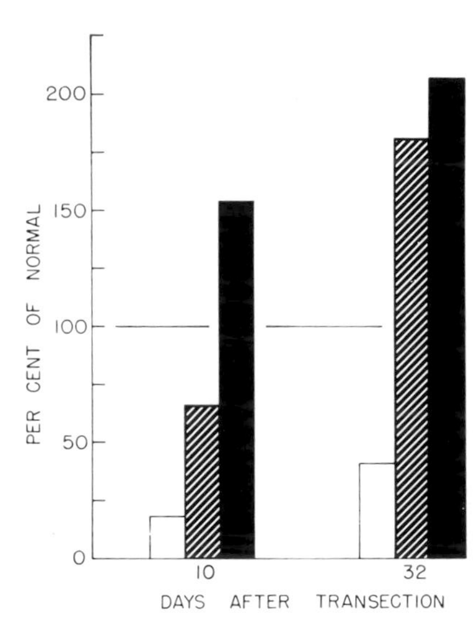

FIG. 9-8. Regenerating sciatics: ten days (*left*) and 32 days (*right*) after transection: *open bar*, lipid content; *striped bar*, incorporation of acetate into the lipids expressed as relative specific activity; *solid bar*, oxygen uptake per 100 mg./fresh weight. Results are calculated as a percentage of the values obtained for normal sciatics.

nerve. This preparation presents certain difficulties in interpretation, since it represents a mixture of degenerating and regenerating fibers. We have studied the filament which bridges a gap of 3–8 mm. between the stumps of a transected nerve after various periods, and in Figure 9-8 are shown the results obtained for a number of measurements carried out at ten days or at 32 days after transection. At ten days the myelin was not observable through the use of osmium tetroxide, whereas at 32 days myelination was well advanced. This situation has been compared with the development of myelin in the peripheral nerves of very young rats where it has been observed that lipogenesis is lower at birth than it is at five days of age (10). Normal and regenerative growth had some features in common. In both cases the uptake of oxygen was elevated, and, prior to the very active lipogenetic functions which accompanied the appearance of observable myelin, the incorporation of lipid precursors into the lipids of the tissue was low.

These over-all observations, and many others made in a great number of laboratories, are interesting as chemically descriptive of the passage of events in degenerating and regenerating nervous tissue. Such over-all observations are, however, not likely to lead us to a detailed understanding of metabolic control processes in either type of tissue. When one considers the large number of individual enzymatic steps in lipid assembly such as are represented in Figure 9-1 and those of fatty acid synthesis, the question must obviously be asked as to what the changes are in individual enzyme reactions which underlie aberrant lipid metabolism. The activities of the enzymes themselves and the availability of individual coenzymes and substrates are the variables which necessarily must be known. Rossiter and his colleagues have begun to answer these questions. For example, in a straightforward approach Pritchard and Rossiter (17) were able to show that, as in brain slices, various precursors labeled different parts of the glycerophosphatide molecule. Thus, in phosphatides substrate glycerol-C^{14} appeared only in the glycerol backbone, acetate-C^{14} only in the fatty acids, choline only in the choline moiety, and so on. Table 9-1 shows some of the data obtained in their experiments in which nerve degenerating after section and intact nerve were compared. It is of great interest that this table shows that there is an increase in the incorporation of several lipid precursors into the lipids of nerves at 16–32 days after section, but that the extent of the increases for each substrate and the changes of incorporation with time after transection are different. Pritchard and Rossiter have commented on the important fact that although the hypertrophy and hyperplasia of the Schwann cells might be expected to result in the formation of myelin lipid, the data of Table 9-1 would indicate that lipids other than myelin lipids only are being made in greater quantities as the Wallerian degeneration proceeds. It might be surmised that the "nonmyelin" lipids represent lipids of particular entities of the Schwann cells—perhaps of the Schwann cell organelles.

In further refinements of their investigation, Rossiter and his colleagues examined various enzymes of lipid synthesis and assembly in regenerating and degenerating cat sciatic nerves. They found, for example, that there was no change in the

Table 9-1. Effect of Nerve Section on the Incorporation of C^{14}-labeled Precursors into the Phospholipid of the Sciatic Nerve of the Cat[a] (17)

	Specific radioactivity[b] *D/I*		*Radioactivity*[c] *D/I*	
C^{14}-labeled precursor	*16 days*	*32 days*	*16 days*	*32 days*
Acetate-1-C^{14}	2.8	10.0	1.4	2.5
Glycerol-1-C^{14}	2.0	21.2	1.0	5.4
Choline-1,2-C^{14}	4.0	22.8	2.0	5.8
Ethanolamine-1,2-C^{14}	15.1	17.0	7.6	4.3
Serine-3-C^{14}	21.8	21.4	11.0	5.5

[a] Control sciatic nerves and the distal portion of transected sciatic nerves were incubated in vitro with the relevant labeled substance.

[b] Specific radioactivity $D/I = \frac{\text{c.p.m. per } \mu\text{g. lipid P in degenerating nerve}}{\text{c.p.m. per } \mu\text{g. lipid P in intact nerve}}$.

[c] Radioactivity $D/I = \frac{\text{c.p.m. per 100 mg. degenerating nerve}}{\text{c.p.m. per 100 mg. intact nerve}}$.

formation of acetyl coenzyme A from acetate, coenzyme A and ATP in cat sciatic nerves 8 to 16 days after transection (2). After 32 days a real increase in acetyl-coenzyme A formation was noted. Thus, in these tissues acetic thiokinase was not depressed.

With respect to choline kinase, however, enzymatic activity in cat sciatic nerves was unchanged 16 days after section, but was greatly *decreased* by 32 days (60–70 per cent) (1). Further, Rossiter, McLeod, and Strickland (19) found that homogenates prepared from degenerating sciatic nerves have a *greater* capacity to incorporate phosphorylcholine-P^{32} of cytidine-diphosphate choline-P^{32} into lipids than do those from intact nerves. Since there is an increased incorporation of phosphate-P^{32} into nerve phosphatides following transection, these results, i.e., decreased enzyme activity at one step, and an increased activity at later steps, are very intriguing. It is clear that the enzymatic steps of the very complex phenomenon called Wallerian degeneration have yet to be explored in full and the contributions of various steps to the over-all picture evaluated in detail. It is gratifying that the methods for exploration of individual enzymes are available and that a start has been made on this highly significant problem.

EFFECTS OF ORGANOPHOSPHORUS COMPOUNDS ON LIPID METABOLISM

Mipafox (bis(monoisopropylamino)-fluorophosphine oxide) is a close relative to di-isopropylphosphorofluoridate (DFP), a potent inhibitor of pseudocholine esterase. Mipafox itself is a cholinesterase inhibitor with a preferential effect on the pseudocholinesterase, and the question has been raised in the past as to whether its effects in causing paralysis are due to this enzyme-inhibiting activity. The results of mipafox poisoning on nervous tissue from poisoned animals have been studied histologically in a comprehensive fashion, but little detailed information is available on the effect of this compound on nervous tissue with respect to lipid synthesis and turnover. We have made a number of investigations of this problem. For example, a study was undertaken on the effects on mipafox poisoning in rats upon the ability of peripheral nerves from such animals to incorporate acetate-1-C^{14} into lipids. Some results are shown in Table 9-2, and it may be noted that very well-defined changes were obtained. The rat is normally held to be somewhat resistant to mipafox treatment, and indeed the animals represented by Table 9-2 showed no signs of paralysis, nor did they exhibit any weight loss or obvious signs of poisoning. An attempt to repeat the experiment exemplified in Table 9-2 was totally unsuccessful. A new batch of mipafox had been used, and no significant depression of incorporation of label into nervous tissue lipids was obtained. After a great

Table 9-2. Effect of Mipafox Treatment on Rat Nerves[a]

Incubation[b] period	*Respiration (μl O_2)* *Normal*	*Treated*	*P*	*Specific activity of lipid[c] c.p.m.* *Normal*	*Treated*	*P*
2 hours	78.1[d]	68.3	0.02	1000	613	<0.01
	±3.1	±2.6		±71	±81	
4 hours	144.3	118.8	0.02	1784	792	<0.001
	±7.9	±4.5		±147	±43	

[a] Four subcutaneous injections each of 5 mg. mipafox were given 5-6 days apart, prior to carrying out the experiment in vitro.

[b] The sciatic nerves were incubated in Krebs-Ringer phosphate medium containing 10 μM glucose per ml. and 1 mg. sodium acetate-1-C^{14} equivalent to about 1 μcurie per 3 ml.

[c] Respiration as μl O_2 per 100 mg. fresh tissue. Specific activity as c.p.m. per 100 mg. lipid.

[d] Twelve measurements were available for the respiration at 2 hours: six measurements were available for each of the other results.

deal of study the clue to this situation was found. This may best perhaps be summed up in the results exemplified in Figure 9-9. In Figure 9-9 are shown the sciatic nerves from an animal poisoned with mipafox and a normal animal. It may be noted

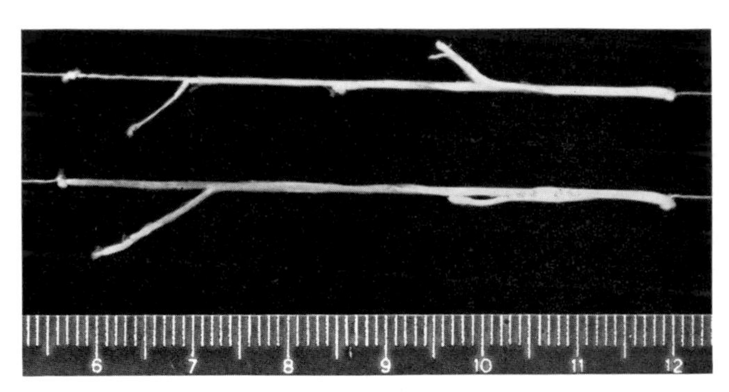

FIG. 9-9. Effect of mipafox treatment on rat sciatic nerve. *Upper nerve:* normal sciatic; *lower nerve:* sciatic nerve from mipafox-treated animal.

that there is pronounced swelling of the *distal* portions of the nerve in the case of mipafox poisoning. This is clearly reminiscent of the appearance of the distal part of the nerve in Wallerian degeneration. It was finally realized that the lesion appears to spread centripetally from the periphery and that the outermost portions of the nerve are affected earliest and most. The whole effect of mipafox on rat nerves was finally confirmed on animals which had been treated for extended periods of time (3 months; total dose ca. 350 mg. mipafox). Figure 9-10 shows results of studies with segments of rat sciatic nerve. It is of importance that rat cerebral cortex also is affected by mipafox poisoning. Under the conditions mentioned, mipafox treatment reduced the ability

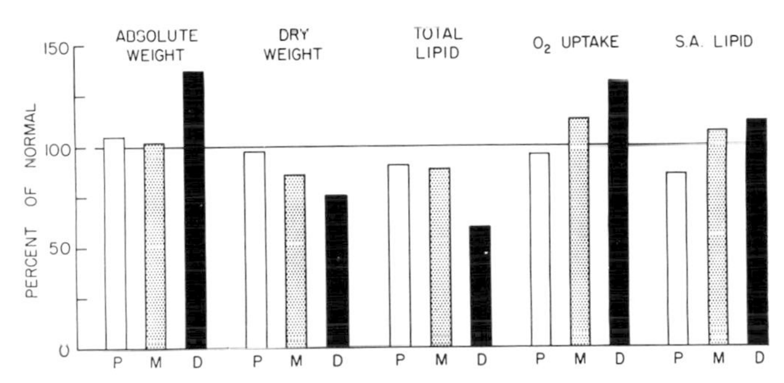

FIG. 9-10. Differential effects of mipafox administration on various parts of rat sciatic nerve. *Open bar*—proximal; *stippled bar*—middle; *solid bar*—distal portion of nerve.

of brain cortex slices to incorporate acetate-1-C^{14} into lipids in vitro to 55 per cent of normal values ($P < 0.01$).

In parallel with these experiments using rats, we carried out a number of experiments using hens, which are known to be more sensitive to the effects of mipafox and develop a well-defined paralysis. Table 9-3 indicates the type of results obtained when studies were made of the sciatic nerves and funiculi stripped from the cords of hens which had received mipafox, compared with those which were not so poisoned. In the upper half of the table are shown the data for hens which were not pair-fed. In this case the mipafox-treated hens lost a tremendous proportion of their weight—up to 30–40 per cent. This fact instigated a study of the effect of mipafox on hens which were pair-fed with their controls, and the data in the lower half of the table were obtained. It is noticeable that hen sciatic nerves

Table 9-3. Effect of Mipafox Administration on Nervous Tissues of Hens[a]

			Cord			
			Upper		*Lower*	
	Tissue	*Sciatics*	*Anterior*	*Lateral*	*Anterior*	*Lateral*
Series A Not pair-fed[b]	*Respiration*[c]	95.5	82.7	82.8	104.3	106.7
		±6.2	±3.0	±3.5	±9.0	±13.5
	P	>0.5	<0.05	<0.05	>0.5	>0.7
	Lipids[d]	43.5	60.5	53.8	72.3	129.0
		±9.3	±10.6	±6.3	±9.0	±18.5
	P	<0.01	<0.05	<0.01	=0.05	>0.5
Series B Pair-fed[e]	*Respiration*	95.0	81.0	107.7	—	—
		±0.3	±4.5	±8.2		
	P	<0.01	=0.05	>0.3		
	Lipids	161.0	84.7[f]	103.0	—	—
		±52.0	±5.9	±13.5		
	P	>0.3	>0.1	>0.8	—	—

[a] Results expressed as percentage of normal values in each experiment.
[b] Two separate doses (10 mg./Kg.) of mipafox were injected subcutaneously one week apart. Hens sacrificed after 23–27 days. At this time the experimental animals had lost 33–40 per cent of their initial weight, while the controls were stationary.
[c] Expressed originally as μl. O_2 per 100 mg. fresh tissue per hour. Three experiments performed.
[d] Expressed originally as specific activity, c.p.m. per 100 mg. lipid. Acetate-1-C^{14} was the precursor. Four experiments in series A; three in series B.
[e] Mipafox given first and eighth day. Treated hens lost 10–30 gm. body weight per day in second week. Food of controls reduced to match weights with experimentals. In third week all hens were force-fed with powdered milk preparation. Hens were killed, and nerves studied 21–24 days after first injection, at which time weights were very similar.
[f] Although this figure does not appear as significantly different from the control value, each experimental animal was lower than its normal counterpart. Further experiments are needed.

apparently are very sensitive, with respect to their ability to incorporate acetate-1-C^{14} into lipids in vitro, to the nutritional state of the animal. Some parts of the cord were also subject to this controlling factor. Although insufficient experiments are available, it is believed that the effect of mipafox on acetate incorporation by the upper anterior funiculi of the cord is real.

The dramatic effects of starving upon nervous tissue were somewhat unexpected, and an experiment was carried out simply to examine the effects of starving on the nervous tissue of hens. The data are shown in Table 9-4. Although starvation appeared to have exacerbated the effect of mipafox on the cords, it alone did not appear to affect acetate incorporation into the white matter of normal animals.

Table 9-4. Effect of Starvation on Respiration and Lipogenesis of Hen Nervous Tissue in vitro[a]

	Oxygen uptake				*Lipid specific activity*			
Precursor	*Nerves*[b]	*P*	*Cords*	*P*	*Nerves*	*P*	*Cords*	*P*
Acetate-1-C^{14}					39.6 ±13.6	<0.05	103.0 ±29.0	>0.5
	87.5[c] ±2.9	<0.01	98.0 ±10.4	>0.8				
Phosphate-P^{32}					68.4 ±16.8	>0.05	98.5 ±6.2	>0.8

[a] Animals were starved one week, but water was allowed ad lib. Compared with fed controls, whose weight remained essentially stable, the starved hens lost 13–27 per cent (average 17.5 per cent) of their weight.

[b] The data are expressed as a percentage of the normal value in each experiment.

[c] The data from both labeling experiments are combined. Five results were obtained in the case of respiratory measurements: three experiments were carried out for each labeled substrate.

All these experiments with rats and hens indicate the crucial importance of (*a*) examining tissue at the right time after poisoning, (*b*) selecting the right parts of the tissue (e.g., in the case of the rat sciatic), and (*c*) in controlling other variables, such as the food intake.

It has been claimed by some that mipafox has no effects on lipid metabolism of treated animals. The data here presented appear to indicate that this substance definitely does cause impaired lipid biosynthesis in some parts of the nervous system, by acting centrally, with secondary degeneration of the fibers.

In line with the previously expressed opinion that increasing refinement of observation is essential, we have carried out a number of fractionations of hen sciatic nerves and cords exposed to acetate-1-C^{14} and have determined the influence of previous mipafox treatment on these individual fractions. Table 9-5 shows the results obtained. It may be noted that there is a general depression of all fractions of sciatics and cords of treated animals compared with the same fraction of tissues isolated from normal animals, except in the case of the "residual fraction" of the cord, where the tissues from the experimentally treated animals showed an increased incorporation of acetate 1-C^{14}. Perhaps the main feature of interest in this table is the fact that the so-called

Table 9-5. Incorporation of Acetate-1-C^{14} into Various Lipid Types by Sciatic Nerve and Cord of the Hen[a]

	Cords		*Sciatics*	
	Normal	*Exptal.*	*Normal*	*Exptal.*
Total lipid[a]	382	320	1020	764
Phosphatide	291	153	527	323
Cholesterol	144	92	787	538
Residual fraction	2690	2250	3810	4710

[a] The hens were not pair-fed. Mipafox administration was similar to that of Table 9-3. Means of four experiments are given. The spread of the results was 40 per cent for cords; 27 per cent for sciatics. The residual fractions from the four experiments were pooled. In 75 per cent of the individual analyses made, the results for the tissues of treated hens were lower than those of controls.

"residual fractions" after removal of the phosphatide and cholesterol have by far the highest specific activity in both normal and treated animals.

In a further attempt to identify some specific entity affected by mipafox in hens, a detailed analysis of the brains, cords, and sciatic nerves of treated animals was compared with that of control animals. The data are given in Table 9-6. It may be noted that very close agreement exists between treated and control tissues for most variables measured even though these animals were not pair-fed. These data thus differ from those concerning the incorporation of acetate-1-C^{14} (Table 9-3). No real diminution of the content of any of the substances estimated could be detected except for one most interesting case. The results of the analysis for polyenoic fatty acids from the brains of treated animals as compared with those of the control animals showed that the pentaenoic fatty acids were noticeably depressed in the brains of mipafox poisoned animals ($P < 0.01$). What the significance of this finding might be is as yet not apparent. That it is real is indicated by the fact that the absorption peak characteristic of these acids after conjugation was significantly shifted to higher wavelengths in lipids from treated animals (i.e., from 349.2 ± 0.3 mμ to 350.7 ± 0.1 mμ). This is

Table 9-6. Analysis of Lipids of Nervous Tissues of Normal and Mipafox-treated Hens[a]

	Brain		*Cord*		*Sciatic*	
Substance	*Control*	*Treated*	*Control*	*Treated*	*Control*	*Treated*
(a) Lipid, % of fresh tissue	9.2 ±0.1	9.3 ±0.1	23.4 ±0.6	23.8 ±0.6	16.1 ±1.0	17.0 ±1.4
(b) Phosphatide, % of lipid	50.4 ±0.6	50.4 ±0.8	40.3 ±0.6	40.6 ±0.6	47.5 ±0.4	47.3 ±0.7
(c) Cholesterol[b] % of lipid	18.9 ±0.3	19.0 ±0.3	21.5 ±0.1	21.9 ±0.1	22.1 ±0.4	22.3 ±0.5
(d) Cerebroside, % of lipid	16.1 ±0.4	16.1 ±0.2	28.4 ±0.8	28.9 ±1.2	25.5 ±1.4	24.8 ±0.2
(e) Sphingomyelin P, % lipid P	11.1 ±0.8	9.4 ±0.6	29.1 ±0.4	27.2 ±0.9	35.7 ±1.8	34.8 +0.9
(f) Pentaenoic acids, % of total lipids	0.88 ±0.05	0.68 ±0.01	0.35 ±0.02	0.34 ±0.01	0.41 ±0.02	0.37 ±0.01

[a] The hens were not pair-fed. Treatment as in Table 9-3. Five pairs of samples of nerves and cords were available, and three pairs of samples of sciatic.

[b] All the cholesterol was unesterified. No differences existed in this respect between normal and treated animals.

the result of a decrease of pentaenoic acids relative to hexaenoic acids, since these two classes of fatty acids share this peak in the alkali-isomerization method (5). An important observation is that nerves, cords, and livers of treated animals were no different, with respect to the pentaenoic fatty acids, from the same tissues of normal animals. It is worth noting that Hove (6) using tri-orthocresylphosphate observed that treatment with vitamin E alleviated the effects of the poisonous agent. It might be that there is some interrelationship between poly-unsaturated fatty acids, their maintenance in an unoxidized condition, vitamin E, and the maintenance of nerve function. A parenthetical note might be sounded at this point to the effect that nervous tissue is very rich in highly unsaturated fatty acids and that little real information has been accumulated over the years as to the exact function of these substances.

DIPHTHERITIC POLYNEURITIS

Wallerian degeneration does not affect myelin or the Schwann cells directly but primarily causes destruction of the axis cylinder followed by breakdown of myelin. In a second kind of demyelination, so called "segmental demyelination" or "Gombault demyelination," there is primary damage to the Schwann cells, or the myelin itself, initially sparing the axis cylinder. A study* of the incorporation of lipid precursors into lipids of peripheral nerves obtained from guinea pigs was undertaken after administration of diphtheria toxin incompletely neutralized with added antitoxin. Such treatment is known to induce demyelination of the segmental type. A single injection of the toxin-antitoxin mixture was given. Figure 9-11 indicates some of the changes observed. It may be noted that there was a decline in the content of lipid of the sciatic nerve and it should also be mentioned that there was a slight but definite increase in the water content between 15 and 25 days. The respiration might have shown a slight decrease in the first few days after injection after which it rose definitely. Incorporation of acetate-1-C^{14} declined rapidly immediately after the injection of the toxin-antitoxin mixture, while that of phosphate-P^{32} rose more slowly. As in the case of the hens used in the mipafox experiments it was necessary to pair-feed the guinea pigs used in these experiments, since starvation led to a decreased incorporation of acetate-1-C^{14} into nerve lipids in vitro. It is of particular interest that attempts to duplicate the effects of diphtheria toxin in vitro on isolated sciatic nerves or strips of guinea-pig cord were unsuccessful, whereas similar ex-

* This study was carried out in collaboration with Dr. Byron Waksman, of the Harvard Medical School and the Neurology Service, Massachusetts General Hospital, Boston, Mass.

periments with mipafox were successful. The reason for this is not yet apparent, although it may have its origin in the ability or inability of the active agent to penetrate into nervous tissue. No effect was obtained even when the amount of toxin used in vitro was about 1000 times greater than that which might have been expected in the body fluids of animals given the toxic substance.

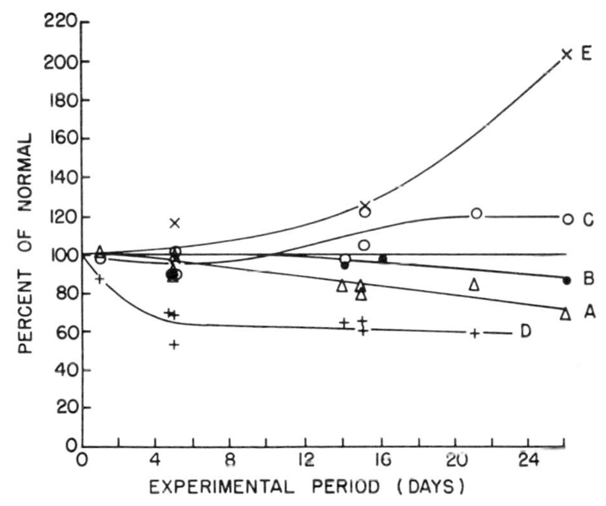

FIG. 9-11. Biochemical changes in guinea-pig nerves after injection of diphtheria toxin-antitoxin mixture. All values are expressed as a percentage of values for normal tissue. (**A**) lipid content, per 100 mg. fresh weight; (**B**) dry weight, per cent of fresh weight; (**C**) oxygen uptake per 100 mg. fresh weight and hour; (**D**) specific activity of lipids after exposure of nerve to acetate-1-C^{14}; (**E**) specific activity of lipids after exposure of nerve to phosphate-P^{32}.

If one compares the picture of metabolic events obtained after administration of diphtheria toxin-antitoxin mixture one might again be struck by the similarity to the events observed after transection of nerves, although the former apparently take place in "slow motion," and are less dramatic (cf. transected central tracts). This may perhaps be explained by the fact that in diphtheritic polyneuritis not all the fibers of a given nerve are affected. The viewpoint has been expressed (13) that " . . . the initial lesion of diphtheritic paralysis is purely 'regressive,' contrary to Wallerian degeneration in which progressive and regressive changes are intertwined from a very early stage and possibly *ab initio*. To put this another way, the two injurious agents, axon transection and diphtheria toxin, act on the Schwann cells in a very different manner. Both impair the maintenance of the myelin sheath. The former, however, acts also as a growth stimulus to the Schwann cells, while in diphtheritic paralysis the proliferative reaction is a relatively late, and probably secondary occurrence." These observations are drawn from the comparison of events during the two processes and particularly from the fact that, whereas, after transection of sciatic nerve, the incorporation of phosphate-P^{32} into the lipid components in vitro rose immediately, in animals which had been injected with diphtheria toxin the appearance of increased incorporation of phosphate-P^{32} was relatively late.

CONCLUSION

The studies presented emphasize the possibility of measuring, in vitro, variables which might reflect the effects of agents causing impairment of metabolism of the lipids of nervous tissue. The experimental approach is somewhat crude in that it depends either on cutting the nerve and destroying its continuity, or on the administration of toxic chemical substances, or on the administration of a bacterial toxin. There are surely more subtle ways in which variations in the over-all metabolism of an animal might cause a breakdown and failure of resynthesis of the lipids of nervous tissues, and the wastage of the myelin sheaths. The models studied here must be regarded as somewhat elementary.

A beginning has been made in recent years to refine the approach. It will be of importance to differentiate failures in the metabolism of myelin lipids from lesions in the metabolism of nonmyelin lipids, which presumably have special functions. The hope is to pin-point specific steps in impaired lipid metabolism. Thus, future studies will probably be more and more at the level of individual enzymes. Information is urgently needed on the relative importance of substrate and coenzyme availability and enzymatic activity at given sites in the nervous system exhibiting aberrant lipid metabolism. Such information will probably be forthcoming through a wider application of methods like those elaborated by Lowry and his collaborators (3). A particularly intriguing question concerns substances which originate in the cell body and whose transport down the nerve is essential for the maintenance of the integrity of the nerve fiber. It is relevant also to inquire into the effects of the conduction of impulses on the metabolism of the lipids of nervous tissue. This problem is a reciprocal one—it is well known that impulse conduction is dependent on the lipids of nervous tissue inasmuch as these are part of the myelin. Conduction of impulses in sciatic nerve stimulates the incorporation of acetate-1-C^{14} and glucose-C^{14} carbon into the lipids by about 10–20 per cent without so affecting phosphate-P^{32} or choline-C^{14} incorporation (12). The superposition of the effects of failure of conduction on primary effects causing such failure is important, and pertinent to the models discussed above.

In addition to the relevance of remarks concerning refinement of investigations to the enzyme level in studies of faulty lipid metabolism induced by various agents or conditions, and leading to malfunction, they are clearly applicable in studies of the ultimate nature of classical lipid diseases of the nervous system, such as Niemann-Pick and Tay-Sachs diseases. In the former, an abnormal sphingomyelin is reported to accumulate in the brain. These familial diseases may be expected to originate from some enzymatic lack or imbalance. Since the mode of assembly of sphingomyelin is now known (21) as well as that of the cerebrosides (4, 14), and the problems of the structure and assembly of gangliosides are under investigation in several laboratories (e.g. 14), the time appears ripe for re-examination of these classical aberrations of nerve-lipid metabolism.

REFERENCES

1. BERRY, J. F., MCPHERSON, C. F., and ROSSITER, R. J. Chemical studies of peripheral nerve during Wallerian degeneration IX. Choline kinase. *J. Neurochem.* 3: 65, 1958.

2. BERRY, J. F., and ROSSITER, R. J. Chemical studies of peripheral nerve during Wallerian degeneration VIII. Acetic thiokinase and choline acetylase. *J. Neurochem. 3:* 59, 1958.
3. BUELL, M. V., LOWRY, O. H., ROBERTS, N. R., CHANG, M. W., and KAPPHAHN, J. I. The quantitative histochemistry of the brain V. Enzymes of glucose metabolism. *J. Biol. Chem. 232:* 979, 1958.
4. BURTON, R. M., SODD, M. A., and BRADY, R. O. The incorporation of galactose into galactolipides. *J. Biol. Chem. 233:* 1053, 1958.
5. HERB, S. F., and RIEMENSCHNIEDER, R. W. Spectrophotometric micromethod for determining polyunsaturated fatty acid. *Anal. Chem. 25:* 953, 1953.
6. HOVE, E. L. The toxicity of tri-orthocresylphosphate for rats as related to dietary casein level, vitamin E and vitamin A. *J. Nutrition. 51:* 609, 1953.
7. KARNOVSKY, M. L., and MAJNO, G. Lipide synthesis *in vitro* by central tracts and peripheral nerves following transection. In *Chemical Pathology of the Nervous System,* edited by J. Folch. Pergamon Press, New York, 1961, p. 261.
8. KENNEDY, E. P. Metabolism of lipides. *Ann. Rev. Biochem. 26:* 119, 1957.
9. KORNBERG, A., and PRICER, W. E., JR. Enzymatic esterification of α-glycerophosphate by long chain fatty acids. *J. Biol. Chem. 204:* 345, 1953.
10. MAJNO, G., and KARNOVSKY, M. L. Lipide biosynthesis *in vitro* by normal nervous tissue. *J. Exper. Med. 107:* 475, 1958.
11. MAJNO, G., and KARNOVSKY, M. L. Lipogenesis *in vitro* by rat nerves following transection. *J. Exper. Med. 108:* 197, 1958.
12. MAJNO, G., GASTEIGER, E. L., LAGATTUTA, M., and KARNOVSKY, M. L. Lipid biosynthesis *in vitro* by electrically stimulated rat sciatic nerves. *J. Neurochem. 3:* 127, 1958.
13. MAJNO, G., WAKSMAN, B. H., and KARNOVSKY, M. L. The effect of diphtheria toxin on lipide biosynthesis by guinea pig nerve. *J. Neuropath. & Exper. Neurol. 19:* 7, 1960.
14. MOSER, H. W., and KARNOVSKY, M. L. Studies on the biosynthesis of glycolipides and other lipids of the brain. *J. Biol. Chem. 234:* 1990, 1959.
15. PAULUS, H., and KENNEDY, E. P. The enzymatic synthesis of inositol monophosphatide. *J. Biol. Chem. 235:* 1303, 1960.
16. POPJÁK, G. Biosynthesis of cholesterol and related substances. *Ann. Rev. Biochem. 27:* 533, 1958.

17. PRITCHARD, E. T., and ROSSITER, R. J. Chemical studies of peripheral nerve during Wallerian degeneration XI. *In vitro* incorporation of C^{14}-labeled precursors into phosphatides. *J. Neurochem. 3:* 341, 1959.
18. ROSSITER, R. J., and STRICKLAND, K. P. Biogenesis of phosphatides and triglycerides. *Ann. New York Acad. Sc. 72:* 790, 1959.
19. ROSSITER, R. J., MCLEOD, I. M., and STRICKLAND, K. P. Biosynthesis of lecithin in brain and degenerating nerve. Participation of cytidine diphosphate choline. *Canad. J. Biochem. Physiol. 35:* 945, 1957.
20. SMITH, M. I., and ELVOVE, E. Pharmacological and chemical studies of the cause of so-called ginger paralysis. *Pub. Health Rep. 45:* 1703, 1930.
21. SRIBNEY, M., and KENNEDY, E. P. The enzymatic synthesis of sphingomyelin. *J. Biol. Chem. 233:* 1315, 1958.
22. WITTENBERG, J., and KORNBERG, A. Choline phosphokinase. *J. Biol. Chem. 202:* 431, 1953.

CHAPTER 10

Modes of the Utilization of Glucose by the Brain

ALEXANDER GEIGER

THE main fuel supplied to the brain by the blood is glucose (47). This substance is taken up into the brain in amounts that are practically equivalent to its oxygen consumption and lactate production. This often confirmed observation led originally to the belief that the main, or only metabolic, function of the brain is the oxidation of glucose, primarily for the generation of high-energy phosphate bonds. However, in recent years it became evident that most of the chemical constituents of the brain, free, or "structural," participate in its metabolism, and at various rates. Amino acids, proteins, and lipids are among these. This was also implied by recent observations, which show that a large portion of the respiratory CO_2 of the brain is derived from the oxidation of endogenous substances other than glucose (23, 32). Glucose being, practically, the only energy-yielding substance taken up from the blood by the brain, the synthesis of the endogenous

The studies made in the writer's laboratory were supported by grants from the National Institute of Neurological Diseases and Blindness (Grant 413 B), of the National Institutes of Health, U.S. Public Health Service, and from the National Multiple Sclerosis Society.

The writer also wishes to express his thanks to Mrs. Lorraine Alexander for her help with the manuscript.

substrates of metabolism has to be supported by the use of glucose-metabolites. Other essential compounds are either being re-used, or are taken up from the blood in comparatively small amounts. The use of C^{14} labeled glucose made the demonstration of these processes possible. These findings then extended the scope of the glucose metabolism of the brain to the biochemical processes through which the glucose-carbon is incorporated into the various chemical components of the brain. Such an inquiry also offered the opportunity to study the relative quantities contributed by glucose on the one hand, and by various endogenous metabolites on the other, to the energy-yielding processes, by measuring the relative proportion of C^{14} derived from labeled glucose in the respiratory CO_2 and in other intermediary "key" metabolites.

It will be shown below that the relative rates at which various endogenous metabolites of the brain participate in the metabolic processes are kept constant under normal, "resting" conditions. Thus, a "metabolic pattern" is discernible. This "metabolic pattern" varies with changing physiological conditions and is also affected by drugs. In the following presentation the results obtained by the writer and his colleagues on the nature of the "metabolic pattern" of the brain under various physiological conditions are described.

In the intact animal, intermediary metabolites of glucose produced by the liver and by other organs reach the brain via the blood stream, from where they may be taken up or exchanged for similar "free" substances in the brain. Thus, when these substances are isolated from the brain it is difficult to know whether these metabolites were produced by the brain, or were transported there by the blood from other organs. In the writer's laboratory the use of a brain perfusion method in vivo, with isolated brain circulation, and intact nervous connections to the rest of the body in order to maintain its normal blood supply, facilitated these investigations. In these experiments the brain is perfused in vivo with a "simplified" blood of known composition, containing uniformly C^{14} labeled glucose as the only substrate, or other C^{14} labeled compounds. The physiological functions of the brain and its metabolic activity can be examined simultaneously (5, 30, 31).

GLUCOSE UPTAKE BY THE BRAIN

Under normal conditions, the glucose content of the brain as measured by chemical methods (copper reduction, ferricyanide, etc.) seems to follow the concentration of glucose in the blood (5), except when the blood glucose is elevated far above the normal range of in vivo variations.

It was seen lately, however, that even in the presence of 0.6 per cent glucose in the blood of a normal cat, the ("true") glucose content of the brain remains at about 50 mg. per cent while that of other carbohydrates increases up to 180 mg. per cent (27). In brain perfusion experiments when the brain circulation is isolated and the brain is perfused with a "simplified blood" consisting of well-washed red blood cells suspended in Ringer-albumin solution, glucose uptake into the brain ceases, and the brain continues to oxidize endogenous substances after one to one and one-half hours of perfusion. The insertion of an isolated liver into the perfusion circuit, or the addition of fresh liver or muscle extract, or, as was shown later, the addition of uridine and cytidine, restores the glucose uptake by the brain (38).

The mechanism of action of uridine and of cytidine is not clear, but observations showing the oxidation of galactose and glycerol derived from lipids and of fatty acids are indications of the mode of action of these nucleosides. It was recently shown (62) that 5-hydroxytryptophane or 5-hydroxyptamine in the blood also helps to increase the content of reducing substances in the brain. These experiments indicated an active transport mechanism for the glucose into the brain, in which substances produced by the liver or the above-mentioned chemicals are involved.

The brain can utilize mannose as well as glucose. When, during a perfusion with simplified blood, and without the addition of liver substances or uridine, glucose uptake into the brain ceases; mannose still can be taken up by the brain and utilized. And vice versa, if the perfusion is started with mannose, a simi-

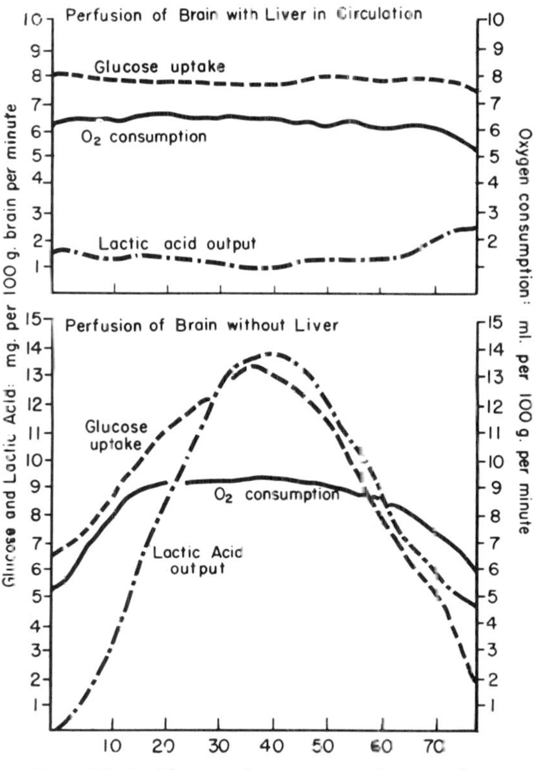

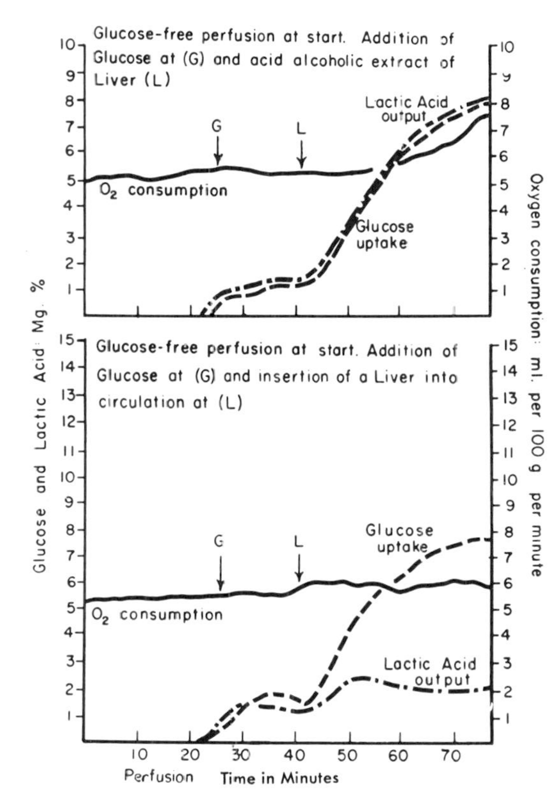

FIG. 10-1. Shows the course of a perfusion of brain with and without the liver in the circulation, and the effect of a liver extract.

Table 10-1. Effect of Uridine and of Cytidine on the Lipid Galactose and Lipid P Content of Brain*

Type of experiment	*Perfusion time*	*Additions*	*mg. in 100 gm. brain*	
			lipid galactose	*lipid-P*
A	0	None		
	30		326	186
	60		282	131
	90		211	131
C	0	15 mg. each of cytidine and uridine		
	30		339	194
	60		319	187
	65	15 mg. each of cytidine and uridine		
	110		330	196
	115	15 mg. each of cytidine and uridine		
	155		343	202
D	0	None		
	60		221	153
	65	15 mg. of uridine		
	78		266	147
	80	15 mg. of cytidine		
	95		280	191
	98	20 mg. each of uridine and cytidine		
	150		288	195

* A. Geiger and S. Yamasaki. *J. Neurochem. 1:* 98, 1956.

lar situation prevails with respect to glucose (33) (Fig. 10-2). This indicates individual transport mechanisms for individual sugars.

Various mechanisms have been proposed for the chemical transport mechanism of sugars into living cells. Mutarotase catalyzes the alpha-beta interconversion of sugars (52), and it is suggested that it converts the sugars into a "preferentially absorbed form," supposedly a free aldehyde. This enzyme has been found in liver and kidney and brain. The Michaelis-Menten constant of this enzyme in the brain, as calculated, corresponds to the average rates at which glucose is utilized in the brain (53). The role of insulin in glucose transport across cell boundaries, as postulated for other tissue (59, 66), cannot be easily reconciled in the brain with the fact that insulin does not penetrate into

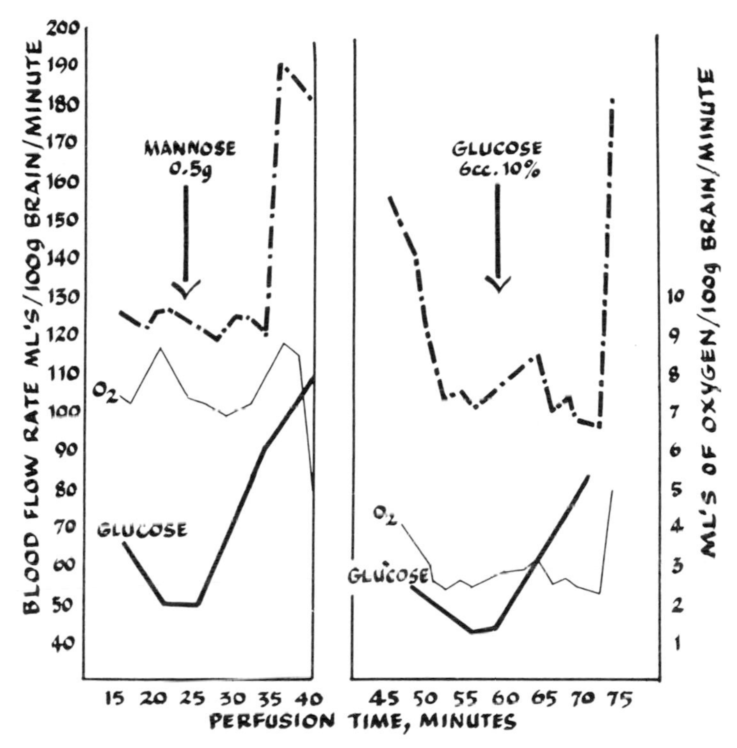

FIG. 10-2. Shows the utilization of glucose and of mannose by the brain. When glucose uptake is blocked, mannose still can be taken up, and vice versa. (*Left*) Perfusion started with glucose. (*Right*) Perfusion started with mannose.

the brain from the blood (44). Nevertheless, insulin added to the perfusion blood in recent perfusion experiments slightly increases sugar oxidations in the brain (61). It should be mentioned that, according to Goldstein (40), an unidentified chemical compound produced by strenuously working muscles is effective even in the absence of insulin to promote glucose uptake by the muscles. This compound, however, does not affect the utilization of glucose (92). It is possible that the same substance is also active in the transfer of glucose into the brain, as muscle extracts had similar affects to that of liver extracts in perfusion experiments.

It seems that the first step in the process of glucose utilization is operating on the "blood brain barrier" level. In this connection, the findings of Wolf and Tschirgi (92) are of interest. Their work shows that the central nervous system utilizes glucose only if it is taken up from the blood, but not if it is supplied directly to the cerebrospinal fluid by perfusing the subarachnoid spaces with solutions containing glucose up to 600 mg. per cent. It is, therefore, possible that the glucose transport mechanism of the brain is located in the glial coverings of the brain capillaries. All the available data indicate that the selectivity of the intact brain in uptake of hexoses resides in the "blood brain barrier," a glial layer interposed between the brain capillaries and the neurons. This latter assumption seems to be well founded (10). In support of this mechanism, a recent observation of Ruth Geiger in tissue cultures may be significant (39). In this work, brain capillaries with the surrounding glial cells and neurons were cultured in a media containing very small amounts of phenol red as indicator. The capillary cement concentrated this dye. A few sucker feet of astrocytes touching the capillary were seen to further concentrate it, and to take it up into the cell bodies. None of the astrocytes which are not in contact with the capillary has shown any trace of this dye.

These observations show the ability of the astrocytic glial cells to take up and to concentrate some material, but only from the capillaries. These findings and those before-mentioned of Wolf and Tschirgi are indications of an interdependence of capillary walls and glial cells in the process of taking up glucose and other substances into the brain. The only disturbance of this process known to the writer was observed during brain perfusion in the absence of liver (Fig. 10-1). Such experiments indicated recently that not only uridine and cytidine but some other compounds supplied by the liver are also necessary for the survival of the perfused brain (26). In the absence of these compounds, glucose uptake into the brain ceases, and the brain is utilizing endogenous metabolites. Perfusion experiments in which glucose was absent from the blood have shown that the brain can survive for one to two hours on its endogenous metabolites and continue its oxidative metabolism at a slightly reduced rate if the cerebral blood flow rate is sufficiently accelerated (37). Under such conditions phospholipids, nucleic acids, and proteins are broken down and oxidized (2) as shown in Table 10-1. Some

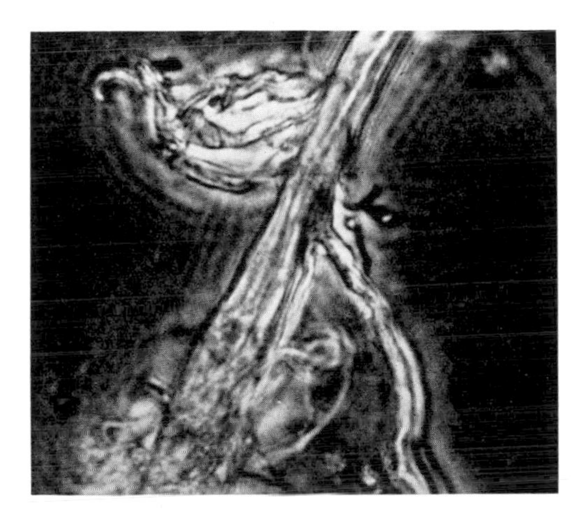

Fig. 10-3. Shows that the capillary ground substance concentrates phenol red and that from there the sucker feet of the astrocytes take up this substance. (This picture was obtained from adult brain cultures and kindly lent by Ruth S. Geiger. See reference 39.)

of the physiological responses of the brain survive until about 50 per cent of the microsomal nucleic acids are used up.

Fructose is taken up by the intact brain very slowly, and is not metabolized by the perfused brain, even if it is forced into it by an extremely high concentration of fructose in the blood prior to perfusion (36). However, brain slices do oxidize fructose and brain homogenates glycolyze it at even higher rates than glucose. The mode of utilization of fructose in brain slices is probably not identical with those of glucose, as was shown recently in Quastel's laboratory (55). For one thing the labeling of aspartic acid by uniformly labeled fructose far exceeds that found after incubation with uniformly labeled glucose. According to these authors the low amount of pyruvate and acetyl CoA formation from fructose is mainly responsible for this difference.

Glucose transport in other organs and possibly in the brain is interconnected with cation transport or with the concentration of various cations inside and outside of the cell (56). In recent observations of Csaky and Zollicoffer (18), resorption of glucose from a loop of intestine perfused in situ with glucose dissolved in

Table 10-2. Changes in Acid-insoluble Phosphorus Components of Cat Cerebral Cortex during Glucose-free and Glucose Perfusion*

Fraction	*Phospholipid-P*			*Phosphoprotein P*			*(Nucleic Acid) (as Nucleotides)*		
	a	*b*	*Decr. %*	*a*	*b*	*Decr. %*	*a*	*b*	*Decr. %*
Exper. 10 (glucose-free)									
R_2	37.0	35.2	5	2.50	2.21	12	1.08	1.10	1
R_3	11.9	4.3	64	0.35	0.22	37	0.59	0.25	58
S	2.7	1.0	63	0.30	0.08	73	0.74	0.38	40
Exper. 11 (glucose-free)									
R_2	32.0	28.6	12	2.40	2.05	15	1.10	0.99	10
R_3	9.3	7.2	22	0.58	0.37	36	0.75	0.50	33
S	2.7	1.8	33	0.37	0.17	54	0.90	0.77	14
Exper. 12 (glucose)									
R_2	37.0	36.0	3	2.40	2.28	8	1.20	1.23	2
R_3	12.0	11.1	9	0.36	0.30	17	0.68	0.60	11
S	2.9	2.8	4	0.26	0.21	19	0.65	0.58	11

Sample *a* removed 10 min. after perfusion was begun; sample *b* 60 min. later. Values expressed as μmole/Gm. of tissue. R_2 = mitochondria, R_3 = microsomes, S = supernatant.

* L. G. Abood and A. Geiger, *Am. J. Physiol. 182:* 557, 1955.

isosmotic solution of Na_2SO_4, or Li_2SO_4, or K_2SO_4, or $MgSO_4$ (upper jejunum of a rat) was rapid from sodium sulfate solution, but it was inhibited by 75–90 per cent when the sodium was replaced by lithium or potassium or magnesium.

The possibility of proteins or peptides participating in the first steps of glucose metabolism (possibly in their transport) is indicated by recent findings of Walaas *et al.* (88). According to these authors, C^{14} glucose is very rapidly (within seconds) incorporated into a glucosan-peptide complex in the diaphragm of the rat. No such compound has yet been demonstrated in the brain. It was shown by Wertheimer *et al.* (7) that in the blood serum of starved rats a protein is present which inhibits glucose incorporation into glycogen of rat diaphragm. Similarly, a globulin fraction has been isolated from normal blood serum (86) which inhibits glucose uptake by the diaphragm of normal rats. This protein acts like an antagonist of insulin. Recently, Rafaelson (73) reported that insulin increased the glucose uptake by the spinal cord and by peripheral nerves of alloxan diabetic rats, when the cord and nerves were incubated in vitro in physiological saline solution. According to these authors, insulin also increased the glucose uptake of brain cortex slices possessing an intact, pia-covered surface, whereas slices not covered by pia having artificial surfaces were uninfluenced by insulin.

Considerable hexokinase activity in the brain was found by Ochoa (64), and by Weil-Malherbe and Bone (90). In studies on enzymic phosphorylation, Long (59) observed that next to muscle and small intestine hexokinase was most abundant in brain. Crane and Sols (17) have found brain hexokinase tightly bound to subcellular particles. Brain contains one hexokinase, which is more specific to glucose than to other sugars, and is strongly inhibited by hexose monophosphates, as was found by Ochoa, and in Cori's laboratory. The relatively high ATP-ase activity in brain homogenates frustrated earlier attempts at obtaining glycolyzing brain extracts (35). The localization of the hexokinase seems to be in the membrane and mitochondria of the cells. Lowry (60) found a considerable amount of hexokinase in isolated neurons of various cerebral origin. No such measurements on glia are known to the writer. It would be of interest to have a comparison. In this connection, Lowry's observation that the hexokinase activity of a whole brain cortex piece was usually almost twice as high as that of any individual neuron (calculated for dry weight) would indicate that the hexokinase activity is higher in glia than in neurons.

The Hexose Monophosphate Shunt

The question, whether this pathway is possible in the brain, has been examined by Coxon (15) in a recent review of the carbohydrate metabolism of the brain. It was generally assumed that the glycolytic pathway and the tricarboxylic cycle are the main mechanisms by which carbohydrates are utilized in the brain (8), and little or no importance was attributed to the oxidation of the hexose-6-phosphate via the shunt. However, most of the intermediates of the glucose-6-phosphate-oxidase pathway were found to be present in the brain (19) and nervous tissue. Recently it was shown that the pentose phosphate pathway in brain and retina can be stimulated to increased activity by various chemicals (14, 48).

The work of Salmony and Whitehead (75) rules out the oxidation of glucose via gluconate without phosphorylation. As shown above, the brain can utilize mannose as well as glucose, but transport mechanisms involved are in part different.

Phosphomannoisomerase found in red blood cells has been characterized by Bruns and Noltman (11). It is an SH dependent metal enzyme complex. The occurrence of this enzyme in the brain has not yet been shown directly, although the easy utilization of mannose by the brain makes the presence in high activity likely.

Kabib and Leloir (49) isolated first from yeast guanosine diphosphomannose, which is similar in structure to uridine diphosphate glucose. Strominger (80) found this compound to be present in mammalian tissue.

Guanine Nucleotides in Brain

Kerr (51) found that roughly 15–20 per cent of the acid-soluble nucleotides in dog brain were guanine derivatives, the rest being mainly adenine nucleotides. More recent and definite identification techniques in Potter's laboratory (78) found the presence of G-5-P and of GTP in rat brain extracts. Heald (45) confirmed these results. It is noteworthy that in skeletal muscle the concentration of guanine nucleotides is much lower, making up only 2–3 per cent of the total nucleotides (85).

Glycogen

The structure of glycogen in tissues other than brain has been examined rather extensively. In the brain, most recent information comes from Russian authors. Goncharova (42) analyzed the glycogen from rabbit brain and also liver. It was concluded that brain glycogen is more branched and has shorter side chains than had liver. Khaikina and Krachko (54) extracted brain glycogen with a method developed for differential extraction after administration of C^{14} glucose. Most of the glycogen (about 60 per cent) was found to be bound to proteins, and about 15 per cent was found in free form. Fifteen per cent of the protein-bound glycogen could be extracted with dilute NaCl. The turnover rate of the free glycogen was very rapid, whereas that of the protein-bound glycogen was slow. Shimizu and Hamuro (79), by histochemical staining techniques, also found evidence of bound and labile forms of brain glycogen. Papers from Dr. Vladimirov's (86a) laboratory also indicate fast turnover rate in the labile glycogen and a very slow one in the bound glycogen. These experiments indicate the presence of at least two forms of glycogen in the brain, only one of them being active metabolically.

Normally, the brain contains about 0.4 to 0.6 mg. of glycogen of which about 15 per cent is labile, while the other part is bound more directly to structural components, probably proteins (42, 54). According to the findings of Kerr and his collaborators (50), the glycogen content of the brain diminishes during hypoglycemia, and slightly during or after electroshock. In the writer's experience, even after two hours of glucose-free perfusion, about 20–30 mg. per cent of glycogen can be extracted from the brain cortex. In studies with C^{14} labeled glucose (42, 54), it has been found that there is a very rapid turnover rate of the 15 per cent of labile glycogen, while that of the bound glycogen was slow.

The metabolism of glycogen has been discussed in McIlwain's monograph (63). Respiring brain slices under proper conditions can resynthesize glycogen which was lost during the preparation. Short-term electrical stimulation had no effect on the glycogen remaining after the initial depletion. Prokhorova (68) calculated that about 5 to 10 per cent of the utilized C^{14} glucose was accounted for by glycogen production. Coxon and Henderson (16) found that brain glycogen was heavily labeled in vivo from both C^{14} glucose and C^{14} bicarbonate. Labeling of the glycogen by $C^{14}O_2$ in the brain can occur only by an indirect way, if glucose from the liver is taken up. Svorad (84) found that, when brain tissue is frozen in situ, hypnosis in animals induces increased glycogen content in the diencephalon, mesencephalon, and medulla oblongata.

Among all the organs studied brain alone cannot produce a cofactor 3′5 cyclic adenosine monophosphate which is necessary for the synthesis of phosphorylase-A from the 2 phosphorylases B (82, 83). The formation of this cofactor from ATP in the presence of magnesium by subcellular particulates of liver, heart, and skeletal muscle is markedly accelerated by glucagon and epinephrine. However, epinephrine did not stimulate the generation of cofactor in the brain.

Hyaluronic acid had been extracted from peripheral nerve, and its existence demonstrated with a special staining technique by Abood and Abul-Haj (1). The existing knowledge has been summarized by Brante in two reviews (9).

Increased anaerobic glycolysis in the presence of narcotic barbiturates was shown by Greig (43), Rosenberg (74), and Webb and Elliott (89).

At a concentration of 0.5 mM, sodium Amytal exerts but a small inhibitory effect on the oxidation of glucose by the unstimulated brain cortex slices, but suppresses almost completely the potassium-stimulated increment in respiration in the presence of glucose, as shown by Quastel (69, 70).

Potter *et al.* (67) find that excess TPN and TPNH inhibit glycolysis of brain. In perfusion experiments, addition of 1 to 2 mg. of ATP, ADP, and adenosine-5-P reduces the oxygen consumption of the brain to a negligible level, with accompanying increase of the vascular resistance.

Quastel proposes the following mechanism of narcosis by Amytal: Oxidation of DPNH is inhibited by Amytal, thereby reducing the amount of DPN available, so that less pyruvate is oxidized to acetyl CoA and less alpha ketoglutarate to glutamate. The latter reaction is reflected by an increased formation of gamma aminobutyrate.

In Kini and Quastel's (55) experiments on brain slices, the labeling of glutamic acid with either uniformly C^{14} labeled fructose or glucose is highest among the amino acids investigated, aspartic acid showing the next highest activity with

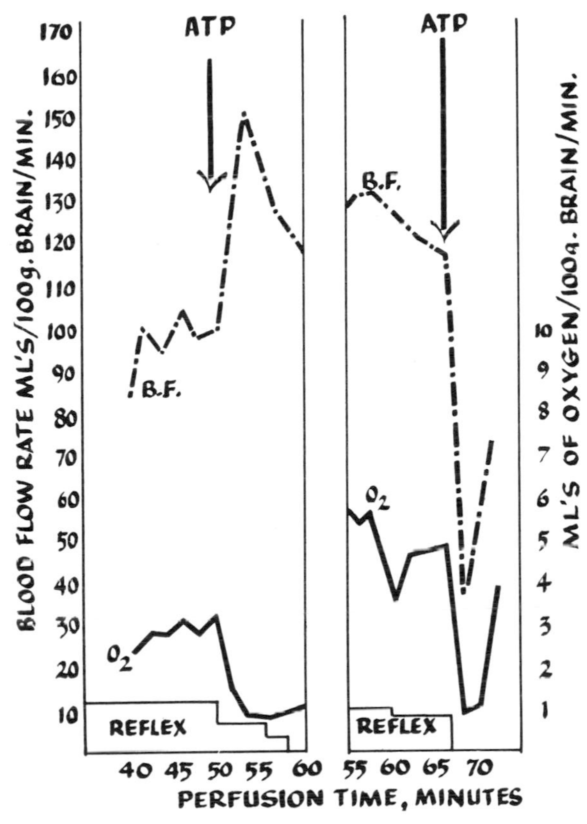

FIG. 10-4. Shows the effect of ATP on cerebral oxygen consumption and on the vascular resistance in the brain. When added to the perfusion blood in concentrations of 2 mg. in 100 ml. The graph on the left side shows that there is an inhibition of oxidation even when the blood flow rate is increased by increased perfusion pressure.

glucose. It is noteworthy that the labeling of aspartic acid in incubated brain slices with uniformly labeled *fructose* greatly exceeds that of this amino acid found after incubation with uniformly labeled glucose.

Another pathway in the carbohydrate utilization is the formation of lipids first via incorporation of galactose into galactolipids. It has been shown by Radin *et al.* (71, 72) and by Burton *et al.* (12) that labeled galactose was incorporated into galactolipids. In the writer's laboratory, after the administration of uniformly C^{14} labeled glucose in perfusion experiments, the label is found in the galactose obtained from galactolipids by hydrolysis. Studies on the mechanism of incorporation of galactose into lipids has been described recently by Burton *et al.* (12).

The "Metabolic Pattern" of the Brain

This brings us to the question of utilization of glucose via noncarbohydrates. It has been shown as early as 1952 by Winzler *et al.* (91), and later by Chain *et al.* (6) and by Quastel *et al.* (69, 70) that amino acids are formed from administered uniformly C^{14} labeled glucose in brain slices. In the work of the writer and his colleagues, in brain perfusion experiments, it was shown that amino acids are formed rapidly from uniformly C^{14} labeled glucose by the brain, and proteins and lipids more slowly, when C^{14} labeled glucose was the only substrate present in the perfusion blood. As most enzyme systems which were found in other tissues are also present in the brain in varying amounts, many of the intermediary metabolites of glucose can be metabolized via a number of alternative interlocking pathways. The rapid progress of biochemistry uncovered a very large number of biochemical mechanisms, which offer a bewildering number of alternative choices for a metabolite to travel. Thus the questions confront us: What is the normal pattern of the metabolism in the brain really like, what are its regulatory mechanisms, and what kind of changes are brought about in this pattern by different physiological conditions, such as drugs, etc.? The well-known differences between different areas in the brain with respect to their reactivity to various chemical compounds similarly emphasize the need for knowing their metabolic pattern. With these questions in mind, a considerable number of experiments were made by the writer and his colleagues, first to determine roughly the metabolic fate of glucose entering the brain from the blood.

All these experiments were done on the brain in situ and in vivo with brain circulation completely isolated from the rest of the body while maintaining intact nerve connections with the rest of the body, while the brain is perfused with a so-called "simplified perfusion blood" consisting of well-washed bovine red blood cells suspended in a bovine serum-albumin-Ringer solution. By using uniformly C^{14} labeled glucose as the only substrate offered to the brain in the perfusion blood and by simultaneous measurements of the arteriovenous differences of various compounds, and by measuring the rates of C^{14} incorporation into the various "key" metabolites of the brain, a pattern emerges, which indicates the origin of various metabolites and the relative amounts in which they enter the metabolic pool.

Previous work has shown (32) that, after a perfusion time of around 30 to 40 minutes with uniformly C^{14} labeled glucose, all the pre-existing glucose and its glycolytic metabolites have been exchanged by the incoming glucose and the specific activity of the CO_2 produced by the brain relative to the glucose-carbons reached a figure indicating that only about 30 per cent of the CO_2 is derived from glucose (Fig. 10-5). From then on, this C^{14}/C^{12} ratio and the rate of CO_2 production remained constant even in experiments lasting for up to five hours (Fig. 10-5). Similar observations have been made by Allweiss and Magnes (4), and experiments on living human brain by Sachs *et al.* (76). Experiments with various brain preparations have also shown that carbon from endogenous sources other than glucose participates in CO_2 production.

Sutherland *et al.* (81) found that, in excised surviving brain tissue incubated with uniformly C^{14} labeled glucose, the glucose oxidized amounted to only about 50 per cent of the total oxygen consumption. The lactic acid produced, however, was entirely derived from the C^{14} glucose added to the incubation mixture via the Embden-Meyerhof cycle. Erbslöh *et al.* (20) found that, although the glucose consumption and the oxygen consumption of the brain of patients suffering from chronic liver diseases (mainly cirrhoses) and in patients suffering from acute heptatitis are normal, in precoma hepaticum the glucose consumption of the

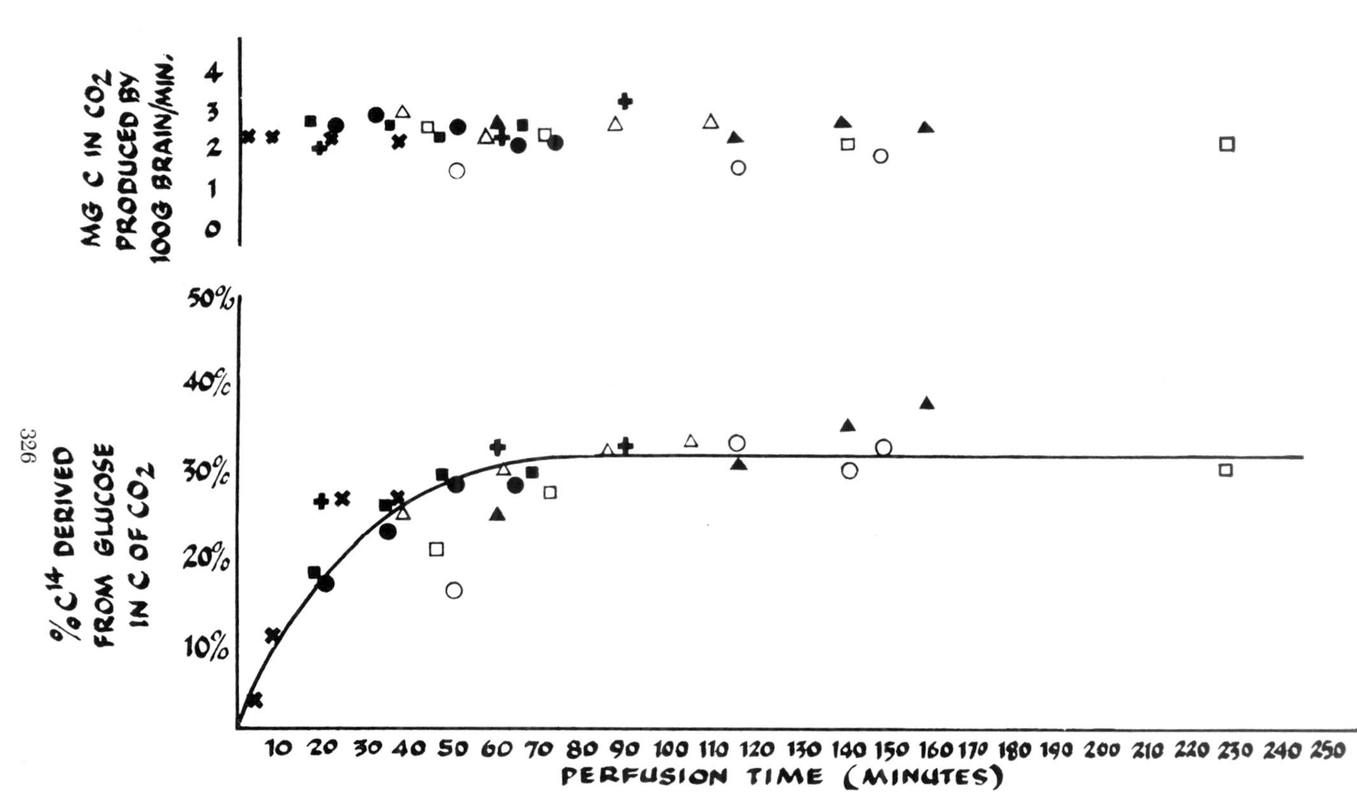

FIG. 10-5. Shows the C^{14} derived from glucose in the respiratory CO_2 of the brain, expressed as per cent of the total C in the respiratory CO_2.

brain drops sharply, whereas oxygen consumption remains normal. Only later when coma sets in, is there also a drop in its oxygen consumption. A similar dissociation of the rates of the glucose consumption from that of the oxygen consumption of the brain has also been observed by these authors in Wilson's disease and in encephalopathies. These findings show that the brain in these pathological conditions can, for a while, use substrates other than glucose, to a great extent, much like that in the glucose-free perfusion experiments. Allweiss and Magnes (4) in brain perfusion experiments, similar to those of the writer, found that only about 30 per cent of the respiratory CO_2 of the brain is derived from glucose. The rest of the glucose taken up by the brain is transformed partly into lactic acid and other compounds, thus leaving about 70 per cent of the oxidations in the brain to be accounted for by endogenous (probably noncarbohydrate) substrates. Important contributions to the problem of pathways of glucose utilization in the intact human were made by Sachs (77). This author investigated the C^{14} contents of CO_2, glucose, lactic acid, pyruvic acid, and their relative specific activities in intact humans in the arterial and cerebral venous blood, using Kety's technique (53a), after intravenous administration of glucose labeled with C^{14}, uniformly, in C-1, C-6, C-3, and in C-4 positions. They found that most or all of the glucose oxidized went through the glycolytic pathway and probably none through the shunt pathway. They also found, in the course of experiments extending to 100 minutes, that in normal subjects there was a considerable and constant production of CO_2 from sources other than glucose by the brain, amounting to about 46 per cent of the total CO_2 production. In mental patients, this fraction amounted to an average of 74 per cent. The indications, therefore, seem to be very strong that under normal conditions, as well as in perfusion experiments, substances other than glucose (or possibly carbohydrates) are contributing a great portion of the respiratory CO_2 of the brain, and that part of the glucose taken up is utilized via synthetic reactions.

The relative amounts of $C^{14}O_2$ derived from glucose in the respiratory CO_2 of the brain in writer's experiments changed in various states of activity and under the influence of some drugs. Thus, after convulsions evoked by electric current or by Metrazol, when there was a twofold increase of the total CO_2 formation, the rate at which $C^{14}O_2$ was formed from glucose remained constant or even diminished in some cases. The absence of any increase in the amount of carbon derived from glucose in the respiratory CO_2, when the total CO_2 output is as considerably increased, could only mean an increased rate of oxidation of substances other than glucose, i.e., lipids and proteins, and other substances. These experiments, together with others reported previously (22), indicate that the extra energy required during increased activity of the central nervous system is derived from oxidation of noncarbohydrate substance.

In order to find where in the glycolytic and tricarboxylic cycles the major dilution of the glucose-carbons occurs, intermediary metabolites were isolated from the brain, and their C^{14} content was determined and compared to that of glucose. The specific activity of the lactic acid C, isolated from the brain at various times during the perfusion, as compared to that of the glucose remains constant, at a level of 50 per cent of that of glucose (28); that of the glutamic acid reaches a constant figure after about 50 to 60 minutes of perfusion at about the same level as the specific activity of the CO_2; and that of the aspartate at a lower level, than that of glutamate. This indicates a constant influx of cold carbon into the metabolic pool from sources large enough not to acquire appreciable amounts of C^{14} during a perfusion period of up to five hours.

As seen from the relative specific activities of lactate and of glucose, the largest dilution of glucose-carbon occurs between the uptake of glucose and pyruvate formation. The source of this carbon is at present not known with certainty, but considering the constancy of the relative specific activity of lactate during perfusions lasting up to five hours, it has to come from very large pools, which do not become appreciably radioactive during this period of time. It may be galactose and glycerol derived from lipids.

The conversion of galactose to glucose involves the action of four enzymes: galactokinase, galactose-1-phosphate uridyl transferase, UDP galactose-4-epimerase, and UDPG pyrophosphorylase. Two of these enzymes—UDPG pyrophosphorylase and the epimerase—occur in brain in comparatively high concentrations, the concentration of the other two enzymes being rather small (12). Thus, the conversion of galactose to glucose phosphate proceeds at best at a very slow rate. Burton thinks that it is possible that in congenital galactosemia, where (according to Kalckar and his associates—47a) the concentration of galactose-1-phosphate uridyl transferase is very low, the accumulating galactose-1-phosphate may be inhibitory to the glycolytic pathway.

This possibility is also indicated by the necessity of the presence of uridine and cytidine in the perfusion blood (38). In the absence of these substances all the glucose metabolism of the brain is impaired, and lipids—mainly galactolipids—are depleted from the brain. This loss can be prevented, or corrected, by adding these nucleosides to the perfusion blood. This is shown in Figure 10-1.

An important finding in these perfusion experiments has been the remarkable degree of constancy in the amount and composition of the amino acid pool under varying conditions. The total amino acid pool (approximately 150 mg. C/100 Gm. brain) is very much larger than that made up of pyruvate and of the intermediates of the tricarboxylic acid cycle (probably less than 1 mg./100 Gm. brain).

By transaminase activity it would be reasonable to expect a rapid exchange and equilibration of alanine, aspartic acid, and glutamic acid carbon with that of pyruvate and of the di- and tricarboxylic acids. From these amino acids radiocarbon would gain entry into a number of others by further familiar reactions, e.g., transamination, amination, decarboxylation, etc. Since glycolysis represents, presumably, the major, if not exclusive, pathway for breakdown of glucose in brain, one-third of the respired CO_2 is contributed by the 3 and 4 carbons of glucose by way of pyruvate and two-thirds come by way of the cycle (glucose-carbons 1, 2, 5, 6). If we assume that the only source of carbon exchanging with pyruvate and cycle intermediates is the amino acid pool and that such exchange occurs at an at least equal and nonlimiting rate in relation to the turnover of the former, then the specific radioactivity of the respired CO_2 should closely parallel and be almost equal to that of all these metabolites. This is evidently not the case, as can be seen from Figure 10-5 and Table 10-3 in which the acquisition of radioactivity by the amino acid pool and more particularly of glutamic acid lags behind and does not come up to the level of carbon dioxide during the course of the first 50 to 60 minutes of perfusion. After this time, however, it was seen in experiments, lasting four to five hours, that the specific activity of these amino acids reaches a constant value which does not change further, indicating that equilibrium with the whole metabolic pool has been reached. These findings are not surprising, however, since the principal amino acid with which pyruvate would be expected to exchange rapidly, namely, alanine, makes up a small fraction of the amino acid pool (less than 5 per cent) whereas glutamic and aspartic and their derivatives, which would exchange with cycle intermediates, comprise the major part of the free amino acids. Consequently, the dilution of pyruvate carbons by amino acid carbon may be considered negligible compared to the dilution of the cycle intermediates from this source. That portion of the respired carbon dioxide which comes from the oxidative decarboxylation of pyruvate should, therefore, contain a higher radioactivity than that arising from the cycle until such time as the cold carbon from the amino acids exchanging with cycle intermediates has been replaced. Consequently, the slower rise of amino acid radioactivity in relation to that of respired CO_2 can be readily understood. The specific activity of glutamic and aspartic acids was found to be a good gage of the activity of the tricarboxylic acid cycle components.

An important feature of the data presented in Figure 10-5 and Table 10-3 is not, however, explained by the foregoing consideration, namely, that the radioactivity of both the respired CO_2 and the amino acids increases during roughly the first half of perfusion and then remains at a constant level during the balance of the perfusion time. If one again assumes a simple situation in which carbon from exogenous glucose exclusively (or almost so)

Table 10-3. Incorporation of C^{14} Derived from U-C^{14} Glucose into Various Metabolites During Perfusion

Experiment	*Duration of perfusion with U-C^{14} glucose*	*% of glucose-carbon found in the carbon of:*			
		CO_2	*Glutamic acid*	*Aspartic acid*	*GABA*
Apr. 30, 1959	18′	18.5%			
	30–35′	26.0%	5.7%		
	40–45′	29.5%	9.0%		
	50–55′		28.0%		
	65–75′	29.2%	30.2%		
Feb. 9, 1960	20′	26.7%			
	60′	33.0%			
	90′	32.5%	32.5%	23.5%	
Nov. 3, 1960	46′	20%			
	83′	28.5%			
	143′	30%			
	229′	31%	35%	21%	
Apr. 25, 1961	−60′	26%			
	116′	32%			
	142′	35%			
	160′	38%			
	177′		40%	28%	16%
May 23, 1961 Hypoxia	30′	15%			
	90′	45%			
	141′	41%	42%	37.5%	15%
June 15, 1961 Hypoxia	42′	31.7%			
	70′	47.5%			
	100′	48.5%			
	136′	49.5%			
	156′		47%	43%	22%

replenishes the glycolytic and cycle intermediates and that the amino acids represent the only carbon pool which rapidly equilibrates with these carbons, then at the rates in which glucose is being taken up by the brain, and accepting certain values for the concentrations of the glycolytic intermediates, we can predict the pattern and some of the dimensions of the rates of increase of radioactivity in carbon dioxide and the amino acids. Under these circumstances, the level of radioactivity in carbon dioxide would increase at a fairly rapid and constant rate during the period in which the pre-existing pool of glucose and glycolytic intermediates was being replaced by C^{14} glucose; then at a slower but nonetheless appreciable rate during the period in which the amino acid carbon was equilibrating with tricarboxylic acid cycle intermediates. At the point of near-completion of the exchange of amino acid carbon, the radioactivity of the respired CO_2 would be expected to rise at a very slow rate, reflecting the rate of entry of cold carbon from the combined turnover of brain lipid, protein, and nucleic acids.

In most of these experiments, glucose-carbon is taken up by the brain at a rate of 4–5 mg. C/min./100 Gm. brain. A fairly constant value of 2.6 mg. C/min. of this entering glucose-carbon (which equals the rate at which CO_2 carbon is given off) is available for supporting brain metabolism whereas the balance is put back into the perfusing blood as lactic acid. At this rate of glucose C^{14} input, and taking into consideration the exchange of glucose betwen blood and brain, it has been estimated (32) that the pre-existing brain glucose would be completely replaced in 5 to 10 minutes. Since the glycolytic intermediates make up a total pool of about 32 mg. C (3) it can be calculated that within 25 minutes after the addition of C^{14} glucose to the perfusion blood these intermediates would have 90 per cent or better of the specific activity of the glucose. During this period, the radioactivity of the respired carbon dioxide would increase until by 25 minutes it should be 30 per cent of the glucose (at a minimum) since one-third of the CO_2 carbon would be coming from pyruvate which, at this point, would have a specific activity comparable to glucose. Furthermore, during the first 60 minutes of perfusion with C^{14} glucose, approximately 100 mg. of C^{14} carbon would have entered the cycle and exchanged with 150 mg. amino acid carbon, thus raising the level of radioactivity of amino acid carbon to about 50 per cent that of glucose-carbon.

There would, therefore, be a steady rise in the radioactivity of the respired carbon dioxide from a minimal value of about 30 per cent at 25 minutes to 65 per cent at 60 minutes. As was shown before, this situation can be obtained under the influence of drugs.

It is quite apparent from Figure 10-5 and Table 10-3 that in resting conditions neither the carbon dioxide nor the amino acids conform to this pattern. The data obtained clearly indicate that a source of cold carbon must be feeding into and forming glycolytic and tricarboxylic acid intermediates at a rate which is almost as large as the one in which they are formed from exogenous glucose taken up by the brain. The source of this cold carbon is at present unknown. As mentioned before, the C^{14} content of the pyruvate carbons when equilibrium has been reached is only 50 per cent of that of the glucose-carbons. Thus, a major dilution of the intermediates of the glucose has to occur in the glycolytic cycle. The total uptake of C^{14} into lipids, proteins, and nucleic acids (29) during this period is only a fraction of the amount of cold carbon which is forming carbon dioxide.

Another possibility had to be considered, namely, that part of the dilution of the pyruvate came from the citric acid cycle, by decarboxylation of the oxaloacetate or malate. In order to see the extent of these reactions in the brain, perfusion experiments were made using C^{14} labeled l-aspartate and unlabeled glucose as substrates. It was expected that the labeled aspartate taken up by the brain will by transamination label the oxaloacetate and malate coming through the citric acid cycle, and thus also label the pyruvate at the rate at which decarboxylation proceeds. Such experiments, done with 4-C^{14}, 3-C^{14}, and uniformly C^{14} labeled aspartate, have shown that about 10 per cent of the pyruvate may be derived from such reactions (41).

Similar results were obtained in perfusion experiments in which $NaHC^{14}O_2$ was used with nonlabeled glucose (65). The results on these findings are shown in Figure 10-6.

These findings show a considerable rate of CO_2 assimilation in the brain. The highest concentration of C^{14}, as expected, was found in the aspartate by transamination from oxaloacetate. The glutamate contained 50 per cent of the C^{14} of the aspartate, indicating that no "cold" carbon came into the cycle via acetyl CoA. Similar results were reported previously by Waelsch's group (87).

These experiments also confirm the results obtained with aspartate, namely, that not more than about 10 per cent of the

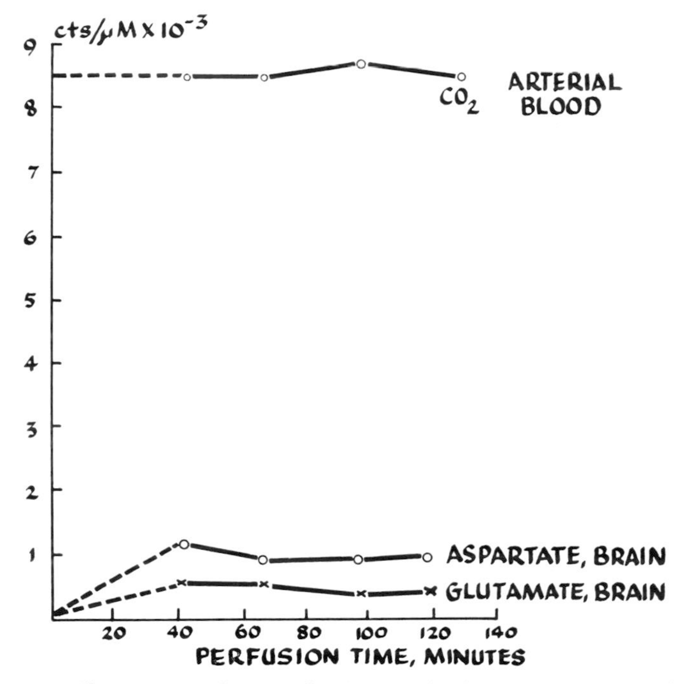

FIG. 10-6. Shows assimilation of $C^{14}O_2$ in the brain and its distribution in various metabolites.

pyruvate may be derived from decarboxylation of the labeled oxaloacetate and malate.

The next step in the chain of metabolic reactions, the condensation of oxaloacetate with acetyl CoA and the formation of alphaketoglutarate through the usual steps, may also introduce "cold" carbon from fatty acids, etc., via acetyl CoA. The data obtained in long-lasting perfusion experiments show that the carbons of the glutamate (formed by transamination from alphaketoglutarate) contain about 65 to 70 per cent of that of the pyruvate, indicating a 30 to 35 per cent dilution of the carbons of the pyruvate at this stage.

Considering that in this step the specific activity of the alpha-ketoglutarate was not analyzed directly, but that of the more easily accessible glutamate, the question arises whether the specific activity of the glutamate reflects truly that of the alpha-ketoglutarate. This question has been answered in the affirmative, as shown elsewhere (25).

The next "key metabolite" analyzed was the free aspartate of the brain. The reason for analyzing the aspartate instead of the oxaloacetate directly is the difficulty in obtaining enough oxaloacetate in pure form from the brain cortex for the determination of its specific activity. Thus, it is assumed that, after a sufficient length of perfusion time, when the aspartate carbons attained a constant specific activity relative to that of the glucose- (or pyruvate) carbons, which did not change during the consequent one to three hours of perfusion, the whole free aspartate pool of the cortex came into equilibrium which the oxaloacetate and that the C^{14} content of the aspartate represents that of the oxaloacetate. This assumption has not been subjected to experimental tests, but there is very little doubt about its being correct, since its validity was proven in the case of glutamic and alphaketoglutaric acids, where the pool of free glutamic acid in the brain is about five times as large as that of the aspartic acid. The respective transaminases are known to be abundantly present in the brain (13).

Table 10-3 shows that the specific activity of the aspartic acid of the normal brain is lower than that of the glutamate by about 30 per cent, indicating a further dilution as reactions proceed from alphaketoglutarate to aspartate.

If we then calculate the contribution of nonglucose-carbon to the metabolites of tricarboxylic acid cycle in the normal perfused brain, using the relative specific activities of such "key metabolites" as the respiratory CO_2, brain pyruvate, glutamate, and aspartate, we find that under normal conditions most of this contribution occurs between the reactions leading from alpha-ketoglutaric to oxaloacetic acid (glutamic to aspartic) with very little if any cold carbon entering the cycle as acetyl CoA.

Under hypoxic conditions, this situation is reversed, and most of the cold carbon seems to enter as acetyl CoA while very little cold carbon, if any, enters the cycle between alphaketoglutarate and oxaloacetate (24).

One of the "key metabolites" in the characterization of the metabolic pattern of the brain is the respiratory CO_2. This is composed of one carbon derived from the decarboxylation of the pyruvate, one from that of the oxalosuccinate in the citric acid cycle, and the third from the alphaketoglutarate, also in the cycle. The two last-mentioned carbon atoms originate from carbons 1 and 4 of the oxaloacetic acid. Under normal conditions, the specific activity of the pyruvate carbon is 50 per cent of that of the glucose-carbon, and the specific activity of the respiratory CO_2 is around 30 per cent. This represents the sum of one carbon atom of the pyruvate carrying a 50 per cent label and of two other carbon atoms carrying the label of the oxaloacetate, each of these two, 25 per cent of that of the glucose. Thus the C^{14} content of the CO_2 can be predicted from that of the pyruvate and of the oxaloacetate.

The same calculation, applied to a ketoglutarate or glutamate, shows that if "cold" carbon does not enter the Krebs cycle as acetyl CoA, the ketoglutarate should contain 32.5 per cent of the C^{14} of glucose. In fact, 34 per cent of C^{14} derived from glucose was found in the brain glutamate consistently in a large number of experiments. These findings then strongly indicate that practically all the acetyl CoA is derived from pyruvate, and that no "cold" carbon enters the Krebs cycle at this stage.

The correctness of this calculation was confirmed by the experiments mentioned before in which the assimilation of CO_2 was studied in the brain. Here the C^{14} content of the glutamic acid was exactly 50 per cent of the aspartate (Mol. per Mol.) which is consistent with the fact that the assimilated C^{14} is in the 1 and 4 carbons of the aspartate, and that only one of these carbons is present in the glutamate. The other was eliminated by decarboxylation of the oxalosuccinate. These findings also show that no "cold" carbon enters the Krebs cycle in any noticeable amounts as acetyl CoA.

It should be emphasized that the "metabolic pattern" described here was that of the whole brain. Considering the great variations in the sensitivities of various brain areas to hypoxia, the differences between the normal and the hypoxic state in those more sensitive areas must be much larger than found in the whole brain. A schematic presentation of these events is shown in Figure 10-7.

The relative proportions in which glucose and various other endogenous compounds participate in the oxidative metabolism vary under changing physiological conditions (as under the effect of stimulation or of drugs) even if the total oxidation rate remains constant. This raises the question whether the relative proportion of the various substrates (endogenous substrates and glucose) utilized by the brain under various physiological conditions can be regarded as characteristic of any particular physiological conditions.

Stimulation of the brain by electroshock, Metrazol, or through the brachial plexus nearly doubled the total respiratory CO_2 output of the brain, but the C^{14} output remained constant at the "resting" level, thus greatly reducing the C^{14} concentration in the respiratory CO_2. The C^{14} concentration in the lactic acid, also, remained around 50 per cent, as in the "resting" state, indicating that the dilution occurred in the tricarboxylic acid cycle by influx of cold carbon from a large pool which did not become appreciably radioactive during the preceding perfusion time. No significant effects of the label of glutamic acid was seen, although that of the aspartic was diminished. Some drugs (among them isoniazid, iproniazid, phenyl cyclopropylamine) influenced this pattern in the direction of increased proportional participation of glucose C^{14} in CO_2 and lactate formation, presumably by blocking the influx of cold carbon from pools which otherwise dilute the pyruvic acid. In these experiments, the C^{14} concentration in the respiratory CO_2 and in the pyruvic acid (or brain lactic acid) increased steadily and linearly until, after two hours of perfusion, the carbon of these compounds reached a C^{14} concentration of up to 85 per cent of that of the glucose. The C^{14} concentration in glutamic and aspartic acids and in alanine

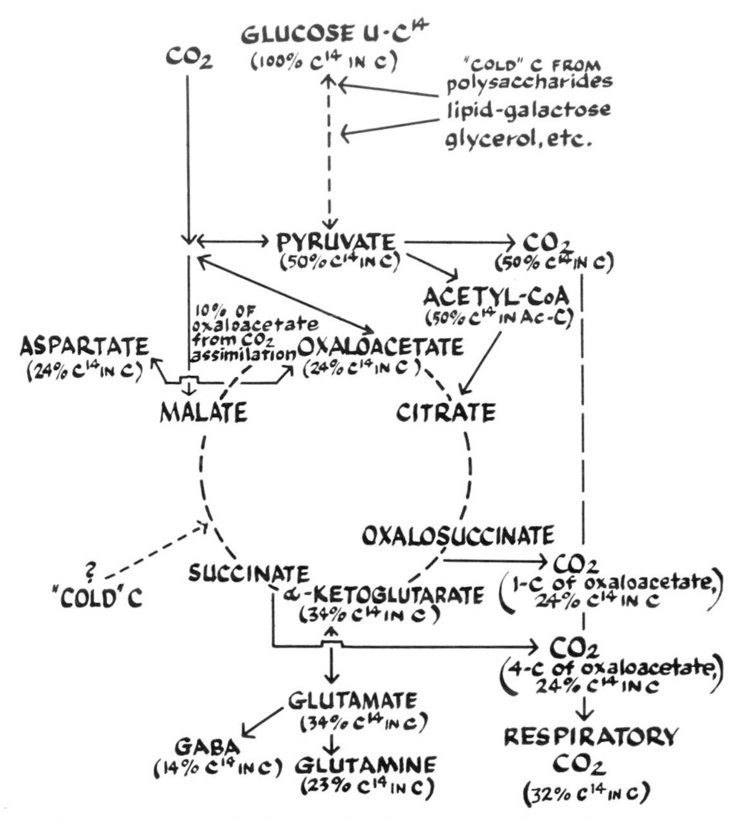

FIG. 10-7. Shows the basic metabolic patterns of the brain in perfusion experiments; the relative amounts of glucose-C^{14} found in various "key" metabolites; the biochemical sites, and the relative rates at which "cold" carbon, from preformed endogenous metabolites, enters the glycolytic and tricarboxylic cycles in the brain.

The C^{14} concentrations found in the C of the glutamate and in the C of the respiratory CO_2 correspond closely to the figures which can be calculated from the C^{14} concentrations found in the C of the aspartate (oxaloacetate) and of the pyruvate, indicating that all of the acetyl-CoA is derived from pyruvate, while a dilution by "cold" carbon occurs between alpha-keto glutarate and oxaloacetate.

did not follow that in the CO_2, but the radioactivity remained at the "resting" level (i.e., 25 to 30 per cent C^{14}), indicating a possible inhibition of transaminases by these drugs.

These experiments demonstrate the flexibility of the metabolic pattern of the brain, and indicate their possible usefulness for the study of the metabolic correlates of physiological function. It should be pointed out that at the present time labeled glucose seems to be the only substrate which is capable of uncovering this pattern. Labeled amino acids, when added to the perfusion blood, show anomalies which can, as indicated by the studies of Lajtha *et al.* (57), be attributed to compartmentalization of various free amino acids within the neurons or between neurons and glia cells.

INCORPORATION OF AMINO ACIDS DERIVED FROM GLUCOSE C^{14} INTO PROTEINS

In brain perfusion experiments in vivo and in situ, uniformly C^{14} labeled glucose was added to a simplified perfusion blood of known composition, and the incorporation of C^{14} into the proteins of the brain cortex was followed at rest and during activity.

The rates of incorporation of glucose C^{14} into the proteins of the brain cortex at "rest" was considerably slower than into free amino acids.

Convulsive activity increased the incorporation rates of C^{14} into proteins. During the convulsions, the incorporation rate was increased. Immediately after the cessation of the convulsions a lag period lasting around 15 minutes followed, during which C^{14} incorporation into proteins entirely ceased and some loss of C^{14} occurred, mainly from the microsomes. After the lag period, the incorporation rates of C^{14} again increased two- to fourfold over the resting incorporation rates.

The incorporation of C^{14} into various cell fractions has been examined. The specific activity of microsomal protein was the highest and that of the mitochondria the lowest. However, most of the C^{14} incorporated into protein was in the mitochondria, as this fraction constitutes about 54 per cent of the total brain proteins.

The same characteristic pattern of C^{14} incorporation which was found during stimulation in the whole cortex was also seen in each cellular fraction.

The possible role of the protein metabolism of the brain and its relations to physiological functions has been discussed elsewhere (21, 46).

REFERENCES

1. Abood, L. G., and Abul-Haj, S. K. *J. Neurochem. 1:* 119, 1956.
2. Abood, L. G., and Geiger, A. *Am. J. Physiol. 182:* 557, 1955.
3. Abood, L. G., Gerard, R. W., Banks, J., and Tschirgi, R. D. *Am. J. Physiol. 168:* 728, 1952.
4. Allweiss, C., and Magnes, J. *Abstr. 20th Internatl. Physiol. Congr.*, 1956.
5. Barkulis, S. S., Geiger, A., Kawakita, Y., and Aguilar, V. *J. Neurochem. 5:* 339–348, 1960.
6. Beloff-Chain, A., Catanzaro, R., Chain, E. B., Mase, T., and Pocchiari, F. *Proc. Roy. Soc., London, s. B. 144:* 22, 1956.
7. Berman, E. R., and Wertheimer, E. *Am. J. Physiol. 198:* 1075, 1960.
8. Bloom, B. *Proc. Soc. Exper. Biol. & Med. 88:* 317, 1955.
9. Brante, G. In *Metabolism of the Nervous System,* edited by D. Richter. Pergamon Press, New York, 1957.
10. Brierley, J. B. In *Metabolism of the Nervous System,* edited by D. Richter. Pergamon Press, New York, 1957.
11. Bruns, T. H., and Noltman, E. *Nature. 18:* 1467, 1958.
12. Burton, R. M., Sokol, M. A., and Brady, R. O. *Federation Proc. 16:* 161, 1957.
13. Cohen, P., and Hekhuis, L. *J. Biol. Chem. 140:* 711, 1941.
14. Cohen, L. H., and Noell, W. K. *J. Neurochem. 5:* 253, 1960.
15. Coxon, R. V. In *Metabolism of the Nervous System,* edited by D. Richter. Pergamon Press, New York, 1957.
16. Coxon, R. V., and Henderson, J. R. *Abstr. of Internat'l Congr. of Biochem., 4th meeting,* 1958.
17. Crane, R. K., and Sols, A. T. *J. Biochem. 203:* 273, 1953.
18. Csaky, T. Z., and Zollicoffer, L. *Am. J. Physiol. 198:* 1056, 1960.
19. DiPietro, D., and Weinhouse, S. *Arch. Biochem. Biophys. 80:* 268, 1959.
20. Erbslöh, F., Bernsmeier, A., and Hillesheim, H. R. *Archiv. fur Psychiatri w.z.f.d. ges. Neurologie. 196:* 611, 1958.
21. Geiger, A. In *Neurochemistry,* edited by K. A. C. Elliott, T. H. Page, and J. H. Quastel. Thomas, Springfield, Ill., 1955.

22. GEIGER, A. In *Metabolism of the Nervous System,* edited by D. Richter. Pergamon Press, New York, 1957.
23. GEIGER, A. *Physiol. Rev. 38:* 1, 1958.
24. GEIGER, A. *C.I.O.M.S. Symp. on the Selective Vulnerability of the CNS to Hypoxeamia,* Baden, 1961.
25. GEIGER, A. Unpublished observations.
26. GEIGER, A., GOMBOS, G., and OTSUKI, S. Unpublished observations.
27. GOMBOS, G., and GEIGER, A. Unpublished observations.
28. GEIGER, A., GOMBOS, G., OTSUKI, S., GOTHELF, B., WHITNEY, G., and SCRUGGS, W. In preparation.
29. GEIGER, A., HORVATH, N., and KAWAKITA, Y. *J. Neurochem. 5:* 311–322, 1960.
30. GEIGER, A., and MAGNES, J. *Am. J. Physiol. 149:* 517, 1947.
31. GEIGER, A., MAGNES, J., TAYLOR, R. M., and VARALLIL, M. *Am. J. Physiol. 177:* 138, 1954.
32. GEIGER, A., KAWAKITA, Y., and BARKULIS, S. S. *J. Neurochem. 5:* 323, 1960.
33. GEIGER, A., and MAGNES, J. Unpublished observations.
34. GEIGER, A., and MAGNES, J. Unpublished observations.
35. GEIGER, A., and MAGNES, J. *Biochem. J. 33:* 884, 1939.
36. GEIGER, A., and MAGNES, J. *Federation Proc. 8:* 1, 1949.
37. GEIGER, A., MAGNES, J., and GEIGER, R. S. *Nature. 170:* 754, 1952.
38. GEIGER, A., and YAMASKI, S. *J. Neurochem. 1:* 93, 1956.
39. GEIGER, RUTH S. *International Review of Neuro Biology.* In press.
40. GOLDSTEIN, S., and LEVINE, R. *Am. J. Physiol. 177:* 447, 1954.
41. GOMBOS, G., OTSUKI, S., GEIGER, A., WHITNEY, C., and SCRUGGS, W. In preparation.
42. GONCHAROVA, E. E. *Doklady Akad. Nauk S.S.S.R. 112:* 899, 1957.
43. GREIG, M. E. *J. Pharmacol. & Exper. Therap. 91:* 317, 1947.
44. HAVGAARD, N., VAUGHN, M., HAVGAARD, E. S., and STADIE, W. J. *J. Biol. Chem. 208:* 549, 1954.
45. HEALD, P. J. *Biochem. J. 67:* 529, 1957.
46. HYDÉN, H. In *Biochemistry of the Central Nervous System*, edited by F. Brücke. Pergamon Press, New York, 1959.
47. HIMWICH, H. E. *Brain Metabolism and Cerebral Disorders.* Williams and Wilkens, Baltimore, 1951.
47a. KALCKAR, H. M., ANDERSON, E. P., and ISSELBACHER, K. J. *Proc. Natl. Acad. Sci. U.S. 42:* 49, 1956.
48. HOSKIN, F. C. G. *Biochim. et Biophys. Acta 40:* 309, 1960.
49. CABIB, E., and LEBOIR, L. F. *J. Biol. Chem. 206:* 779, 1956.

50. KERR, S. E., and GHANTUS, M. J. *J. Biol. Chem. 116:* 9, 1936.
51. KERR, S. E., HAMPEL, C. W., and GHANTUS, M. J. *J. Biol. Chem. 119:* 405, 1946.
52. KESTON, A. S. *Science, 120:* 355, 1954.
53. KESTON, A. S. *Federation Proc. 16:* 203, 1957.
53a. KETY, S. S., and SCHMIDT, C. F. *J. Clin. Invest. 27:* 484, 1948.
54. KHAIKINA, B. I., and KRACHKO, L. S. *Ukrian. biokem. zhur. 29:* 10, 1957.
55. KINI, M. M., and QUASTEL, J. H. *Nature. 184:* 252, 1959.
56. KREBS, H. A., and EGGLESTON, L. O. *Biochem. J. 44:* 2, 1949.
57. LAJTHA, A., FURST, S. S., GERSTEIN, A., and WAELSCH, H. *J. Neurochem. 1:* 289, 1957.
58. LEVINE, R., and GOLDSTEIN, M. S. In *Major Metabolic Fuels, Brookhaven Symp. Biol. 5:* 73, 1952.
59. LONG, C. *Biochem. J. 50:* 407, 1952.
60. LOWRY, O. H. In *Metabolism of the Nervous System,* edited by D. Richter. Pergamon Press, New York, 1957.
61. MAGNES, J. Personal communication.
62. MAGNES, J., and HESTRIN-LERNER, S. *J. Neurochem. 5:* 128, 1960.
63. MCILWAIN, H. *Biochemistry and the Central Nervous System.* Little, Brown & Co., Boston, 1955.
64. OCHOA, S. *J. Biol. Chem. 141:* 245, 1941.
65. OTSUKI, S., GEIGER, A., GOMBOS, G., WHITNEY, G., and SCRUGGS, W. In preparation.
66. PARK, C. R., BORNSTEIN, J., and POST, R. L. *Am. J. Physiol. 182:* 12, 1955.
67. POTTER, V. R. In *Metabolic Regulations,* edited by G. Wolstenholme and C. O'Connor. Little, Brown & Co., Boston, 1958.
68. PROKHOROVA, M. E. *Chem. Abstr.* p. 57, 268, 1956.
69. QUASTEL, J. H. *Proc. IVth Internat'l Congr. of Biochem.,* Vienna. *3:* 1958.
70. QUASTEL, J. H. In *Biochemistry of the Central Nervous System,* edited by F. Brücek. Pergamon Press, New York, 1959.
71. RADIN, N. S., LAVIN, F. B., and BROWN, J. R. *J. Biochem. 277:* 789, 1955.
72. RADIN, N. S., MARTIN, F. B., BROWN, J. R., and ALLEN, J. R. *Federation Proc. 15:* 333, 1956.
73. RAFAELSON, O. J. *Lancet.* Nov. 1, 1958.
74. ROSENBERG, A. F., BUCHEL, L., ETLING, N., and LEVI, J. *C. R. Acad. Sc., Paris. 230:* 480, 1950.

75. SALMONY, D., and WHITEHEAD, J. K. *Biochem. J. 58:* 408, 1954.
76. SACHS, W. J. *J. Appl. Physiol. 10:* 37, 1957, and *14:* 849, 1959.
77. SACHS, W. J. *J. Appl. Physiol. 9:* 43, 1956.
78. SCHMITZ, H., HURLBET, R. B., and POTTER, V. R. *J. Biol. Chem. 209:* 23, 1954.
79. SHIMIZU, N., and HAMURO, Y. *Nature. 181:* 781, 1958.
80. STROMINGER, J. L. *Federation Proc. 13:* 307, 1954.
81. SUTHERLAND, V. C., BURBRIDGE, T. N., and ELLIOTT, H. W. *Am. J. Physiol. 180:* 195, 1955.
82. SUTHERLAND, E. W., and RALL, T. W. *J. Biochem. 232:* 1077, 1958.
83. SUTHERLAND, E. W., and RALL, T. W. *J. Biol. Chem. 232:* 1065, 1958.
84. SVORAD, D. *Nature. 181:* 775, 1958.
85. THRELLFALL, C. J. *Biochem. J. 65:* 694, 1957.
86. VARGAS, L., TAYLOR, R. W., and RANDLE, P. J. *Biochem. J. 77:* 43, 1960.
86a. VLADMIROV, G. E., and URINSON, A. P. *Brokhimiya 22:* 655, 1957.
87. WAELSCH, H. *Federation Proc. 20:* 342, 1961.
88. WALAAS, O., BORREBACK, B., KRISTIANSEN, T., and WALAAS, E. *Biochem. et Biophys. Acta 40:* 562, 1960.
89. WEBB, J. L., and ELLIOTT, K. A. C. *J. Pharmacol. & Exper. Therap. 103:* 24, 1957.
90. WEIL-MALHERBE, H., and BONE, A. O. *Biochem. J. 49:* 339, 1957.
91. WINZLER, R. J., MOLDOVE, T., RAFELSON, M. E., and PERSON, H. E. *J. Biochem. 199:* 485, 1952.
92. WOLF, P. H., and TSCHIRGI, R. D. *Am. J. Physiol. 184:* 220, 1956.

DISCUSSION

DR. GRENELL: I would like to ask Dr. Mendelson to make some remarks concerning some work we did together for a number of years and the relation to some of the recent work done in Russia.

DR. MENDELSON: I think what Dr. Grenell was referring to was the conceptional model employed in attempting to relate levels of convention appearing in the central nervous system. Certainly an adequate and traditionally good model is to make the assumption that during a reduced level of concentration something happens to the energy-sensitizing mechanisms in the brain. Basically when you have hypoglycemia the patient loses consciousness. If you can introduce a narcotic in sufficient quantities the individual again loses consciousness. Certainly a reasonable assumption that was made, I estimate, initially about fifty years ago, was that something happened to the energy-synthesizing mechanism. In some way he did not have enough energy to support it and, therefore, loss of consciousness supervened.

As techniques improved and work moved along, the hypothesis was formulated that the narcotic in some way interfered with some group of enzymes or perhaps some specific enzyme so that enough ATP was not available to support normal activity. For many years people searched for the enzyme, not coming up with very much. When unconsciousness was introduced it became even more appealing that some phenomena would in turn give ATP in the brain and change the phenomenon of altering consciousness. The proof of the theory was to try to assess levels of ATP in the brain during narcosis and stimulation. Certainly a great deal of work has been recorded in this area. It does not appear that this hypothesis of loss of high-energy phosphate in the brain will support the phenomenon of unconsciousness. It has been shown that you can measure ATP in the brain during narcosis. This has been done by Grenell and myself using the firefly technique. It has been done in the Soviet Union using photographic techniques. What you find is exactly the reverse of what your hypothesis would suggest; namely, during narcosis ATP is not increased. I think the same thing could be applied to some of Dr. Bessman's concept in what happens in brain trauma. The net high-energy phosphate is less.

When you assess ATP in the brain again what you find is an increased level of ATP which would strongly suggest that the ATP changes are related to ATP in activity rather than ATP synthesis. I think that we still do not know in what way ATP is utilized in the membrane after the firing of the cell—perhaps in the operation of pump mechanism—but it certainly seems that a deficiency of ATP does not occur during narcosis. Furthermore, in recent studies if you induce convulsions in cats and rats and measure the phosphate in the cortex you find lower levels of ATP than in the controls.

I think this area needs a lot more work, and I think it is something we have to look into further.

DR. R. S. GEIGER: In view of Drs. Grennell and Mendelsohn's results showing an increased ATP concentration in brain during barbital narcosis, it could be of interest to mention some of our findings on in vitro cultures of adult mammalian brain cells.

Sodium barbital, when added to the brain cultures, in concentrations comparable to those used for narcosis in vivo, affects the structural elements of the neurons (2). These effects are reversible, when the narcotic drug is washed out of the cultures. The most striking effect of sodium barbital consists in the disappearance (within 2 to 10 minutes) of the mitochondria from the neuron after the addition of the narcotic. Fifteen to 20 minutes after the narcotic was in contact with the culture, these mitochondria gradually reappear as very small granules, finely dispersed throughout the cytoplasm. After washing and feeding the culture, the mitochondria reappear in their original size, within about 15 minutes. The Nissl substance appears unaffected by barbiturates. Some of the processes of neurons in the presence of barbiturates show some retraction from synaptic regions. The effect of the narcotic drug on the mitochondria, observed first with phase contrast optics and time-lapse photography, was confirmed by fixing and staining with osmic acid, or with phosphotungstic acid hematoxylin, as recommended by Mallory for demonstrating mitochondria. The same picture was observed in the living cells with phase contrast or vital staining with Janus green B. Other osmophilic granules (not mitochondria) appear fewer, but larger, than in normal cells. The membrane of the neuron in the presence of barbiturates stains more deeply with osmic acid and phosphotungstic acid hematoxylin than under normal conditions. The perineuronal oligodendroglia are also very deeply stained. A decrease of the acetylcholine esterase in the perikaryon was also observed. The oligodendroglia stained heavily for butyrylcholinesterase.

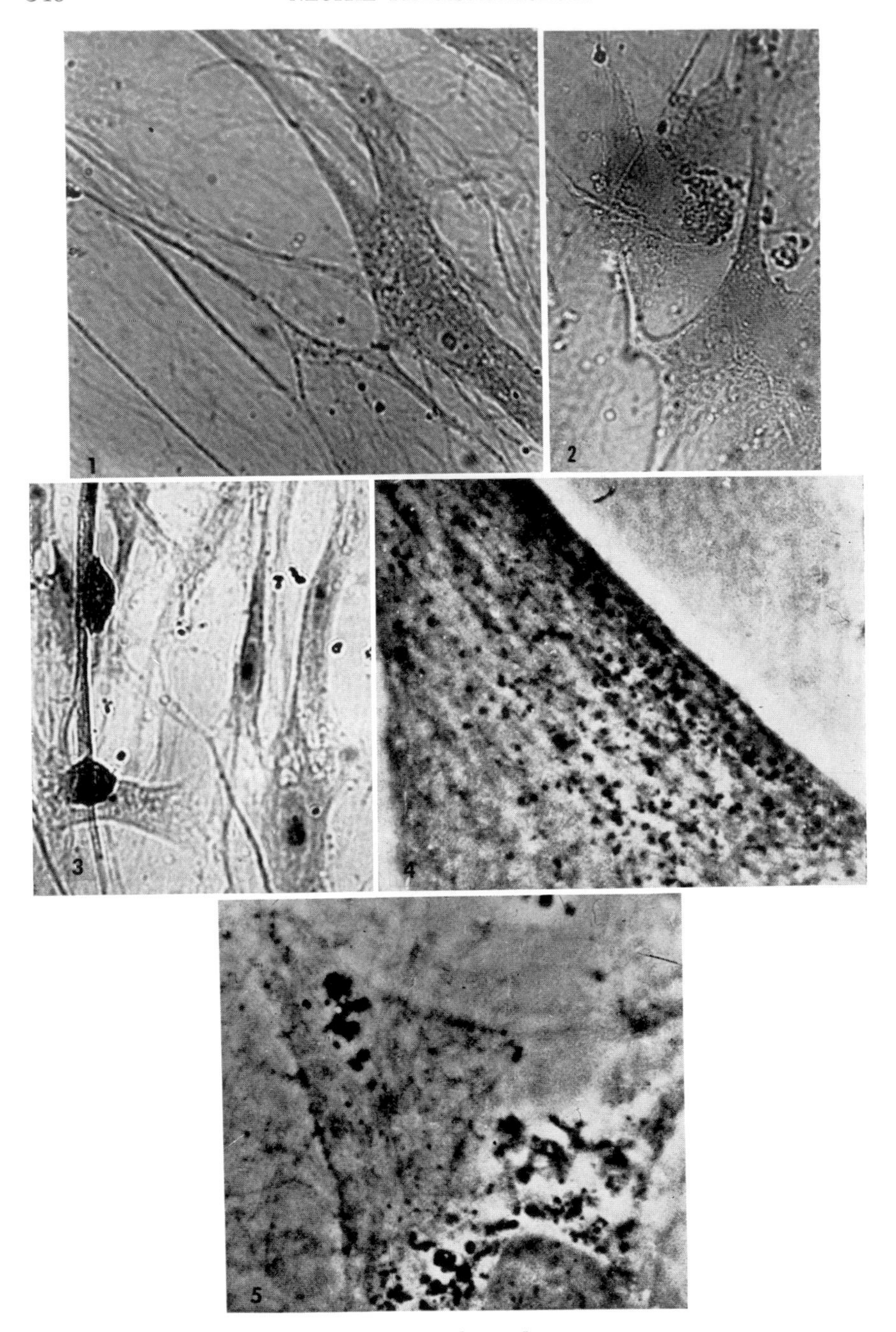

FIG. 10-8. For descriptive legend see opposite page.

The narcotic stopped the pulsating movements of oligodendroglia and progressively increased their size for about an hour, as seen with time-lapse photography. After this time, the pulsating movements begin again at a somewhat accelerated rate, even when the narcotic remains in the culture. These effects of the narcotic on the glia, namely, the inhibited pulsations, increase in size, and heavier staining, may indicate an interruption of material-transfer from the glia to neurons.

Metrazol, in concentrations of 50–100 γ/ml., when added simultaneously with sodium barbital, inhibited the phenomena described above. Also, when added at any time to barbital-treated cells, Metrazol reversed the barbital effect and mitochondria reappeared within a few minutes.

Although a barbiturate, 1,3-dimethylbutylethyl barbituric acid (the sodium salt), acts in animals as a convulsant, when added to brain cell cultures it does not affect the neurons or glia in the manner described for sodium barbital. On the contrary, its action was similar to that of Metrazol. These data indicate that narcotic drugs act specifically on mitochondria of neurons by dispersing them, lending support to a hypothesis advanced previously that one of the effects of narcotic drugs may be the alteration of the relationship between the enzymes in the mitochondria and those in the rest of the cytoplasm, thereby modifying enzyme activity. It is well known that thorough dispersal and mixing of the enzymes of the particulates with those of the cytoplasm may lead in extreme cases to complete blocking of

---

FIG. 10-8. (*1*) Subculture rabbit gray cortex stained with phosphotungstic acid hematoxylin for mitochondria (according to Mallory). ×400. (Whole-mount Maximow Lying drop culture.)

(*2*) Same type preparation as (*1*). Fixed five minutes after addition of sodium barbital 10 γ/ml. showing little staining in cell body of neuron. ×400.

(*3*) Same type preparation as (*1*) and (*2*), 12 minutes after addition of sodium barbital 10 γ/ml., showing dense staining of glial cells.

(*4*) Same type preparation as (*1*), stained with 2 per cent osmic acid vapor. ×1000.

(*5*) Same type preparation as (*4*), after addition of sodium barbital 10 γ/ml. for 12 minutes.

glycolysis in brain tissue (3). Bain (1) found no difference between Na barbital and 1-3-dimethyl butylethyl barbiturate in the inhibitory effect on oxidative phosphorylation of rat brain mitochondria.

REFERENCES

1. Bain, J. A. *Federation Proc. 11:* 655, 1952.
2. Geiger, R. S. In *Ultrastructure and Celular Chemistry of Neural Tissue,* edited by Henrich Waelsch. Hoeber-Harper, New York, 1957, pp. 83–99.
3. Geiger, A. *Biochem. J. 33:* 877, 1939.

CHAPTER 11

Evolutionary Forces in the Function and Failure of Neurons

BERNARD L. STREHLER

IN this age of scientific specialization, it is apparent even at a conference on a restricted aspect of biology, such as this one devoted to "abnormal nervous function," that a number of different scientific languages are in use. Thus, the neuron which the chemically oriented neurobiologist describes is an almost unrecognizably different entity from that which the physically or behaviorally inclined worker sets forth. Even members of different schools of thought about membrane phenomena give evidence of failure to apprehend or appreciate each others' points of view.

My own reason for contributing to this symposium stems from quite different roots than those nourishing most of the other participants, since in our laboratory we are concerned with the general nature of the processes leading to the senescence and, ultimately, death of organisms. It affords an opportunity for an exposition of a view of the function and failure of the nervous system in a somewhat different dialect if not language. Thus, even though the view of biological substructures (e.g., neurons) entertained by a gerontologist is likely to be quite different from that of most of the other participants in this conference, there is probably value in restating and re-evaluating the general principles which unite our efforts from time to time.

The predominant modern opinion ascribes an important or even central role in the aging process to the gradual loss of function of nondividing, differentiated cells, the so-called fixed postmitotics, which include as some of their most important representatives muscle and nerve cells (1, 8, 45).

In our earlier attempts to develop a picture of the relation of senescence to the function and failure of various cell types we have retraced and re-explored a number of evolutionary arguments originally set forth by Darwin (9), Weismann (49), and more recently elaborated, criticized, and clarified by Medawar (30) and Williams (50). Because these thoughts are central to some of the detailed discussions of function and failure in neurons set forth later, we will briefly trace some of the probable mechanisms operating in the evolution of the neuron. This will be followed by a brief survey of some of the special biological attributes of these remarkable cells, a review of some seldom-mentioned biochemical facts possibly relevant to membrane structure and function, and the suggestion of a theory harmonizing these facts with other aspects of neuronal structure and function. Finally some recent findings on the nature and function of lipofuscin age pigments will be reviewed and their relationship to neuronal failure discussed.

ENERGY, ENTROPY, AND THE EVOLUTION OF THE NEURON

A living organism may be defined as a catalytic molecular system capable of structural variation (mutation) within certain limits, which makes use of the matter and energy in its environment in order to produce more of itself. In the course of the evolution of higher forms of life, this primitive capacity to produce more living material has been modified by natural selection and variation in at least two discrete directions. The first of these consists essentially of a series of devices serving to speed up the rate or efficiency of reproduction or to broaden the types of food materials which may be used as raw material.

The second process, by contrast, does not place such a high premium on the rate of production of protoplasm, but, rather, emphasizes the development of systems which will ensure the survival of the genetic line during the adverse periods connected with low food supply, drought, presence of predators, etc. As a consequence of this specialization, the reproductive core of the line of animals and plants which have taken this road may assume a minor position as far as mass and complexity are concerned. By contrast, the nonreproductive cells, or soma, become the dominant recognizable features of these animals and plants. This soma-emphasizing line of evolution has been so enormously effective primarily because it has made possible a fantastically varied burgeoning of adaptation and behavior.

Bioenergetic Aspects of Behavior

Behavior, in bioenergetic terms, may be defined as the controlled release of the potential energy available to an organism so as to do work upon the environment or upon the organism itself. There is, of course, practically no aspect of an organism's life which does not fall within this definition. The achievement of work is made possible, in turn, by the development of devices which will be termed energy transducers and which, by virtue of their structure, have the capacity to convert energy available in one form into another, more appropriate to the survival of the organism. Thus, the energy available in sunlight, initially trapped by the green plants, eventually finds its way into the energy reservoirs of all living things through the action of such transducers. It must then or ultimately be transformed into a local form of energy currency which can be used to activate the various effector systems that have evolved.

This ability to transform one kind of available free energy into another, more usable in promoting the survival of the organism in question, is after all one of the most remarkable properties of living things. There is little in common, most would agree, between the absorption of a light quantum by a chlorophyll molecule and the practice of conscious behavior which plays such a central role in our lives (15). Yet, infinite trial and error, modification, elimination, death and success, the substance of evolutionary history, all have yielded products which are almost incomprehensibly complex and awe-inspiring in their capacity to catalyze such transformations.

What generalizations can be made concerning the selective factors operating on this capacity for variation in the structure and function of transducers? The first is that nearly all of the transducers which living systems possess have survived the onslaught of evolutionary fluctuation because they have provided the animals or plants possessing them with a defense against sources of failure operating prior to reproductive maturation. In turn, the development of such energy transducers is based upon one other property of the relationship between the organism and environment. This crucial property is a sufficient regularity in relationships and events to permit a process which might be called *evolutionary induction.* Thus, sources of failure which are not *predictably* associated with other features of the environment will not in general be subject to elimination by natural selection.

Compartmentalization, Coordination, Sensation, and Prediction

Because the occurrence of multiple specialized functions within a physically continuous compartment such as a cell might well lead to contradictions and conflict with their attendant inefficiencies, there seems frequently to occur the evolution of functional independence or even isolation of different transducers from each other. The success of metazoans, with their highly diversified cellularity, is a natural consequence of the above selective factors.

On the other hand, in order for multicellular organisms of appreciable size to function effectively in a fluctuating natural environment, it is necessary that their various parts become coordinated, particularly as regards movement. In consequence, one of the most salient features of evolutionary change is the fact that the behavioral aspects of organisms have by and large come under the control of the nervous system, which, in the present context, can be viewed as an effector system concerned during the early period of its evolution with the coordination of vital activities, particularly movements.

In later stages of evolution, however, the nervous system has developed in another direction, quite separate from the first, namely the prediction of the future.

Possessing cells capable of using chemical energy to produce movement, and a coordinating system to unite the contractile activities of the various parts of the organism, there still remained for our primitive ancestors the task of ensuring a high probability of appropriate behavior. Appropriate behavior in this context means the expenditure of energy in the various transducer systems in such a manner as to do work serving to increase the probability of continued survival of the line of animals under consideration.

What evolved adaptations, particularly of the nervous system, would contribute to the selective survival of their possessors by increasing the probability of appropriate behavior? As a first instance, the development of sensory apparatus capable of monitoring the changes in the immediate environment would certainly be of use, since it would surely be of considerable value to be able to distinguish on the basis of tactile or chemical sense the difference between prey and predator. Taste and smell have the advantage over a simple tactile sense of permitting the organism some time to prepare himself either to feed or flee before he comes into actual contact with the object of his appetite, anxiety, or affection. With greater time at one's disposal, even slow or deliberate measures can be undertaken successfully.

An even further largess of time during which appropriate behavior might be undertaken could become available if an organism were capable of detecting disturbances in his environment at even greater distances than is possible with the chemical senses. This potentiality is achievable because natural phenomena as well as the activities of living systems do generally cause disturbances at some distance from the site of their occurrence or action. Among these disturbances are sound waves and alterations in the patterns of reflected or transmitted light. Since such patterns are the projections of "distant" events which may have immediate or future consequences in the projection areas, living systems which possessed the capacity to perceive these signals and respond adaptively to them possessed selective advantages over those which did not.

Indeed, one may conjecture that the development of truly intelligent beings probably would have been impossible if it had not been for the presence of such distance receptors, since both the detailed information available through sight and sound and the time interval between the receipt of a stimulus and the necessity for action are prerequisites to the predictive functions so characteristic of highly developed nervous systems.

Viewed in another way, the time interval between the receipt of information about a change in the environment and the necessity for a response made it possible for systems to evolve whose responses were no longer stereotyped. Rather, their actions could be predicated on reason and the recorded experience of the individual organism as opposed to a response based exclusively upon the adaptive experience of the race.

Thus, in essence, intelligence and prediction are based upon the probability that a pattern or configuration of sensory input which resembles in part the pattern of another recorded event or situation will have a significantly greater than random probability of correlating with the rest or other parts of the latter pattern. In a parallel manner the survival value of intelligent prediction is based upon the probability that actions successful in preserving an individual on one occasion will be more adaptive in similar situations than other possible responses.

Perhaps the most striking feature of the nervous system, the feature which has given it such tremendous adaptive value in higher forms of life, is its record-keeping capacity. The utility of this capacity is ultimately related to the fact that there is a considerable degree of regularity, order, and predictability in the events occurring to organisms of any given type in their normal environments. In the present context, we mean by regularity or order that similar events or configurations of objects will occur repeatedly. If an animal species, therefore, has "learned" an advantageous response either by evolutionary selection or by the recording of events in some more plastic memory system, then whenever the combination of stimuli occurs which is reminiscent of the earlier pattern or sequence, there will be, on the average, a selective advantage to a repetition of the "learned" response.

This, then, in brief outline, is a view of the evolutionary forces operating on the nervous system, whose cells's structural and functional properties have made possible much of the living world as we know it. These versatile cells, drawing upon the same reservoirs of energy and matter as other metazoan cells, nevertheless also possess some unique bioenergetic features and problems, a few of which are examined in the following discussion.

SOME SPECIFIC BIOENERGETIC PROBLEMS OF NEURONS

Neurons are thus specialized types of energy transducers serving the multiple functions of coordinating, sensing, predicting, and choosing among alternative courses of action. In carrying out these activities neurons face more specific problems including those associated with the following categories of processes: (*1*) growth, differentiation, and morphogenesis; (*2*) chemical work—synthesis of compounds related to function; (*3*) formation or accentuation of synaptic pathways; (*4*) conduction and related osmotic work; and finally (*5*) maintenance and repair processes. This is an impressive list of capacities for any cell to possess, and in many respects the neuron evidences these specializations to a higher degree than any other type of mammalian cell.

Growth, Differentiation, and Morphogenesis

Compared to other body cells, nerves achieve enormous sizes. For example, the much-studied squid axon is of easily visible proportions while even the much less impressive motor neurons of a human being achieve lengths greater than 1 yard. The design of a genetic and metabolic system which can control, sustain, and supply such relatively enormous cellular structures is a major problem in architecture and function. Concerning the mechanism of the chemical differentiation (47) of the neuron and the nature of the function of the nucleus, whether as a direct genetic source of information, or as a repository of a code which is rarely if ever referred to after the initiation of differentiation, there is considerable ignorance. The nucleus does seem to be necessary for maintainance of nerve function, since the distal ends of transected nerves degenerate, but the nature of its influence may just as well be metabolic as genetic once development has taken place. It is known that the nervous system is more sensitive during its formation to respiratory inhibitors and short periods of anaerobiosis than are a number of mesodermal structures. Similarly, the adult nervous system is exquisitely sensitive to oxygen lack as evidenced by the disastrous effects of short periods of anaerobicity on the function of the brain.

The morphogenetic specificity of the neuron is a related property of considerable note. Stone's and Sperry's remarkable findings (36, 37) of the specificity of regenerative pathways of neurons (as revealed both by anatomical studies and behavioral alterations) in Amphibia whose organs or limbs have been transplanted, transposed or inverted in situ are instructive in this regard. The conclusions from these studies, particularly those in which eyes were transplanted, were that there exists a nearly absolute specificity between a neuron whose cell body lies in the retina and a portion of the brain which it innervates, and that surgical manipulation and transection of the axons of these nerves would not, under many circumstances, interfere with this apparently cell-for-cell trophic response. The number of combinations of information-carrying factors required to specify the exact points of synapse among the myriad nerves making their way from the retina to the cortex suggests a highly complex code and readout mechanism. Recently, the presence in several tissues of specific and potent stimulators of nerve outgrowth has been reported by Levi-Montalcini (29), Hamburger (20), and Cohen (7). The exact chemical nature of this material, its mode of action, and the possibility of other substances of similar natures or effects, but operating on other types of nerves, are questions whose answers may be of considerable value in untangling the confusing web surrounding the problem of nerve morphogenetic specificity.

Metabolic Capacities

Since a number of other papers in this symposium deal directly and in extenso with the metabolic activities of the neuron, we will only here call to mind the rather impressive catalogue of substances present in nervous tissue. Some of these substances are undoubtedly synthesized in other cells of the body, but in more primitive animals, such as the coelenterates, it appears likely that much of the specialized substance of the conducting cell is synthesized in the conducting cell itself.

Record Keeping

Probably the most unique capacity of the nervous system in higher mammals is the fact that it records events as they occur. Presumably these records are established either through the formation of new synaptic pathways or by the alteration of preexisting ones. Whatever the method of record keeping is, it must involve a rather stable change in structure in order to permit the detailed recall of long-past experiences which are said to be evoked under hypnosis or by specific cortical electrical stimulation. The alternative suggestion of feedback circuits resonating over a period of 90 or 100 years seems unlikely in the judgment of most competent neurobiologists.

The establishment of new synaptic pathways would appear to depend upon the simultaneous discharge of several afferent fibers on a single secondary fiber (spatial summation) or possibly upon a type of temporal summation. Since presumably, the individual presynaptic fibers might fire many times without eliciting the discharge of the postsynaptic neuron, it appears likely that the learning process involves some change in the latter rather than in the former. Possibly, depolarization results in a temporary neutralization of like charges on both (or all) neurons involved, so that the synaptic membranes can come into closer contact, a process which might facilitate a secondary's discharge at a later time when *any* of the afferents involved are discharged. Such a process might even lead to fusion of synaptic membranes so as to yield a single membrane. Alternatively, there might be an increase in the area of contact which would facilitate later transmission. Or, finally, structural changes might occur (e.g., adaptive enzyme formation in the case of long-term memory although this would seem to be ruled out as far as immediate recall is concerned) which would permanently lower the membrane threshold to subsequent local stimulation.

Impulse Conduction

By far the most characteristic feature of the individual neuron is its ability rapidly to conduct an impulse along its length. There seems to be little doubt that the transmission of an impulse involves at least three successive types of events, although descriptions of the conduction process usually treat it as unitary.

The first of these events is the initiation of the characteristic ion movements across the membrane. According to the Hodgkin-Huxley (24) model (Fig. 11-1), initiation consists of a local increase in permeability to sodium as a result of ion movement induced some distance from the initiating disturbance (either electrical stimulation, current passage in an adjacent portion of the same neuron, or the activity of another nerve).

The second of these events consists of the amplification of the small, initial, and critical increase in permeability, so that the resistance to sodium movement through the membrane is further decreased in an autocatalytic way. This increased sodium conductivity is shortly followed by a decrease in permeability of the membrane to this ion and then by an increasing, then decreasing, change in the conductivity to potassium, which essentially restores the original polarity.

The final phase of activity connected with nerve impulse propagation is the restorative phase, in which the various ion movements and other chemical reactions occurring during the conduction process are reversed through the utilization of stored metabolic potential energy (12, 28, 44).

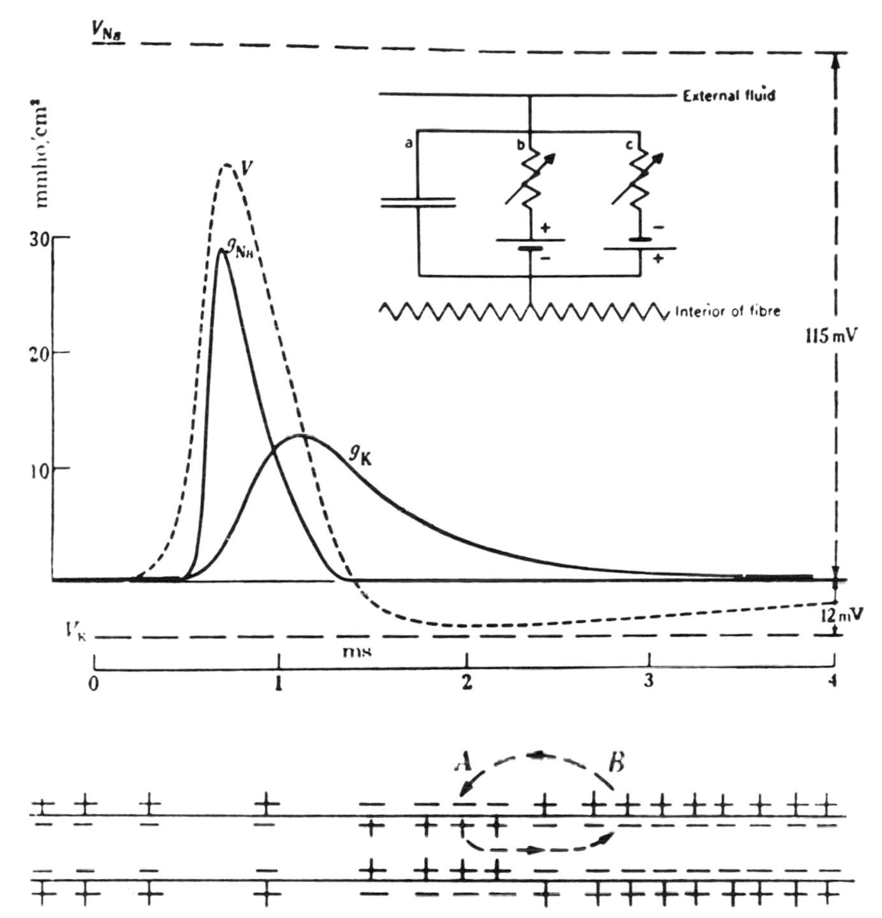

FIG. 11-1. Several representations of the Hodgkin-Huxley model (23). In the upper portion, the horizontal dotted lines represent the sodium and potassium concentration cell potentials. The *dotted curved line* represents voltage changes occurring during neuronal discharge, and the *solid lines* represent sodium conductivity and potassium conductivity respectively contributing to the aforesaid membrane potential changes. The *inset* represents an electrical analogue of the system; **a** representing the membrane capacitance, and **b** and **c** representing the opposed potentials of the concentration cells. The variable resistances represent changing membrane conductances to the two ionic species.

The lower portion of the figure illustrates the type of ionic movements to be expected at **B**, a point in advance of the region of membrane depolarization, **A**, because of the cable properties of neurons (12).

The Hodgkin-Huxley model furnishes a plausible mathematical function describing the kinetics of sodium and potassium ion movement, membrane resistances to these ions, and the electrical changes correlated with the ion movements. It is not, however, intended to be a molecular mechanism for the initiation-propagation, amplification, and restoration processes. It is to be hoped that such a detailed molecular model will be forthcoming.

Let us consider in slightly greater detail the second of these processes. It requires a physical or chemical amplifier of the initial induced depolarization and certainly must involve some change in molecular arrangement at the site of conductance change, the membrane. It may well be of crucial importance to analyze separately the three fundamental aspects of the depolarization-repolarization process, for although the speed of impulse propagation could hardly be accounted for by ordinary lateral diffusion of a "transmitter substance," there seems to be no such stringent limitation on the participation of diffusible molecules and enzymatically catalyzed reactions in the depolarization-amplification process (once the cable properties of the neuron have permitted the onset of depolarization) since diffusion distances may in this case be vanishingly small. Likewise, the repolarization and ion pump features of the conductive membrane are probably not beyond the province of the more classical biochemical concepts. It may well be that the impasse between the proponents of the chemical mediation of nerve impulse transmission such as Nachmansohn (33) and the more dominant physically oriented school lies in the failure to take into account the possible dichotomy between the initiatory and amplificatory aspects of neuronal function.

In addition to the items mentioned above, a number of other observations should be incorporated into any theory of membrane function. These include the facts that: (*1*) the neuronal membrane is, in all likelihood, a mixture of cholesterol and phospholipid (13) applied to a protein matrix (Fig. 11-2); (*2*) in certain synaptic areas (and also, in this connection, the experiments reported in Chapter 1 by Dr. Thesleff on the neuromuscular junction are relevant) the presence of acetylcholine will cause a depolarization of nerve membranes, and, if one accepts Nachmansohn's evidence and arguments (33), there is reason to believe that acetylcholine functions in nerve depolarization in other loci including the axon as well; (3) extensive work around the turn of the century (3, 11) indicated that the mechanism whereby the hemolytic and neurotoxic and depolarizing effects of a number of snake venoms exerted their effects was through the production of lysolecithin or lysocephalin. These monoacylated

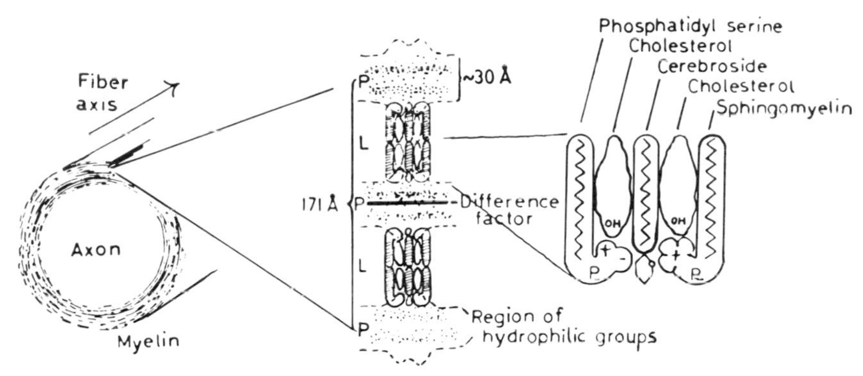

FIG. 11-2. A model of membrane structure suggested by Engström and Finean. In the context of the present discussion, note the close apposition of cholesterol to phospholipid moieties (13).

derivatives of glycerophosphocholine or glycerophosphoethanolamine are closely related to lecithin and cephalin, presumably normal constituents of the membrane and are indeed produced from the latter by the action of the enzyme lysolecithinase present in considerable quantities not only in snake venom but in a variety of human tissues including the nervous system. These early workers also showed that the lysolecithin produced by the action of cobra venom on naturally occurring lecithin will form a strong molecular complex with cholesterol. They also noted the interesting fact that the rate of production of lysolecithin is considerably accelerated by the addition of small amounts of sodium chloride.

These observations, taken together with the others mentioned above, are consistent with the following scheme:

(*a*) The cable properties of the nerve permit the local accumulation of positive charge in areas on the inside of the membrane adjacent to the area in which depolarization has taken place. This sequence is precisely similar to that outlined by Hodgkin in his Croonian lecture (23).

(*b*) This movement of positive ions, particularly sodium, toward the inside of the membrane releases acetylcholine from negatively charged binding sites (possibly protein) on the membrane's inner surface by a sort of ion-exchange process, thus:

$$R^{-}AcCh^{+} + Na^{+} \rightarrow R^{-}Na^{+} + AcCh^{+}$$

(*c*) The temporarily increased local concentration of $AcCh^{+}$, resulting from the above ion-exchange process, reacts enzymatically at the membrane surface with a monoacylglycerophosphate molecule to yield a transiently increased lyso-lecithin concentration, thus:

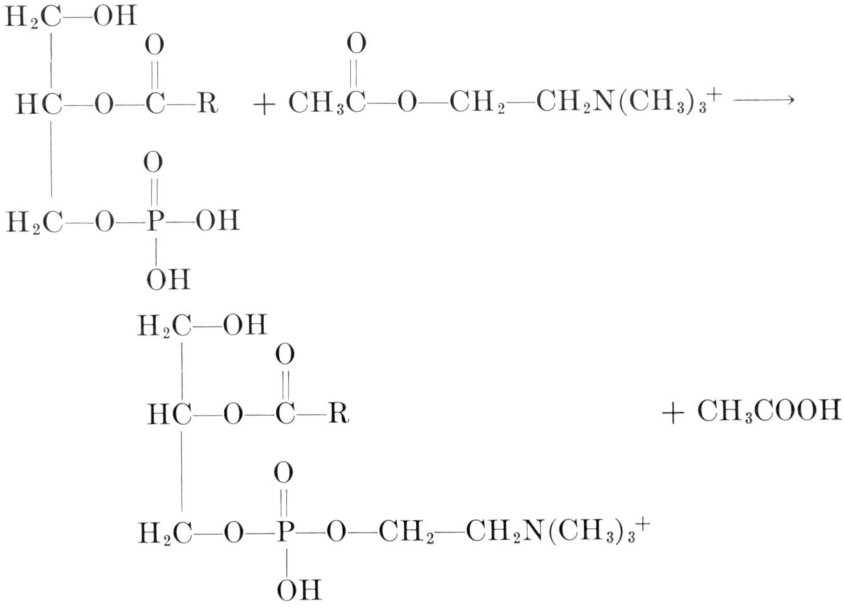

$$\begin{array}{l} H_2C\text{—}OH \\ \;\;| \qquad\quad O \\ \;\;| \qquad\quad \| \\ HC\text{—}O\text{—}C\text{—}R \\ \;\;| \qquad\quad O \\ \;\;| \qquad\quad \| \\ H_2C\text{—}O\text{—}P\text{—}OH \\ \qquad\qquad | \\ \qquad\qquad OH \end{array} + \begin{array}{l} \quad O \\ \quad \| \\ CH_3C\text{—}O\text{—}CH_2\text{—}CH_2N(CH_3)_3^{+} \end{array} \longrightarrow$$

$$\begin{array}{l} H_2C\text{—}OH \\ \;\;| \qquad\quad O \\ \;\;| \qquad\quad \| \\ HC\text{—}O\text{—}C\text{—}R \\ \;\;| \qquad\quad O \\ \;\;| \qquad\quad \| \\ H_2C\text{—}O\text{—}P\text{—}O\text{—}CH_2\text{—}CH_2N(CH_3)_3^{+} \\ \qquad\qquad | \\ \qquad\qquad OH \end{array} + CH_3COOH$$

(*d*) The lyso-lecithin (LL) thus formed combines with cholesterol (Ch) which had been occupying a membrane pore as a lecithin (L) complex (Fig. 11-2) and removes it therefrom thus:

```
                                            (Na+ Pore)
Memb.—L—Ch—Memb. → Memb.—L. . . . . . . . . . .Memb.
                |                                   |
               LL                                  LL
                                                    |
                                                   Ch
```

The holes which are produced are of sufficient size to permit Na^+ to move into the cell (but not K^+) which amplifies reactions (*b*) to (*d*) with the resultant increase in sodium conductivity and action potential production. (See Katz, 27, 28, for an excellent discussion.)

(*e*) As the movement of sodium ions decreases the effective positivity on the outside of the membrane, lecithin molecules on the membrane are released from the Na^+ holes, enlarging them and simultaneously increasing the membrane permeability to potassium and decreasing its permeability to sodium by a mechanism similar to the ingenious "close fit" hypothesis of Mullins (32), thus:

```
           (Na+ Pore)                       (K+ Pore)
Memb.—L. . . . . . . . . . .Memb. → Memb. . . . . . . . . .  Memb.
                              |        +L                      |
                             LL                               LL
                              |                                |
                             Ch                               Ch
```

In accordance with the observations that the conductivity of clamped neurons remains high to K^+ as long as the potential is not strongly positive on the outside, this potassium conductivity continues as long as the hole is not blocked by a lecithin-cholesterol complex. The reinsertion of such a complex should not occur as long as there is insufficient positivity outside to hold the negatively charged lecithin molecule adnate to the membrane pore.

(*f*) The movement of K^+ ions to the outside soon restores the potential to its original value, and, as a result, the electrostatic stabilization of a cholesterol-lecithin complex once again occurs at the membrane pore and thus blocks the passage of both K^+ and Na^+, thus essentially restoring original conditions.

(*g*) The lysolecithin in the cholesterol-lysolecithin complex may be converted to lecithin by acylation, degraded to an inactive entity, or reconverted to monoacylglycerophosphate by supporting enzyme systems. Incidentally, if the last-named reaction occurred the over-all reaction would appear as choline-esterase activity associated with the inside of the membrane.

(*h*) The ion pump or pumps now proceed to restore the ionic concentrations on the two sides of the membrane to their original values.

This model differs from some earlier ones. It does not depend upon the lateral diffusion of a biochemical reagent or reaction sequence along the membrane. Further, it makes use of the fact that there is sufficient time for a biochemical sequence to act as a local amplifier of the action current, provided that an electrical or electrophoretic mechanism can be called into play as a means of propagating the initiation of the impulse in the further reaches of the neuron. It provides a rational connection between the observed effects of acetylcholine on neural structures, of the facts that the choline-containing lipid, lyso-lecithin, is a strong depolarizing agent, that salts facilitate the action of lyso-lecithinase, and that locally high sodium concentrations may occur inside the membrane during the action potential wave.

The final phase of this process is the recharging of the whole system, and consists of a mechanism by which ions may be moved against concentration gradients or electrical potential gradients by a membrane associated structure, in turn driven by the metabolic machinery of the cell. That adenosinetriphosphate may be involved in this process is strongly suggested by the evidence of Hodgkin and Keynes (25) and Caldwell and Keynes (6). In the formers' experiments it was shown that dinitrophenol destroys the capacity of the sodium pump to extrude sodium from the inside of the axon. In the latter report, a small but significant increase in the rate of sodium extrusion was demonstrated when a cyanide-poisoned squid axon was injected with an ATP solution!

Repair and Maintenance

Unlike blood cells or the cellular linings of the abraded surfaces on the inside and outside of the body, nerve cells are not usually replaced during the lifetime of the individual. Replacement, if it did occur, would certainly do violence, among other things, to any system of reflex or memory that depended on fixed spatial relations between synapses. Because of the functional importance of the synapse in the integrative activity of the nervous system, the individual functioning unit is the individual cell. Since damage will occur with the passage of time to any physical system subject to a destructive environment, the neuron must either be shielded from such or be capable of repair and maintenance, or both. Physical shielding is achieved in vertebrates by the development of a protective skull and backbone; shielding from drastic fluctuations in the chemical milieu is facilitated by the blood-brain barrier; repair capacity expresses itself, according to Weiss's classical studies, in the presence of an intact nucleus and a suitable path for the regenerating fiber (48); maintenance is probably achieved by a regular turnover of many structural and functional elements at the molecular level during the entire life span of the cell.

Despite these varied adaptations serving to preserve the integrity of the neuron, there are obviously many ways in which neural function may be hampered, altered, or obliterated, as other papers in this symposium have shown so clearly. There are literally hundreds of ways in which one could interfere with the metabolic transformations that lead to manifestations of conduction within the axon or at synapses, and the remarkably specific effects of many drugs bears witness to the effective isolation of these metabolic interferences or accelerations. Detailed inhibitor analysis of complex neural function in the classical sense is, of course, an almost impossible task. Measurements of adenosinetriphosphate concentration changes during narcosis have been made (18, 19) using the firefly enzyme assay method (42, 43), but the extent to which measured changes are a reflection of changes in nervous activity and the extent to which they cause changes in activity is not so readily decided. Ultimately, factors which interfere with the generation of high-energy phosphate bonds should be of paramount importance in producing abnormal neural function in vivo and in vitro, particularly if the suggestive observations of Keynes and collaborators are generally applicable as normal features of the metabolism of nerves and of their ion pumps. The fact that a neuron may carry many impulses on the basis of the prior work done by its ion pumps suggests that the decrease in maximal performance attendant to fatigue, hypoxia, and perhaps to aspects of senile behavior is a function of the maximum rate at which the ion pumps can operate. This rate, in turn, may be limited by the rate at which adenosinetriphosphate is resynthesized.

Among the changes which may supplant or limit the reserve capacity of neurons as they grow older, is one which seems to occur to a number of postmitotic cell types. This change is the gradual accumulation of the golden yellow fluorescent age pigment, lipofuscin, in the brains and spinal ganglia of older persons (5). This substance has not yet been isolated from brain cells, but a similar substance occurring in the human myocardium has been the subject of intensive study in our laboratory (31, 40, 41). Cardiac age pigment accumulates as a linear function of age (Fig. 11-3) and is apparently a lipoprotein complex whose fluorescent component is probably a peroxidation and/or autooxidation product of cephalin. Earlier studies by Hydén (26), who conjectured that neuronal age pigment is a pteridine derivative, have not been borne out by our findings.

Our analyses of lipofuscin are based upon a new preparative procedure which yields particles consistently less contaminated with nonfluorescent impurities than did the earlier procedures of Heidenreich and Siebert (21). Current studies indicate a high cathepsin and acid phosphatase activity which suggests that this pigment is derived from or associated with cytoplasmic inclusions similar to or identical with the lysosomes of DeDuve, Novikoff, and their associates (10, 34).

The fluorescent lipid component which is readily extracted with 2:1 chloroform-methanol has been chromatographed on paper impregnated with silicic acid and on silicic acid columns (22). The major fluorescent fraction moves with the cephalin fraction as do fluorescent fractions present in auto-oxidized cephalin.

The specific gravity of the pigment particles is ca. 1.17–1.22 as measured by centrifugal behavior in discontinuous sucrose

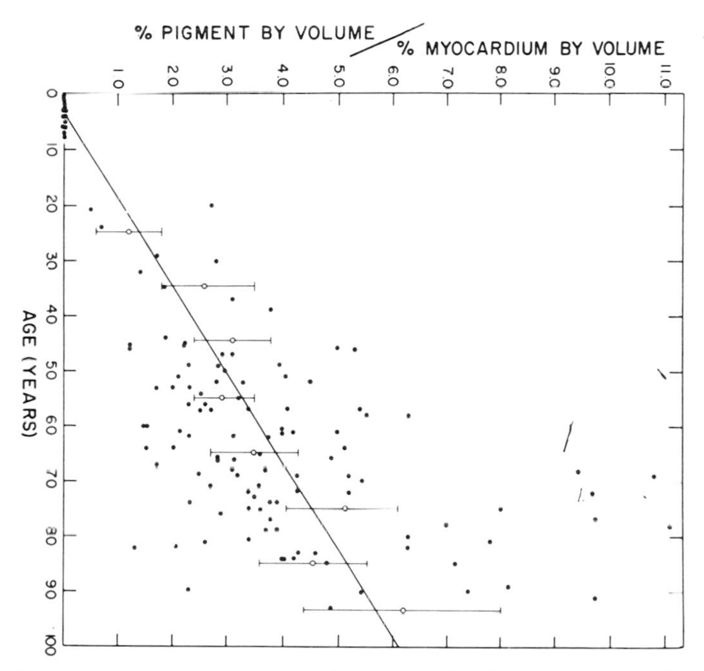

FIG. 11-3. Age pigment accumulation in the human myocardium with age. The individual points represent measurements on individual autopsy specimens. The average rate of accumulation is approximately 0.3 per cent per decade of the total myocardial volume.

density gradients. The color of the particles, whose appearance as photographed by their own fluorescence is illustrated in Figure 11-4, is a dark brown. Measurement of the absorption spectrum of isolated particles using a special light integrating box indicates essentially end absorption (41).

These findings are generally consistent with the studies of Heidenreich and Siebert (21), Gedigk and Bontke (16), and Essner and Novikoff (14), which had indicated a similarity or identity between lysosomes and lipofuscin granules, primarily on the basis of histochemical tests.

We believe age pigment particles may arise from lysosomes damaged by slow auto-oxidation reactions. Possibly these organelles, with their complement of powerful lytic enzymes, whose

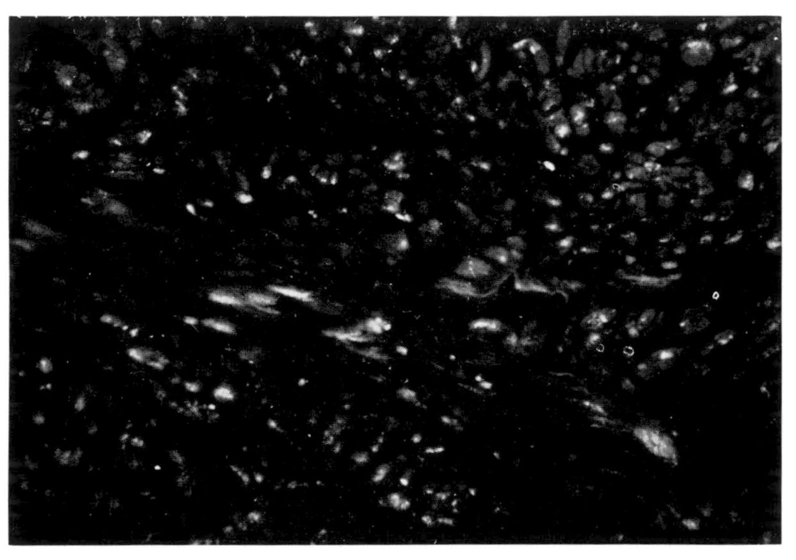

FIG. 11-4. Photomicrograph of an aged human heart section (86 years of age) photographed by its own fluorescence in near ultraviolet light. The brightly fluorescent areas are the age pigment particles; the more dimly fluorescent areas are myocardial fibers; the dark areas are intracellular space. There is a striking contrast between the color of age pigment fluorescence (yellow-orange) and the fluorescence of the myocardial fibers (blue-green) (39).

activation occurs following accidental damage and during certain morphogenetic cell deaths (17, 35), do not normally turn over and thus are the site of slow irreversible changes that other more metabolically labile cell constituents avoid by virtue of their higher turnover number (46).

In the old heart, lipofuscin occupies up to 10 per cent of the intracellular volume. By visual inspection, the volume so occupied by similar particles in very old neurons appears to be even higher, so that it seems probable that this usurpation of space by essentially nonfunctional lipid or lipoprotein displaces, to a considerable degree, functional elements such as mitochondria or Nissl substance (2).

We may conclude, then, that the nervous system, like other nondividing cell lines, appears to be one of the main sites of age changes in higher metazoans, and it appears likely that this fact hinges upon the incomplete evolution of repair systems capable of maintaining these important cellular transducers of energy (38, 39).

If true, is it not an irony of natural selection that the very system which contributes so much to our survival, which floods the consciousness it makes possible with a myriad of impulses, impressions, and sensations, is itself one of the main seats of that decay from which it shrinks reflexively, both by instinct and intelligence? Such an irony is explicable as Bidder commented in 1932 (4) in the following terms:

> I suggest that we were not born with infinitely senescent brains and rejuvenated epithelium; rapidity of division in our skin has been evolved to keep it clean and whole; undividing brain cells have been evolved because their function is to remember.

REFERENCES

1. *Aging, Some Social and Biological Aspects, A Symposium,* edited by N. W. Shock. American Association for the Advancement of Science, Publication 65, Washington, D.C., 1960.
2. ANDREW, W. Structural alterations with aging in the nervous system. *J. Chronic Diseases. 3:* 575–596, 1956.
3. BELFANTI, S., CONTARDI, A., and ERCOLI, A. *Lecithasen. Ergenbn. Enzymforsch. 5:* 213–232, 1936.
4. BIDDER, G. P. Senescence. *Brit. M. J. 2:* 5831, 1932.
5. BONDAREFF, W. Morphology of the aging nervous system. In *Handbook of Aging and the Individual,* edited by J. E. Birren. University of Chicago Press, Chicago, 1959.
6. CALDWELL, P. D., and KEYNES, R. D. The utilization of phosphate bond energy for sodium extrusion from the giant axon. *J. Physiol. 137:* 12, 1957.
7. COHEN, S. A nerve growth promoting protein. In *The Chemical Basis of Development,* edited by W. D. McElroy and H. B. Glass, pp. 665–679. The Johns Hopkins Press, Baltimore, 1958.

8. Comfort, A. *The Biology of Senescence.* Rinehart, New York, 1956.
9. Darwin, C. *On the Origin of Species by Means of Natural Selection or Preservation of Favored Races in the Struggle for Life,* John Murray of London, 1859.
10. DeDuve, C. The enzymatic heterogeneity of cell fractions isolated by differential centrifugation. *Symp. Soc. Exper. Biol. 10:* 50–61, 1957.
11. Delezenne, H., and Forneau, A. La composition en cholesterol et lipide quelque cervaux d'aliénées. *Bull. Soc. Biol. Chim. Francaise. 15:* 421–425, 1914.
12. Eccles, J. C. Introduction—neuron physiology. Chapter 11, pp. 59ff., in *Handbook of Physiology.* Neurophysiol. I., edited by J. Field *et al.* American Physiological Society, Washington, D.C.
13. Engstrom, A., and Finean, J. B. *Biological Ultrastructure* (pp. 223 ff.). Academic Press, New York, 1958.
14. Essner, E., and Novikoff, A. Human hepatocellular pigments and lysosomes. *J. Ultrastructure Res. 3:* 374–391, 1960.
15. Gaffron, H. (ed). *Research in Photosynthesis,* Interscience Publishers, Inc., New York, 1957.
16. Gedick, P., and Bontke, E. Uber den Nachweiss von Hydrolytischen Enzymen in Lipopigmenten. *Z. Zellforsch. 44:* 495–517, 1956.
17. Glucksmann, A. Cell deaths in normal vertebrate ontogeny. *Biol. Rev. 27:* 59-86, 1951.
18. Grenell, R. Some considerations regarding metabolic factors in the action of chlorpromazine. In *Tranquilizer Drugs,* edited by H. E. Himwich. American Association for the Advancement of Science, Publication 46, 61–71, 1957.
19. Grenell, R. Mechanisms of action of psychotherapeutic and related drugs. *Ann. New York Acad. Sc. 66:* 826–835, 1957.
20. Hamburger, V., and Levi-Montalcini, R. Proliferation differentiation and degeneration in spinal and geniculate ganglia of chick embryos under normal and experimental conditions. *J. Exper. Zool. 111:* 457–502, 1949.
21. Heidenreich, O., and Siebert, G. Untersuchungen an Isolierten, Unverhandelten Lipofuscin aus Herzmuskulatur, *Virchow's Arch. 327:* 112-126, 1955.
22. Hirsch, J., and Ahrens, E. H., Jr. The separation of complex lipid mixtures by the use of silicic acid. *J. Biol. Chem. 233:* 311–320, 1958.

23. HODGKIN, A. L. Ionic movements and electrical activity in giant nerve fibers. *Proc. Roy. Soc., London s. B. 148:* 1–37, 1958.
24. HODGKIN, A. L., and HUXLEY, A. F. Currents carried by sodium and potassium through the membrane of the giant axon of Loligo. *J. Physiol. 116:* 449, 1952.
25. HODGKIN, A. L., and KEYNES, R. D. Active transport of K from giant axons of Sepis and Loligo. *J. Physiol. 128:* 28, 1955.
26. HYDEN, H., and LINDSTROM, B. Studies on yellow nerve cell pigment. *Discussions Faraday Soc. 9:* 436–441, 1950.
27. KATZ, B. Mechanism of synaptic transmission. *Rev. Mod. Phys. 31:* 524–531, 1959.
28. KATZ, B. Nature of the nerve impulse. *Rev. Mod. Phys. 31:* 466–474, 1959.
29. LEVI-MONTALCINI, R. Chemical stimulation of nerve growth, pp. 648–664. In *Chemical Basis of Development,* edited by W. D. McElroy and H. B. Glass. The Johns Hopkins Press, Baltimore, 1958.
30. MEDAWAR, P. B. *An Unsolved Problem of Biology.* H. K. Lewis and Co., London, 1951.
31. MILDVAN, A., and STREHLER, B. Fluorescent lipids from heart age pigments. *Federation Proc. 19:* 231, 1960.
32. MULLINS, L. J. The structure of nerve cell membranes. In *Molecular Structure and Functional Activity of Nerve Cells,* edited by R. G. Grenell and L. J. Mullins. American Institute of Biological Science, Publication #1, Washington, D.C., 1956.
33. NACHMANSOHN, D. The Harvey Lectures Series XLIV, Metabolism and function of the nerve cell (pp. 57–99). Academic Press, Inc., New York, 1955.
34. NOVIKOFF, A. Biochemical heterogeneity of the cytoplasmic particles of rat liver. *Symp. Soc. Exper. Biol. 10:* 92–109, 1957.
35. NOVIKOFF, A. Personal communication.
36. SPERRY, R. W. The growth of nerve circuits. *Scient. American. 201:* 68–75, 1959.
37. SPERRY, R. W. Functional results of crossing and transposing muscles in the fore and hind limbs of the rat. *J. Comp. Neurol. 73:* 379, 1942.
38. STREHLER, B. L. Origin and comparison of the effects of time and high energy radiations on living systems. *Quart. Rev. Biol. 31:* 117–141, 1959.
39. STREHLER, B. L. Dynamic theories of aging, pp. 273–304. In *Aging*

—*Some Social and Biological Aspects.* Edited by N. W. Shock. American Association for the Advancement of Science. Publication 65, Washington, D.C., 1960.

40. Strehler, B. L., Mark, D., Mildvan, A., and Gee, M. Rate and magnitude of age pigment accumulation in the human myocardium. *J. Gerontol. 14:* 430–439, 1959.
41. Strehler, B. L., and Mildvan, A. Studies on the chemical properties of Lipofuscin age pigment, *Proceedings of the Fifth International Gerontological Congress,* In press, August, San Francisco, 1960.
42. Strehler, B. L., and Totter, J. R. Firefly luminescence in the study of energy transfer mechanisms. I. Substrate and enzyme determination. *Arch. Biochem. Biophys. 40:* 28–41, 1952.
43. Strehler, B. L., and Totter, J. R. Determination of ATP and related compounds: Firefly luminescence and other methods, In *Methods of Biochemical Analysis I,* Interscience Publishers, Inc., New York, 1954.
44. Tasaki, I. Conduction of the nerve impulse, pp. 75–121. In *Handbook of Physiology,* Neurophysiol. I. Edited by J. Field and others. American Physiological Society, Washington, D.C., 1959.
45. The Biology of Aging, A Symposium, Edited by B. L. Strehler *et al., American Institute of Biological Science,* Washington, D.C., 1960.
46. Thompson, R., and Ballou, J. Studies of metabolic turnover with tritium as a tracer, V. The predominantly non-dynamic state of body constitution in the rat. *J. Biol. Chem. 223:* 795–809, 1956.
47. Weiss, P. *Principles of Development.* Henry Holt, New York, 1939.
48. Weiss, P. Motor effect of sensory nerves experimentally connected with muscles. *Anat. Rec. 60:* 437–448, 1934.
49. Weismann, A. *Essays upon Heredity and Kindred Biological Problems,* Oxford University Press, London, 1891.
50. Williams, G. C. Pleiotropy, natural selection and the evolution of senescence, *Evolution, 11:* 398–411, 1957.

DISCUSSION

Dr. Mullins: It is not possible to separate the increase in sodium permeability of the membrane into a local increase and an amplification thereof. The increase in sodium permeability is a smooth and continuous function of the membrane potential. In an action potential, regeneration occurs because a small increase in P_{Na} leads to depolarization, and this in turn to a further increase. A further critical point of the Hodgkin-Huxley analysis is that it makes no difference whether sodium flows into or out of an axon during excitation; the phenomena are still only a function of potential. This fact would make it difficult to suppose that the entry of sodium displaced something like acetylcholine which in turn affected permeability. Indeed, an action potential can be initiated by a very large depolarization such that sodium only flows outward.

A second point: it is generally agreed that Nachmansohn has no substantial evidence in favor of his proposals. Each experimental test to which his hypothesis has been subjected has failed completely.

There is no a priori reason why a biochemical reaction might not be involved in the permeability changes, but such a system would have to be sensitive not to ion movements in the membrane but to the electric field, and it is this experimental fact that has been a difficult one to relate to known reactions. Electric fields in the membrane, while of the order of 50 kV./cm., are far smaller than the ionic fields that might affect chemical reactions.

DR. STREHLER: Experimental separation of changes in sodium permeability into a local increase and an amplification thereof is one possible interpretation of the conductivity changes in clamped neurons, for the change in permeability is a "smooth and continuous function of the membrane potential" only up to the discharge potential at which point a rapid and self-amplifying change in P_{Na} occurs.

The source of an increased local sodium concentration inside the membrane whether by ingression from the environment (during transmission?) of by electrophoretic movement toward the membrane from the inside of the cell (during the initiation mentioned) does not affect the argument. The critical factor in the hypothesis is a transitory rise in the concentration of Na^{*} or another ion capable of displacing acetyl choline inside the membrane.

Regarding the second point, the defense of one biochemist at a time is a sufficient task.

It would be presumptuous to propose that the electrical fields across the membrane are sufficient to initiate chemical reactions that are not already taking place at some rate, for 50–150 mv. represents 1 to 3 kcal. maximally. However, even this small potential difference could alter local concentrations by factors between 4 and 80 fold, which certainly should be sufficient to change the rate of reactions affecting steady state provided that the electrical field increases the local concentration of a limiting reactant in the depolarization process.

Whether an endogenous or imposed field affects permeability by interacting with charged groups attached to a membrane or by changing the local concentration of mobile ions does not seem to involve a fundamental difference, because work in moving charge from loci of high probability to those of somewhat lower probability is involved in both cases. The choice of one or another scheme is partly a subjective and partly an aesthetic matter.

Dr. Chance: It is my hope in this brief presentation to bring to the neurophysiologists a better understanding of current views of energy sources and the possibilities of interfering with them. While in muscular physiology the energy source is, if not of primary interest, surely high on the list of secondary considerations, in nerve physiology there has been less consideration of energy sources. Perhaps this is so because of the complexity of the system, perhaps because of the small extra oxygen requirement for the propagation of electrical impulses. Furthermore a primary consideration in electrical activity of nerves is the mechanism of pumps that supply the concentration gradients associated with the electrical potentials. The role of ATP in electrical activity of the axon is not clear at the present time although the experiments of Keynes and Hodgkin are very suggestive on this point. Ultimately energy must be fed into the system from respiratory activity. It is at this level that I shall make my presentation.

The sequence of enzyme reactions involved in respiration is of widespread occurrence in many tissues and from carbon monoxide inhibition data (due to F. O. Schmitt) we infer that a similar sequence exists in the mitochondria associated with the axon synapses and cell bodies of the nervous system.

The electron transfer system from which ATP is derived in the oxidation of citric acid cycle intermediates is illustrated in Fig. 11-5 and consists of five cytochromes, two or more flavins,

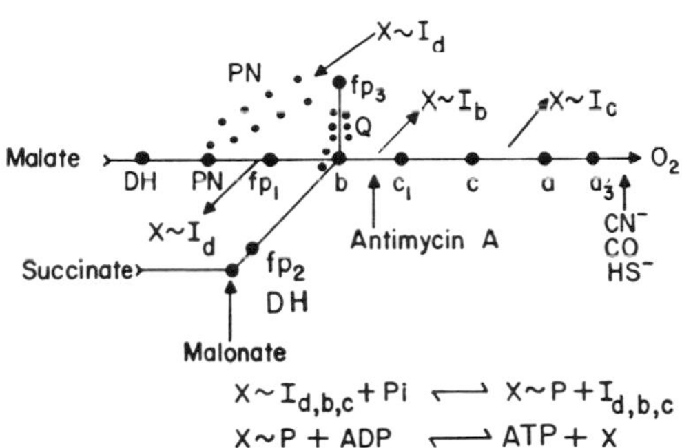

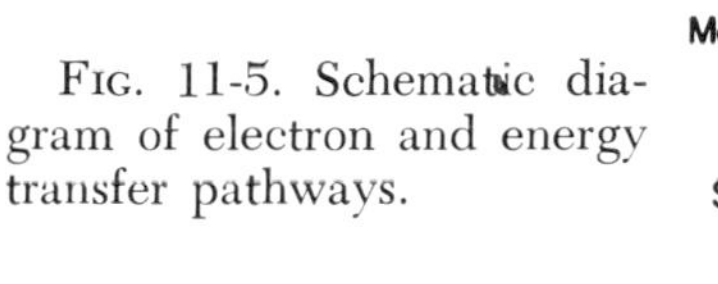
FIG. 11-5. Schematic diagram of electron and energy transfer pathways.

and a large number of pyridine nucleotide molecules. Associated with the chain are also a large number of quinone molecules, equal to about half the number of pyridine nucleotide molecules. In addition there are a number of enzymes which serve to transfer energy from the respiratory carriers to phosphate compounds which eventually lead to the phosphorylation of the ATP. These carriers operate over a span of oxidation-reduction potential from —320 mV. corresponding to that of the pyridine nucleotide couple to +800 mV. corresponding to oxygen-water couple.

Points of interference with the electron transfer chain are indicated by the arrows, interference at the oxygen end by means of carbon monoxide and cyanide is best known. These inhibitors block the flow of electrons to oxygen and cause complete reduction of all the components of the chain (except for those that require energy in their reduction (1).

In the middle of the chain, between cytochromes b and c_1, inhibitors such as Antimycin A and hydroxyquinoline oxide block the transfer of electrons between these two components and cause complete reduction of cytochromes on the substrate side and allow complete oxidation of cytochromes on the oxygen side.

Another site of interference with electron transfer is in the region of flavoprotein, where the addition of Amytal to the electron transfer system causes the pyridine nucleotide to become highly reduced and flavoprotein and the five cytochromes to become highly oxidized. Under these conditions the quinone component also is oxidized. Inhibition at this point is a general property of oxybarbiturates similar to Amytal. It has more recently been found that formaldehyde inhibits at this point. This point is by far the most interesting site of interference and one that may ultimately be found to be of the greatest usefulness in investigating physiological responses to interference in enzyme systems. The exact mechanism by which Amytal and other compounds interfere with electron transfer is only beginning to be understood at the present time. The situation is complicated by the fact that Amytal affects phosphorylating systems in a manner different from that with which it affects non-phosphorylating systems. In the phosphorylating systems it is a current belief that the interference is with the energy transfer reactions characteristic of phosphorylation rather than the electron transfer reactions (2).

Better understood interference with the phosphorylation reaction is caused by uncoupling agents which are currently believed to activate the hydrolysis of intermediates between respiratory carriers and formation of high energy phosphate compounds. Many types of the phenols act as uncoupling agents but at present a sufficient number of other compounds act similarly that chemical specificity of uncoupling has not been proved.

Separate interaction of uncoupling agents with specific sites of oxidative phosphorylation is far from proved and evidence that has been put forward is difficult to substantiate, for example C. Martius (3) postulated that Dicumarol was a specific inhibitor of the phosphorylation step at the flavin level. This idea has not been substantiated by subsequent studies. Experiments which suggested that 2,4-di-nitrophenol inhibits first at one step and then at another similarly lack detailed verification. At the present time we tend toward the idea that the high energy intermediate that interacts with the uncoupling agent does not have chemical properties characteristic of individual phosphorylation steps.

It was pointed out above that the reduction of some of the carriers of the respiratory chain requires not only electron transfer but also an energy source. This is a surprising phenomena but one which appears to be adequately documented (1). It has been found that the reduction of the major portion of the pyridine nucleotide in the mitochondria requires ATP or an intermediate of phosphorylation (4). This also may be true of other components, although studies are not yet complete. Uncoupling agents which diminish the energy content of the mitochondria can interfere with electron transfer through the system. Thus we have two general effects of uncoupling agents, first the inhibition of the formation of ATP and second the inhibition of energy requiring electron transfer reactions, principally those leading to a high degree of reduction of DPN. Since this high degree of reduction of DPN may indeed be the source of the reducing power for TPN used in reductive synthesis, we find pathways of interference with the more subtle functions of the mitochondria.

Little has been said about the role of quinone in electron transfer since actually little is known about it. Fig. 11-5 indicates quinone molecules that can either participate in electron transfer or can be bypassed.

REFERENCES

1. Chance, B., and Hollunger, G. Energy-linked reduction of mitochondrial pyridine nucleotide. *Nature (Lond.) 185:* 666, 1960.
2. Chance, B., and Hollunger, G. Single and multisite inhibitors of energy conserving reactions. *Fed. Proc. 20:* 50, 1961.
3. Martius, C. "Thyroxin und oxydative Phosphorylierung," in *Proceedings of the Third International Congress of Biochemistry,* (Brussels, 1955), edited by C. Liebecq, Academic Press, Inc., New York, 1956, pp. 1–9.
4. Chance, B. The interaction of energy and electron transfer reactions in mitochondria II. General properties of adenosine triphosphate-linked oxidation of cytochrome and reduction of pyridine nucleotide. *J. Biol. Chem. 236:* 1544, 1961.

CHAPTER 12

Why Certain Substances Correct Neural Abnormality

KEITH F. KILLAM

WHEN Dr. Grenell suggested that the question of why drugs correct abnormal neural function be discussed in this symposium it appeared very germane to the outlined program. The more one considers the question, however, the more it becomes apparent that the study of drug effects on neuronal activity has, until very recently, been a descriptive rather than analytical science, and that we really know very little about how pharmacological agents alter normal neuronal activity. In point of fact, we know virtually nothing about how chemical substances correct neural abnormalities, and I think most of my neuropharmacologist colleagues would feel the same way.

Since we are still in the stage of asking: "Why *do* drugs correct neural abnormality?" I would feel hesitant to discuss mechanisms of action of drugs on abnormal neural function. I would like, instead, to consider with you what I feel is the present stage of our knowledge of how drugs may act on the nervous system and the approaches which are available to us with their limitations.

Currently, we are really starting our study of drug action in a reverse fashion. That is to say, we are still finding drugs in the clinic which appear to correct neural abnormalities and then attempting to uncover their mechanism of action in the laboratories. More ideally we should select for therapeutic use drugs whose mechanisms we understand from laboratory study. Not only would a knowledge of drug mechanism enable us to develop therapeutic agents with greater specificity of action, but also provide us with pharmacological tools for the study of interrelationships within the normal central nervous system and for the elucidation of the fundamental disorders underlying pathological syndromes.

The major stumbling block to such goals is that we have few, if any, experimental animal equivalents of clinical entities associated with neural abnormalities. We can induce paroxysmal discharge of nerve cells by chemical or electrical stimulation. We can depress neural activity by antimetabolites, by anoxia, by lowering temperature, and the like. We can induce activity in normally closed circuits by certain stimulants or by massive electrical stimulation. But there is as yet no evidence that these neural abnormalities are equivalent to physiological abnormalities found in the clinic. Taking an example from perhaps the most widely studied field, that of anticonvulsants, it is known that such compounds as trimethadione will block seizures induced by electroshock or pentylene tetrazol injection, but these data tell us nothing about *why* this drug corrects the neural abnormality in either the experimental animal or in epileptics. Or we can say that diphenylhydantoin which modifies convulsive responses to pentylene tetrazol injection prevents seizure spread and somehow "stabilizes," but that is as far as we can go.

Approaches to the Study of Drug Action

If one considers possible approaches to the study of drug effects on neuronal activity, there appear to be five levels of investigation. Of major importance would be the correlation of each of the levels of study with the basic function of the central nervous system—that is, with the generation of behavior. The most limited level, and at the same time the most common denominator, would be the study of the biochemistry of the central nervous system. The second aspect is drug action on the physiological activity of single cells or small cell groups. Third, one may consider drug action on cell populations and on organizational systems at the level afforded by macroelectrode recording. A fourth aspect might be pharmacological alterations of the interrelationship of basic behavior patterns such as the sleep-wakefulness cycle with electrical activity of nerve cell populations. Fifth, the interrelationship of conditional behavior with basic behavior patterns, and with alterations of physiological activity of cell populations as evidenced by electrical potentials might be open to drug manipulation. Such studies would provide us with the maximum information as to drug mechanisms.

Biochemical Methods

It seems platitudinous to point out that drugs probably have their basic action through the alteration of biochemical processes. Such alterations may be very different in character depending on whether the therapeutic agent is foreign to, or actually an endogenous substance to, the brain. Because of the very obviousness of such a conclusion it may appear at first surprising that biochemical bases for the effect of most centrally active agents have not been elucidated. This lack, however, is due in large part to the fact that suitable hypotheses have not been proposed linking the metabolism of the central nervous system to the normal conductile processes or the processes subserving nervous transmission. Biochemical investigations of abnormal neuronal activity associated with pathological syndromes have added to our knowledge of the normal by comparative studies; but many red herrings have been brought up which only by the most painstaking research have been discounted. An example of such confusion is the myriad of biochemical alterations reported in schizophrenic patients.

Another approach to the biochemical explanation of drug action has been the examination of profiles of endogenous substances in neural tissue. Many alterations have been observed in the levels of such substances following the administration of drugs, although the significance of such changes has been obscure in view of the lack of information as to metabolism involved in nervous transmission. Probably the most fascinating possibilities arise from alterations in biogenic amines and associated substances. These include serotonin, norepinephrine, 5-hydroxytryptophane, desoxyphenylalanine (DOPA), and gamma aminobutyric acid. Changes in levels of these compounds appear to alter central nervous system function. From such data, however, it does not necessarily follow that pathological states involve alteration in brain levels of these substances. If one takes, for example, the class of compounds which inhibit monoamine oxidase, the therapeutic effects of the drugs need not reside in this property but may instead involve some other common facet of the activity of the substances. Recently, for example, a drug called imipramine has been developed which has many of the therapeutic properties of the monoamine oxidase inhibitors, but the compound does not block the enzyme monoamine oxidase.

Unit Recording Techniques

Studies of the physiological characteristics of single cells or small cell groups have inherent difficulties when used as a basis for the characterization of drug effects. Pharmacological investigations have generally revealed that responsiveness to drugs is a statistical phenomenon. In all cases, except those in which therapeutic agents produce nonreversible changes, the responsiveness of a population of independent cells, and probably also of a population of cells within an individual tissue, appears to follow laws of normal frequency distribution. The technological problems associated with recording from single cells at the moment prevent the simultaneous recording of potentials from even so small a population sample as 100 individual cells. Even setting this question aside, a number of other restrictions are imposed by the technique on the adequate study of cell populations. The length of time one can reliably record from any given cell is finite and variable. Such factors as the pulsatile movements of the brain induced by reflected cardiovascular and pulmonary movements are of increased importance in the study of drugs with peripheral actions. Furthermore, the time over which reasonably "normal" records can be obtained from a single cell is limited by local changes induced by the high-impedance recording electrode. Interpretations of data are further limited by our present inability accurately to identify the specific cell much less the anatomical parts of cells from which potentials are recorded. Additional difficulties involved in getting drugs to the site of recording by the route, and at the concentration at which the drugs are used clinically, further impede the study of drugs at the unit level.

More courageous workers have attempted to circumvent some of these problems by using multiple electrode passes, and by special routes of administration of the chemical agents. Injection directly into the tissue, topical application, ionophoretic discharge of the material, as well as classical routes of administration, all have been tried. Both types of maneuvers are often feasible in the study of drugs with ephemeral action. Unfortunately, however, many of the drugs of great current interest such as chlorpromazine, reserpine, and LSD-25 have delayed onsets of action. Furthermore, once initiated, the effects of such drugs persist for hours, even days, which prevents the ultimate control of experiments by observation of the return of potentials to control activity. Special properties of certain drugs exclude some methods of administration and preclude certain types of study. Thus, a knowledge of the total pharmacological activity profile of drugs under investigation is imperative. A good example of such a drug is benactyzine. The compound is a good local anesthetic agent (12). This activity is apparent when the drug is topically applied to tissue but is not seen when the agent is given systemically. Thus, it would be rather hazardous to hypothesize on the tranquilizing properties of benactyzine from data derived from direct application of benactyzine to nervous tissue.

Lest the impression remain that these difficulties are insurmountable, it must be pointed out that while studies of individual cell response to pharmacological agents are feasible, this field is one in which great advantage will be derived from employing the "know-how" from engineering, physiology, biochemistry, and pharmacology.

Cell Population Studies

The multiplicity of hazards for the study of drugs at the unit level has led to the characterization of the effects of drugs on the central nervous system at the level of cell populations—i.e., the study of evoked and spontaneous activity using macroelectrode recordings. The detailed evaluation of drugs used in the clinical manifestations of neuronal abnormalities draws heavily on classical neurophysiology for both the technology and the philosophical substratum of hypotheses. The pharmacologist brings to the difficult young field of drug action on neuronal abnormality the comparative drug approach. He has now at his disposal drugs with some efficacy in the treatment of hyperactive mental patients. These agents may be studied in comparison with the barbiturates which are effective sedatives in normal patients but have little effect in mental patients. Similarly in the stimulant side of therapy, there are monoamine oxidase inhibitors and a new class of derivatives of tranquilizers to compare with amphetamine and analogous classical stimulant compounds. Thus, the pharmacologist has a comparative control with which to test his hypotheses as well as to describe the drug-induced alterations. For example, the earliest hypothesis regarding the tranquilizing properties of chlorpromazine was that the drug acted by depression of mechanisms in the reticular activating system ascribed to the maintenance of the sleep-wakefulness cycle. In comparing the effects of pentobarbital with chlorpromazine on these systems, the barbiturates proved to be at least five times more potent (3). This negative finding, along with clinical observations as to the very different properties of the two agents in patients, generated the search for other systems which might be selectively sensitive to chlorpromazine (4).

The literature has grown so enormously in the area of drug action on cell populations and on organizational systems that a summary of the controversies even on one class of compounds seems inappropriate here. Such summaries appear in chapters from the various annual review-type publications. Instead it may be useful to point out the special differences in criteria peculiar to a pharmacological approach and to indicate areas in which little information is available to date.

The ideal approach, of course, is to study the actions of centrally acting drugs on the physiology of the central nervous system of unanesthetized animals having syndromes identical with human pathology. It would be desirable to test, as the findings directed, the responsiveness of a number of structures and to have some neurological or psychological measure of the degree to which a change may be correlated operationally with the physiological parameters.

The use of classical neurophysiological preparations has some limitations. Many constraints are placed on the preparation by immobilization whether with a curariform agent, by surgical lesions, or by deep anesthesia. The anesthetized state, of course, is an impossible preparation from many points of view for the study of drugs such as the tranquilizers or psychomimetic agents. Immobilized preparations such as the *encephale isole* or *cerveau isole* or the curarized animal are most useful but have important limitations in the study of centrally active drugs.

The psychotherapeutic agents, for example, along with their therapeutic effects also alter the autonomic nervous system, both central and peripheral, affect temperature regulation, and change the susceptibility of the central nervous system to seizure discharge. It is even possible that these agents owe their effectiveness to their spectra of activity via some of these mechanisms. If they have, on the other hand, their therapeutic effects on independent mechanisms it remains important to measure all drug-induced changes to see which are related to apparent shifts of excitability in the neuronal system under study. For example, it is known that a fall in body temperature will reduce responsiveness of the reticular formation (7). Since chlorpromazine lowers body temperature to that of the environment (10) it is especially important in immobilized animals to support the body temperature when the effects of chlorpromazine on pathways involving the reticular formation are under study.

If these important considerations are taken into account in the interpretation of data regarding mechanisms of drug action in the brain, there are a number of useful ways in which cell populations may be investigated. Synaptic effects may be assessed by multiple macroelectrode recordings along known pathways to evaluate levels at which drugs may act. Or one may, on the other hand, differentiate types of synapses by stimulation at multiple sites and recording at a single end station in the brain. The great bulk of such synaptic data has until now been related to single evoked responses, but even as early as 1941 Marshall (8) demonstrated the importance of evaluating drug alterations on neuronal recovery time by the use of paired or multiple stimuli.

Evoked paroxysmal activity, particularly in cortical and rhinencephalic structures, has been studied as a model of abnormal neuronal discharge. Blockade or enhancement of such repetitive firing has added information concerning the action of certain pharmacological agents although, as mentioned earlier, such patterns are not necessarily equivalent to those of clinical neural abnormalities.

Other types of long-lasting altered neuronal activity such as EEG arousal patterns, spindling, spreading inhibition, and the like are also open to alteration by drug administration. Again we probably cannot yet adequately evaluate when such responses are normal and when they may be considered to represent abnormal neural activity for the particular animal or patient under study.

Probably the most virgin territory for the study of the potent new agents on cell groups and interrelated pathways of the brain is the study of steady potential gradients and the patterns of change in these gradients. Certainly such events, modifying evoked potentials, far outlast the stimulus period. In a study of this type, for example, Arduini and his colleagues (1) indicated that alteration of steady potential gradients on the neocortex induced by stimulation of the reticular formation is sensitive to pentobarbital.

Before passing on to a consideration of the fourth general approach to the study of drug actions on the brain, it should be pointed out that pharmacological agents also serve as useful tools for the investigation of organizational systems of the brain. And we may employ such tools provided we realize that we cannot with the same set of data both explain the mechanism of action of a pharmacological agent and use the effects of that agent as a basis for the explanation of physiological mechanisms in the brain!

It is often clear that, by altering reversibly the activity of certain areas or pathways, information may be obtained which is not easily available from classical neurophysiological preparations in which activity is altered by lesions or electrical stimulation. An example of such studies is the demonstration by the use of pentobarbital and mephenesin that rostral projection of the reticular formation is not entirely dependent upon the diffuse thalamic projection system. In these experiments, stimulating electrodes were placed both in mesencephalic reticular formation and in the nuclei of the diffuse thalamic projection system. By stimulation of these electrodes at appropriate parameters the EEG arousal response could be elicited from both sites and the cortical recruiting response from the thalamic locus. In this preparation the recruiting response and EEG arousal response elicited by stimulation of the thalamus were blocked by mephenesin at a time when the EEG arousal response could still be elicited from the mesencephalic reticular formation by stimulation at the control level. The converse of this finding was observed after small doses of pentobarbital (6). Such studies as these on many circuits of the brain support the case for the use of drugs to implement investigation of complex interaction patterns and systems.

Behavioral Investigations

The fourth and fifth levels at which drugs may be considered to act on neural activity involve the external manifestation of such activity, that is behavior. The older studies have involved observational techniques in the evaluation of basic behavior patterns: i.e., sleep-wakefulness cycle, excessive motor activity, eating, sexual patterns, and the like. These have, in recent years, been correlated with the electrical activity of the brain as recorded from implanted electrodes and have aided in our interpretation of drug effects on neuronal potentials. One would not fall into the error, for example, of describing the actions of barbiturates and atropine in producing high-voltage slow-wave activity on the cortex as similar if one has studied the chronic preparation. Under barbiturates the EEG effect is correlated with sleep (as in untreated animals), while following atropine waking behavior is characteristic (11). A similar superficial resemblance appears between the low-voltage fast activity induced by amphetamine and eserine. The behavior, however, following eserine is atypical. Sleep may often accompany the low-voltage fast EEG (2).

Despite a plethora of studies of the EEG in conscious animals and man, the correlation of most forms of recorded neural activity with basic behavior patterns is still not clearly defined. Current interest in studies of this type, however, should within the next few years provide fundamental hypotheses on which more adequately controlled drug investigations may be based.

With the advent of the tranquilizing agents, which alter abnormal behavior in mental patients as their most significant manifestation, there has been a shift in emphasis in neuropharmacological research. These agents appear subtlely to alter relationships within the central nervous system, and their effects often differ according to the preset behavior pattern of the patient treated. Thus, neuropharmacologists have become interested in behavioral psychology and the techniques which it offers for the evaluation of patterned behavior and of the learning process. Psychologists, at the same time, have become interested in the use of drugs to dissect behavior and to test the theories associated with the generation of behavior. This whole milieu of interdisciplinary awareness has also permeated the ranks of neurophysiology. In consequence, many laboratories are now attempting to describe the electrical events in the central nervous system as behavioral patterns are acquired, during the performance of learned behavior, and as the behavior is altered by drug administration. Again as with other levels of drug study, however, a major problem has been the lack of animal models of neurological or psychiatric diseases for the evaluation of drug actions on clinically recognized neuronal abnormality. Thus, the data most relevant to the mechanism of drug action on abnormal neuronal activity have had to come from deductive reasoning based on clinical observations. Our current situation is illustrated most cogently by the findings regarding the new drug called imipramine which was mentioned earlier. This agent is chemically closely allied to chlorpromazine, and in the laboratory the properties of the two compounds are indistinguishable (9). In normal volunteers the effects of imipramine also closely resemble those of chlorpromazine. However, quite different data are obtained from clinically depressed patients. In these individuals chlorpromazine appears not to alter the neural abnormality while imipramine has an activity comparable to that of the monoamine oxidase inhibitors. Thus, it is clear that to date the most pertinent preparation for the study of the effects of imipramine and probably its congeners is the chronically depressed patient.

My own interest in this general level of drug investigation centers at the moment around the correlation of electrical representations in the brain of environmental cues which act as stimuli for conditioned behavior patterns. The investigations of Dr. Roy John, now of the University of Rochester, and myself, have thus far revealed some facets of the differential handling of incoming information by various brain structures during approach and avoidance learning, and at various stages of the learning process in each of the two situations. We are not yet in a position, however, to consider any of the neuronal activity which we record as "normal" or "abnormal." But as many laboratories accumulate knowledge in the field we should develop a most useful tool for the study of the mechanisms of drug action. One tantalizing scrap of data, for example, which Dr. John and I uncovered (5) might be considered to relate to the interaction of drug effects and abnormal behavior, and thus with the underlying abnormal nervous activity. If a cat fully trained to make a conditioned avoidance response is treated with reserpine, he shows the whole picture of peripheral reserpine effects and his performance of the avoidance response is impaired for a longer or shorter period depending upon the dose administered. By the time the cat's performance of the conditioned avoidance response has returned to almost control level, all the peripheral manifestations of the drug have disappeared. At this point, however (and it may be as long as seven days after a single dose of reserpine), if the cat makes an abnormal behavioral response and receives the unconditioned stimulus there is an immediate and striking return of all the peripheral symptoms of the drug: miosis, diarrhea, and depression. The explanation of this kind of drug-behavior interaction is still obscure.

Concluding Remarks

At this point in the development of neuropharmacology it thus appears to me that we know little or nothing about the exact mechanisms by which drugs correct neural abnormality. We have developed experimental methods which begin to be promising at five levels of investigation. We can look at drug effects on biochemical processes, on the responses of single cells, on cell populations and integrative systems, on the relation of basic behavior patterns to electrical activity of the brain, and finally the actions of chemical compounds on the acquisition and performance of complex behavior patterns and the correlated activity of neurons in the brain. Interpretation of drug data is dependent upon the development of hypotheses concerning fundamental processes which may be uncovered by the various levels of investigation.

REFERENCES

1. Arduini, A., Mancia, M., and Mechelse, K. Slow potential changes elicited in the cerebral cortex by sensory and reticular stimulations. *Boll. Soc. ital. biol. sper. 32:* 966, 1956.
2. Bradley, P. B., and Elkes, J. The effect of atropine, hyoscyamine, physostigmine and neostigmine on the electrical activity of the brain of the conscious cat. *J. Physiol. 120:* 14, 1953.
3. Killam, E. K., Killam, K. F., and Shaw, T. The effects of psychotherapeutic compounds on central afferent and limbic pathways. *Ann. New York Acad. Sc. 66:* 784, 1957.

4. KILLAM, K. F., and KILLAM, E. K. Drug action on pathways involving the reticular formation, pp. 111–122. In *Reticular Formation of the Brain.* Henry Ford Hospital International Symposium. Little, Brown and Co., Boston, 1958.
5. KILLAM, K. F., and KILLAM, E. K. Central actions of chlorpromazine and reserpine. *Fifth Conference on Neuropharmacology,* pp. 131–195. Josiah Macy, Jr. Foundation, New York, 1960.
6. KING, E. E. Differential action of anesthetics and interneuronal depressants upon EEG arousal and recruitment responses. *J. Pharmacol. & Exper. Therap. 116:* 404, 1956.
7. KOELLA, W. P., and BALLIN, H. M. The influence of temperature changes on the electrocortical responses to acoustic and nociceptive stimuli in the cat. *EEG Clin. Neurophysiol. 6:* 629, 1954.
8. MARSHALL, W. Observations on subcortical somatic mechanisms of cats under Nembutal anesthesia. *J. Neurophysiol. 4:* 25, 1941.
9. SIGG, E. Personal communication.
10. TERZIAN, H. Studio electroencefalografico dell'azione centrale de Largactile (4560 RP). *Rassengna Neurol. Veget. 4–5:* 211, 1952.
11. WIKLER, A. Pharmacologic dissociation of behavior and EEG "sleep patterns" in dogs: morphine, N-allylnormorphine and atropine. *Proc. Soc. Exper. Biol. 79:* 261, 1952.
12. Laboratory data supplied through the courtesy of Merck, Sharp & Dohme Research Laboratories.

INDEX